CONTENTS

C000193967

Cover Picture: Halewell, Cheltenham, Gloucestershire (page

KEY TO SYMBOLS

	English	French	German
12 rms	Total number of rooms	Nombre de chambres	Anzahl der Zimmer
MasterCard	MasterCard accepted	MasterCard accepté	MasterCard akzeptiert
VISA	Visa accepted	Visa accepté	Visa akzeptiert
AMERICAN EXPRESS	American Express accepted	American Express accepté	American Express akzeptiert
Diners Club	Diners Club accepted	Diners Club accepté	Diners Club akzeptiert
(tree)	Quiet location	Un lieu tranquille	Ruhige Lage
(wheelchair)	Access for wheelchairs to at least one bedroom and public rooms	Accès handicapé	Zugang für Behinderte

(The 'Access for wheelchairs' symbol (♿) does not necessarily indicate that the property fulfils National Accessible Scheme grading)

	English	French	German
(chef hat)	Chef-patron	Chef-patron	Chef-patronn
(glass)	Licensed	Avec Licence	Schankerlanbnis
en famille	Guest and Hosts usually dine together	Table d'Hôte	Mit der Familie essen
M 20	Meeting/conference facilities with maximum number of delegates	Salle de conférences – capacité maximale	Konferenzraum-Höchstkapazität
(children 8)	Children welcome, with minimum age where applicable	Enfants bienvenus	Kinder willkommen
(dog)	Dogs accommodated in rooms or kennels	Chiens autorisés	Hunde erlaubt
(bed)	At least one room has a four-poster bed	Lit à baldaquin dans au moins une chambre	Himmelbett
(satellite)	Cable/satellite TV in all bedrooms	TV câblée/satellite dans les chambres	Satellit-und Kabelfernsehen in allen Zimmern
(fax)	Fax available in rooms	Fax dans votre chambre	Fax in Schlafzimmern
(no smoking)	No-smoking rooms (at least one no-smoking bedroom)	Chambres non-fumeur	Zimmer für Nichtraucher
(lift)	Lift available for guests' use	Ascenseur	Fahrstuhl
(indoor pool)	Indoor swimming pool	Piscine couverte	Hallenbad
(outdoor pool)	Outdoor swimming pool	Piscine de plein air	Freibad
(tennis)	Tennis court at hotel	Tennis à l'hôtel	Hoteleigener Tennisplatz
(croquet)	Croquet lawn at hotel	Croquet à l'hôtel	Krocketrasen
(fishing)	Fishing can be arranged	Pêche	Angeln
(golf)	Golf course on site or nearby, which has an arrangement with the hotel allowing guests to play	Golf sur site ou à proximité	Golfplatz
(shooting)	Shooting can be arranged	Chasse / Tir	Jagd
(riding)	Riding can be arranged	Équitation	Reitpferd
(H)	Hotel has a helicopter landing pad	Helipad	Hubschrauberlandplatz
(bell)	Licensed for wedding ceremonies	Cérémonies de mariages	Konzession für Eheschliessungen

FOREWORD

This guide specialises in the smaller hotel or private country house, where you can expect to be greeted as if a guest at a family home. Standards are high but tariffs are reasonable.

Our inspectors annually visit every recommended establishment in addition to the many hotels, inns, country houses and business meeting venues which regularly apply for inclusion. Only those that match our standards of diversity and excellence can be recommended.

The new millennium editions of our guides include the launch of 'Recommended Hotels & Game Lodges Southern Africa Mauritius The Seychelles'. You will find these exciting new recommendations together with those for North America and Europe in the index at the back of this guide.

A complete reference to our year 2000 recommendations representing 40 countries may be found together with a direct on line availability service (DOLAS) on our Internet site www.johansens.com The guides are also available on CD-ROM. We hope that you enjoy these recommendations and our thanks go to the many thousands of you who have sent us 'Guest Survey Reports' that are available at the back of this guide.

Your experience has proved that to mention that you use Johansens when making a booking is a positive benefit to the enjoyment of your stay.

We wish you many more of them.

Andrew Warren
<u>**Managing Director**</u>

JOHANSENS AWARDS FOR EXCELLENCE

RECOMMENDED COUNTRY HOUSES & SMALL HOTELS IN GREAT BRITAIN & IRELAND

The 1999 Awards for Excellence winners at the Dorchester

The Johansens Awards for Excellence were presented at the Johansens Annual Dinner held at The Dorchester on November 2nd 1998.

The Most Excellent Country House Award was presented to **Caragh Lodge** in County Kerry, Ireland.

Beechwood Hotel in Norfolk received The Most Excellent Value for Money Award and its high standards were identified by the many guests who sent in Johansens report forms after an enjoyable stay.

Guests' reports are exclusively the means by which the winner of The Most Excellent Service Award is annually chosen. This award was deservedly won by **Burpham Country Hotel** in West Sussex.

Congratulations to these winners and thank you to everyone who sent in Guest Survey Report forms.

Each year we rely on the appraisals of Johansens guests, alongside the nominations of our team of inspectors, as a basis for making all our awards, not only to our Recommended Country Houses and Small Hotels but also to our Hotels and Inns with Restaurants in Great Britain & Ireland, Recommended Hotels – Europe and the Mediterranean and Recommended Hotels & Inns – North America, Bermuda & The Caribbean. In these categories the award winners for 1999 were:

Johansens Most Excellent London Hotel Award
The London Outpost of the Carnegie Club

Johansens Most Excellent City Hotel Award:
Channings, Edinburgh, Scotland

Johansens Most Excellent Country Hotel Award:
Summer Lodge, Dorset

Johansens Most Excellent Traditional Inn Award:
The New Inn at Coln, Gloucestershire

Johansens Most Excellent Restaurant Award:
Ynyshir Hall, Machynlleth, Wales

The Knight Frank Award for Outstanding Excellence and Innovation
Robin Hutson and Gerard Basset – Hotel du Vin Group of Hotels

Johansens – Europe: The Most Excellent Waterside Resort Hotel:
The Marbella Club, Marbella, Spain

Johansens – Europe: The Most Excellent Country Hotel:
Schlosshotel Igls, Igls, Austria

Johansens – Europe: The Most Excellent City Hotel:
La Tour Rose, Lyon, France

Johansens – North America: Special Award for Excellence:
The Lodge at Moosehead Lake, Greenville, Maine

Johansens – North America: Most Excellent Inn:
Carter House, Eureka, California

Johansens – North America: Most Excellent Hotel:
Monmouth Plantation, Natchez, Mississippi

Published by
Johansens Limited, Therese House, Glasshouse Yard, London EC1A 4JN
Tel: 020 7566 9700 Fax: 020 7490 2538
Find Johansens on the Internet at: **http://www.johansens.com**
E-Mail: admin@johansen.u–net.com

Publishing Director:	Peter Hancock
P.A. to Publishing Director:	Carol Sweeney
Editorial Manager:	Yasmin Razak
Regional Inspectors:	Christopher Bond
	Geraldine Bromley
	Robert Bromley
	Julie Dunkley
	Martin Greaves
	Joan Henderson
	Marie Iversen
	Pauline Mason
	John O'Neill
	Mary O'Neill
	Fiona Patrick
	Brian Sandell
Production Manager:	Daniel Barnett
Production Controller:	Kevin Bradbrook
Senior Designer:	Michael Tompsett
Designer:	Sue Dixon
Copywriters:	Claire-Louise Baxter
	Simon Duke
	Norman Flack
Sales and Marketing Manager:	Laurent Martinez
Marketing Executive:	Stephen Hoskin
Sales Administrator:	Susan Butterworth
Webmaster:	John Lea
P.A. to Managing Director :	Glenda Walshaw
Managing Director:	Andrew Warren

Copyright © 1999 Johansens Limited

Johansens is a subsidiary of the Daily Mail & General Trust plc

ISBN 1 861017 7077

Printed in England by St Ives plc
Colour origination by East Anglian Engraving

Distributed in the UK and Europe by Johnsons International Media Services Ltd, London (direct sales) & Biblios PDS Ltd, West Sussex (bookstores). In North America by Hunter Publishing, New Jersey. In Australia and New Zealand by Bookwise International, Findon, South Australia

HOW TO USE THIS GUIDE

If you want to find a Country House or Small Hotel in a particular area you can:

• Turn to the Maps on pages 278–284

• Search the Indexes on pages 285–289

• Look for the Town or Village where you wish to stay in the main body of the Guide. This is divided into countries. Place names in each country appear at the head of the pages in alphabetical order.

The Indexes list the Country Houses and Small Hotels by countries and by counties, they also show those with amenities such as fishing, conference facilities, swimming, golf, etc.

The Maps cover all regions. Each Country House and Small Hotel symbol (a green square) relates to a property in this guide situated in or near the location shown.

Red Triangles show the location of Johansens Recommended Traditional Inns, Hotels & Restaurants. If you cannot find a suitable Country House or Small Hotel near where you wish to stay, you may decide to choose one of these establishments as an alternative. They are all listed by place names on page 277.

Blue dots show the location of Johansens Recommended Hotels which can be found in our other publication Johansens Recommended Hotels, Great Britain & Ireland.

The prices, in most cases, refer to the cost of one night's accommodation, with breakfast, for two people. Prices are also shown for single occupancy. These rates are correct at the time of going to press but always should be checked with the hotel before you make your reservation.

We occasionally receive letters from guests who have been charged for accommodation booked in advance but later cancelled. Readers should be aware that by making a reservation with a hotel, either by telephone or in writing, they are entering into a legal contract. A hotelier under certain circumstances is entitled to make a charge for accommodation when guests fail to arrive, even if notice of the cancellation is given.

All guides are obtainable from bookshops or by Johansens Freephone 0800 269397 or by using the order coupons on pages 291–304.

INTRODUCTION

From Burpham Country House Hotel, Burpham, West Sussex
Winner of the 1999 Johansens Most Excellent Service Award

To have been awarded the Johansens 1999 Most Excellent Service Award is the icing on the cake for all of us. We are truly thrilled. My Swiss wife Marianne sets enormous store on providing the most friendly and courteous service to our clients. Stephen Piggott, our chef, and all our staff are thoroughly professional, kind and thoughtful – for that we are very grateful to them. All this shows through by the large number of repeat bookings and the many letters from appreciative clients.

Our Hotel is situated in a fold of the Sussex South Downs near Arundel. Today stress is an ever increasing worry to all of us so our offer of a 'Stress Remedy Break' is very appealing.

Much of our success has been brought about by the top quality of the Johansens guides and their excellent marketing strategies. Our thanks go to Johansens and the many clients who sent in survey forms from which they impart final judgement. We look forward to another year of hopefully providing excellent service.

George & Marianne Walker

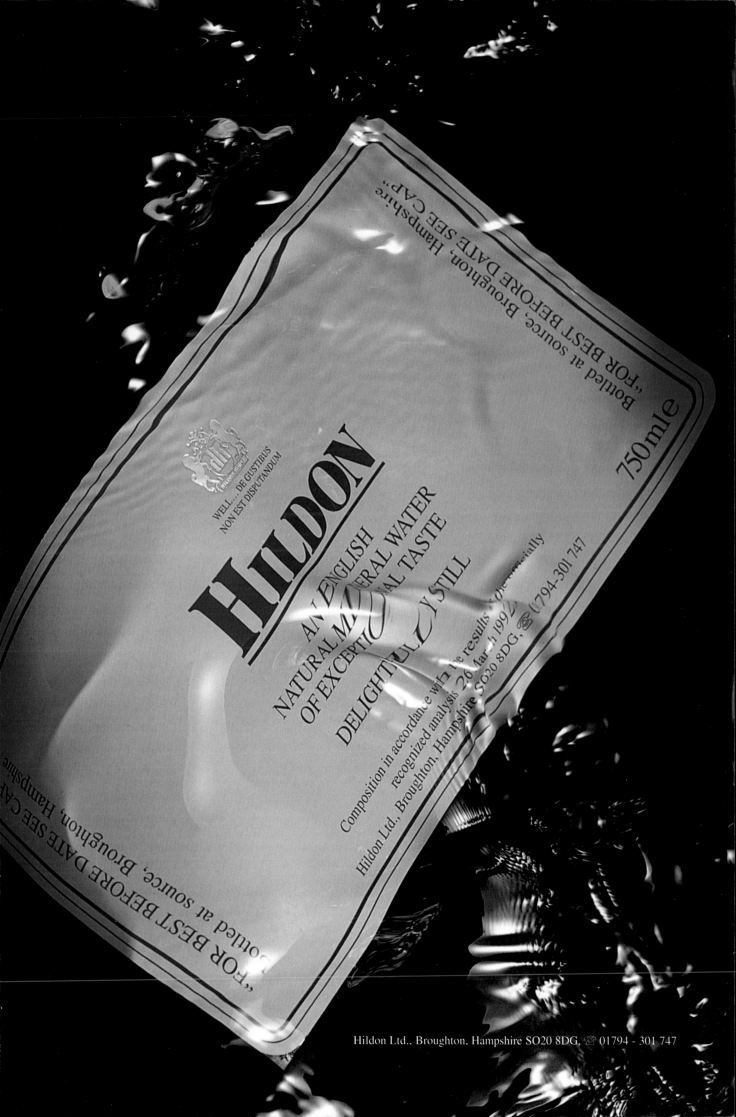

Hildon Ltd., Broughton, Hampshire SO20 8DG. ☎ 01794 - 301 747

INTRODUCTION

From the Beechwood Hotel, North Walsham, Norfolk
Winner of the 1999 Johansens Most Excellent Value for Money Award

Winning the Johansens Most Excellent Value for Money Award for 1999 has been an accolade that has given us immense pleasure, because it has recognised what we set out to do when we bought the Beechwood Hotel; to offer our guests the very highest standards of customer service and the best value for money.

In 1993, when we first turned into the drive, we knew immediately that our search for a hotel to purchase was over, we had found that very special place we had been looking for. It's easy to see why; the combination of a historic Georgian house, an acre of beautiful gardens, the warm and friendly atmosphere and of course nowadays, the welcome you will receive from our small team.

The house was built in 1800 and for many years was owned by a series of local doctors. During these years it hosted many distinguished guests, including Agatha Christie who came to Norfolk for many extended holidays. In 1972 it was converted into a hotel and has been welcoming visitors ever since.

We have nine bedrooms, each individually furnished with traditional and antique furniture and an inviting Dining Room with a relaxed atmosphere, where the emphasis is on culinary innovation and fresh local produce as well as traditional fare. To complement our food, there is a well balanced wine list which features interesting and unusual offerings from the Proprietors' Private Cellar. These have been tasted and selected for their exceptional varietal style and value. We also have a Drawing Room with an extensive range of local guidebooks, magazines and a selection of novels. In summer the French windows open out into the garden and in winter the Drawing Room is a cosy place to curl up by the fire and read one of those classic books you've never got around to reading.

Added to this we have another bonus, because we are situated in Norfolk, an amazing place to visit. The charm of an English county where you won't find a motorway but instead leafy lanes and sweeping beaches, clear skies and a wonderful way of life that we love to share with our visitors.

Whichever Johansens property you choose, we hope you will enjoy your stay.

Don Birch and Lindsay Spalding

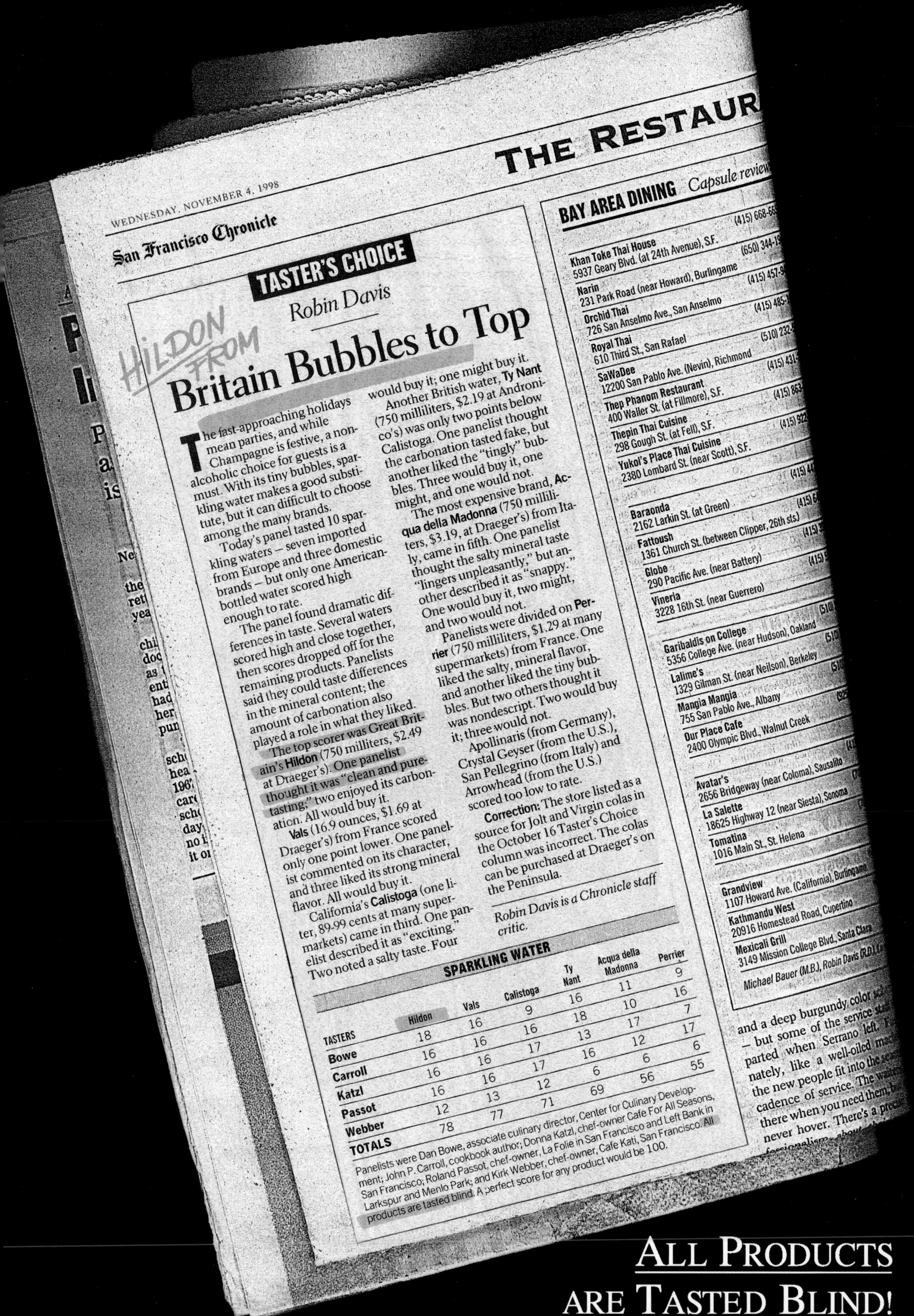

WEDNESDAY, NOVEMBER 4, 1998

San Francisco Chronicle

TASTER'S CHOICE

Robin Davis

Britain Bubbles to Top

(handwritten: HILDON FROM)

The fast-approaching holidays mean parties, and while Champagne is festive, a non-alcoholic choice for guests is a must. With its tiny bubbles, sparkling water makes a good substitute, but it can difficult to choose among the many brands.

Today's panel tasted 10 sparkling waters — seven imported from Europe and three domestic brands — but only one American-bottled water scored high enough to rate.

The panel found dramatic differences in taste. Several waters scored high and close together, then scores dropped off for the remaining products. Panelists said they could taste differences in the mineral content; the amount of carbonation also played a role in what they liked.

The top scorer was Great Britain's **Hildon** (750 milliters, $2.49 at Draeger's). One panelist thought it was "clean and pure-tasting," two enjoyed its carbonation. All would buy it.

Vals (16.9 ounces, $1.69 at Draeger's) from France scored only one point lower. One panelist commented on its character, and three liked its strong mineral flavor. All would buy it.

California's **Calistoga** (one liter, 89.99 cents at many supermarkets) came in third. One panelist described it as "exciting." Four Two noted a salty taste.

would buy it; one might buy it. Another British water, **Ty Nant** (750 milliliters, $2.19 at Andronico's) was only two points below Calistoga. One panelist thought the carbonation tasted fake, but another liked the "tingly" bubbles. Three would buy it, one might, and one would not.

The most expensive brand, **Acqua della Madonna** (750 milliliters, $3.19, at Draeger's) from Italy, came in fifth. One panelist thought the salty mineral taste "lingers unpleasantly," but another described it as "snappy." One would buy it, two might, and two would not.

Panelists were divided on **Perrier** (750 milliliters, $1.29 at many supermarkets) from France. One liked the salty, mineral flavor, and another liked the tiny bubbles. But two others thought it was nondescript. Two would buy it; three would not.

Apollinaris (from Germany), Crystal Geyser (from the U.S.), San Pellegrino (from Italy) and Arrowhead (from the U.S.) scored too low to rate.

Correction: The store listed as a source for Jolt and Virgin colas in the October 16 Taster's Choice column was incorrect. The colas can be purchased at Draeger's on the Peninsula.

Robin Davis is a Chronicle staff critic.

SPARKLING WATER

TASTERS	Hildon	Vals	Calistoga	Ty Nant	Acqua della Madonna	Perrier
Bowe	18	16	9	16	11	9
Carroll	16	16	16	18	10	16
Katzl	16	16	17	13	17	7
Passot	16	16	17	16	12	17
Webber	12	13	12	6	6	6
TOTALS	78	77	71	69	56	55

Panelists were Dan Bowe, associate culinary director, Center for Culinary Development; John P. Carroll, cookbook author; Donna Katzl, chef-owner, Cafe For All Seasons, San Francisco; Roland Passot, chef-owner, La Folie in San Francisco and Left Bank in Larkspur and Menlo Park; and Kirk Webber, chef-owner, Cafe Kati, San Francisco. All products are tasted blind. A perfect score for any product would be 100.

INTRODUCTION

From Caragh Lodge, Caragh Lake, Co Kerry
Winner of the 1999 Johansens Most Excellent Country House Award

Eleven years ago, while living in Leicestershire, Graham and I decided to look for a cottage in the country. And the "country" we both wanted was Ireland. We had previously lived in Dublin and had once had a summer home in Kerry so we knew the area well. Graham made several trips there and discovered a number of properties to consider. When we both arrived in Kerry, ready to make the final decision, Lady Luck stepped in. We just happened to meet the then owners of Caragh Lodge through a mutual friend and it just happened that Caragh Lodge was on the market. Three months, two further trips and a million phone calls later, Caragh Lodge was ours.

At this point the real story began. We moved our family – 2 adults, 2 children, 2 dogs, and our furniture – to Caragh Lodge and opened our country house in Summer 1989. We had no previous experience, no formal training, but we did have memories of our stays in good small hotels and country houses over the years. We decided our goal was to make Caragh Lodge into somewhere we would love to stay ourselves. Ten years on and we hope we are getting somewhere close to that goal.

From the start our greatest problem was how to find our guests. We are delighted, therefore, to be a part of Johansens whereby we continue to be discovered by so many wonderful visitors over the years. Many have become good friends who now return to us again and again.

After ten years we are still pleasantly surprised when guests compliment us on our efforts. Thus we were absolutely thrilled to receive the 1999 Johansens Most Excellent Country House Award.

Mary Gaunt

The Honda Accord has won critical acclaim from both the public and press alike.

What Car? Magazine voted it best in class in their 1999 Car of the Year Awards.

Now there's the choice of a 5 door model within the range, offering increased versatility.

Like all Accords, the 5 door is one of the quietest and most refined in its class.

It's powered by Honda's Formula One bred VTEC engine, which combines high power with high economy (147ps and 32.8mpg* from the 2.0i).

With multi-link double-wishbone suspension-which keeps the wheels as vertical as possible, thereby maximising road grip-plus ABS and air conditioning, it's a pleasure to drive.

Call 0345 159 159 or visit www.honda.co.uk

Same story, different ending.

The Honda Accord.

*COMBINED FIGURE FOR THE 2.0i MA

Johansens Recommended Country Houses & Small Hotels

England

England has so much to offer – castles, cathedrals, museums, magnificent country houses and the opportunity to stay in areas of great historical importance.

Castle Combe, Wiltshire

Regional Tourist Boards

Cumbria Tourist Board
Ashleigh, Holly Road, Windermere
Cumbria LA23 2AQ
Tel: 015394 44444
England's most beautiful lakes and tallest mountains reach out from the Lake District National Park to a landscape of spectacular coasts, hills and dales.

East of England Tourist Board
Toppesfield Hall, Hadleigh
Suffolk IP7 5DN
Tel: 01473 822922
Cambridgeshire, Essex, Hertfordshire, Bedfordshire, Norfolk, Suffolk and Lincolnshire.

Heart of England Tourist Board
Woodside, Larkhill Road.
Worcester WR5 2EZ
Tel: 01905 763436
Gloucestershire, Hereford & Worcester, Shropshire, Staffordshire, Warwickshire, West Midlands, Derbyshire, Leicestershire, Northamptonshire, Nottinghamshire & Rutland. Represents the districts of Cherwell & West Oxfordshire in the county of Oxfordshire.

London Tourist Board
Glen House, Stag Place
London SW1E 5LT
Tel: 0171 932 2000
The Greater London area (see page 13)

Northumbria Tourist Board
Aykley Heads
Durham DH1 5UX
Tel: 0191 375 3000
The Tees Valley, Durham, Northumberland, Tyne & Wear.

North West Tourist Board
Swan House, Swan Meadow Road, Wigan Pier
Lancashire WN3 5BB
Tel: 01942 821222
Cheshire, Greater Manchester, Lancashire, Merseyside & the High Peak District of Derbyshire.

South East England Tourist Board
The Old Brew House, Warwick Park, Tunbridge
Wells, Kent TN2 5TU
Tel: 01892 540766
East & West Sussex, Kent & Surrey

Southern Tourist Board
40 Chamberlayne Road, Eastleigh
Hampshire SO50 5JH
Tel: 01703 620006
East & North Dorset, Hampshire, Isle of Wight, Berkshire, Buckinghamshire & Oxfordshire.

West Country Tourist Board
60 St David's Hill, Exeter
Devon EX4 4SY
Tel: 01392 425426
Bath & NE Somerset, Bristol, Cornwall and the Isles of Scilly, Devon, Dorset (Western), North Somerset & Wiltshire.

Yorkshire Tourist Board
312 Tadcaster Road
York YO2 2HF
Tel: 01904 707961
Yorkshire and North & North East Lincolnshire.

Further Information

English Heritage
23rd Floor, Portland HouseStag Place
London SW1E 5EE
Tel: 0171-973 3000
Offers an unrivalled choice of properties to visit.

Historic Houses Association
2 Chester Street
London SW1X 7BB
Tel: 0171-259 5688
Ensures the survival of historic houses and gardens in private ownership in Great Britain

The National Trust
36 Queen Anne's Gate
London SW1H 9AS
Tel: 0171-222 9251
Cares for more than 590,000 acres of countryside and over 400 historic buildings.

ARROW MILL HOTEL AND RESTAURANT

ARROW, NEAR ALCESTER, WARWICKSHIRE B49 5NL
TEL: 01789 762419 FAX: 01789 765170

OWNERS: The Woodhams Family

18 rms | 18 ens | SMALL HOTEL

S: £65
D: £84–140

Once a working flour mill, Arrow Mill is proud of its listing in the Domesday Book, when it was valued at three shillings and sixpence. Since Norman times standards and inflation have risen. Today it remains a historic and charming building, although it offers its guests the most modern and comfortable accommodation.

Its rustic charm, enhanced by log fires and exposed beams, is complemented by a spectacular yet secluded riverside setting. Creature comforts are plentiful in the individually furnished bedrooms and panoramic views take in the mill pond, River Arrow and surrounding countryside.

A highly trained team of chefs uses only market-fresh ingredients in maintaining their uncompromising standards. The Millstream Restaurant incorporates the original working floor of the mill, with its wheel still driven by the flowing stream. It offers an à la carte menu and carefully selected wine list to satisfy the most discriminating palate. Similarly high standards are assured by the luncheons from the Miller's Table.

Residential conferences, business meetings, hospitality days and product launches can all be accommodated. **Places of interest nearby:** Stratford-upon-Avon, Warwick Castle and the Cotswolds are all nearby. Arrow Mill is closed from 26 December for two weeks. **Directions: Set back from the A435 1 mile south of Alcester.**

NANNY BROW COUNTRY HOUSE HOTEL & RESTAURANT

CLAPPERSGATE, AMBLESIDE, CUMBRIA LA22 9NF
TEL: 015394 32036 FAX: 015394 32450 E-MAIL: reservations@nannybrowhotel.demon.co.uk

OWNERS: Michael and Carol Fletcher
MANAGER: David Lancaster
CHEF: Dan Harmon

S: £55–£90
D: £110–£180
Suite: £150–£180

Away from the tourists visiting Ambleside at the northern end of Lake Windermere, a Victorian architect built Nanny Brow for himself on this magnificent site on Loughrigg Fell, which overlooks the dramatic Langdale Pikes and River Brathay. Set in five acres of landscaped gardens, the house has been converted into a comfortable elegant hotel whilst retaining its country house charm and has been awarded many accolades such as Hotel of the Year 1998 – Lancashire & Lake District Life, AA Romantic Hotel of the Year and holds two AA Red Rosettes. New arrivals appreciate the welcoming atmosphere of the lounge hall, filled with local antiques and find the drawing room with its graceful furniture and log fires very restful. The pretty bedrooms, individually decorated, have been thoughtfully equipped with many extras. The romantic Garden Suites have balconies or patios outside the sitting rooms. Guests mingle in the inviting Library Bar, before dining by candlelight in the RAC Merit Awards RHCC restaurant. The ever-changing five course menu features the chef's inspired rendition of traditional English dishes, complemented by the many fine wines. Fishing, putting and spa facilities, with membership of a private leisure club and a sailing cruiser on Lake Windermere are offered. **Directions: From Ambleside A593 Coniston Road for 1m. Nanny Brow is on the right.**

SHALLOWDALE HOUSE

AMPLEFORTH, YORK, NORTH YORKSHIRE YO62 4DY
TEL: 01439 788325 FAX: 01439 788885

OWNERS: Anton Van Der Horst and Phillip Gill

| 3 rms | 2 ens | 🌳 |

 S: £40–£50
D: £60–£75

With breathtaking views of unsullied countryside from every room, Shallowdale House is an elegant guest house situated at the edge of Ampleforth village, just inside the North York Moors National Park. Peace and tranquillity are the hallmarks and visitors can relax in the peaceful 2½ acre landscaped garden with its stunning views of the Coxwold Gilling Gap.

Guests relax in the drawing room, with its crackling log fire, or read in the comfortable sitting room, crammed with guide books and literature. Shallowdale House prides itself on the quality of its home-cooked food. Although self-taught, chef Phillip Gill concocts fare of remarkable flair and originality, all made with locally-produced goods. The bedrooms are comfortably decorated and have spacious bathrooms. The house is a totally non-smoking establishment.

Places of interest nearby: Shallowdale House is a perfect base from which to explore the glorious routes of the North York Moors National Park. The historic town of York is nearby, while other towns of interest in the vicinity include Helmsley, Thirsk and Whitby. Visitors interested in the history of this culturally rich area should not miss Rievaulx Abbey, Castle Howard, or the Ryedale Folk Museum.
Directions: Shallowdale House is on the west side of Ampleforth. From York, take B1363, turning left at Brandsby. From Thirsk, take A170.

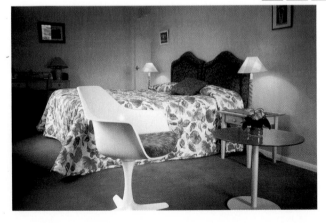

APPLETON HALL

APPLETON-LE-MOORS, NORTH YORKSHIRE YO62 6TF
TEL: 01751 417227 FAX: 01751 417540

OWNERS: Edward and Wendy Horne

9 rms | 9 ens | SMALL HOTEL

S: £65–£70
D: £130–£150
(including 5 course dinner)

Appleton Hall is a focal point of the pretty Yorkshire village of Appleton-le-Moors – which is on the southern side of the North Yorkshire Moors National Park. The hotel is surrounded by beautiful landscaped gardens where guests can sit and relax or wander at their leisure. The elegant refurbished rooms assure visitors they have come to a peaceful and comfortable country house where Edward and Wendy and their staff maintain a high standard of service and hospitality.

The nine en suite bedrooms are all fully equipped to provide the modern necessities – two have their own lounges. One of the rooms has a four-poster bed.

There is a small well-stocked bar to pass the time before dinner. The delectable five-course table d'hôte menu is accompanied by a comprehensive selection of wines. Special breaks available.

Places of interest nearby: The enchanting North York moors and steam railway, Castle Howard, York and the rugged East Coast, returning to log fires on chilly evenings. **Directions: Leave A1 at Thirsk turning, taking the A170, signposted Scarborough. After passing through Kirkbymoorside the village is to the left, and before Pickering.**

 ARUNDEL (Burpham)

BURPHAM COUNTRY HOUSE HOTEL

OLD DOWN, BURPHAM, NR ARUNDEL, WEST SUSSEX BN18 9RJ
TEL: 01903 882160 FAX: 01903 884627

OWNERS: George and Marianne Walker
CHEF: Marianne Walker

S: from £42.50
D: £87–£105

This charming Country House Hotel nestles in a fold of the Sussex South Downs – just perfect for a 'Stress Remedy Break'.

The ten en-suite bedrooms are all tastefully furnished with telephone, television, hairdryer, and tea/coffee facility. A lovely old world garden, with a croquet lawn, surrounds the hotel.

Drinks before dinner can be enjoyed by the open fire in the comfortable Cocktail Lounges. A good wine list is available with most countries represented. Swiss born Marianne Walker has won a well deserved Rosette from the AA for her culinary skills. A constantly changing menu using only the finest ingredients is presented in the Rösti room with its attractive conservatory extension. The Hotel has won a Silver award from the English Tourist Board for quality and the most prestigous Johansens 1999 award for 'Most Excellent Service'.

Special breaks are offered throughout the year. Golf, riding, fishing and sailing are all available in the locality. Racing at Goodwood and Fontwell.

Places of interest nearby: Burpham has a beautiful and historic Norman church, while Arundel, with its Wildfowl Sanctuary and renowned Castle, is three miles away. The coast lies within six miles. **Directions: The Hotel is signposted on the A27 east of Arundel railway bridge. Turn off here and follow this road for 2½ miles.**

Chapel House

FRIARS' GATE, ATHERSTONE, WARWICKSHIRE CV9 1EY
TEL: 01827 718949 FAX: 01827 717702

OWNERS: Chapel House (Atherstone) Ltd
MANAGING DIRECTOR: David Arnold

S: £49.50–£65
D: £70–£80

A former dower house to the now demolished Atherstone Hall, Chapel House is discreetly tucked away in the corner of Atherstone's market square, within a walled garden that remains a particularly attractive feature of the property. With the oldest part of the house dating from about 1720, subsequent additions were made until 1879. Many original features have been retained and others carefully restored so that the house retains the elegance of an earlier age.

Holder of two AA Rosettes since 1995, the restaurant at Chapel House has acquired an enviable reputation for high quality, imaginative food and an extensive and adventurous wine cellar and most attentive service. Chef Adam Bennett uses the very best ingredients and changes the à la carte menu every five or six weeks. Speciality and themed evenings are noteworthy events and special dietary needs can be catered for by prior arrangement. Closed on Christmas Day and Boxing Day, Chapel House is just 25 minutes from the centres of Birmingham and Leicester and is most conveniently situated for those visiting the NEC or using Birmingham's International Airport.

Places of interest nearby: Bosworth Battlefield, Tamworth Castle, Arbury Hall, Lichfield and Coventry Cathedrals and the many industrial museums of the Midlands. Also close is the Belfry Golf Centre. **Directions: On A5 about 8 miles south-east of M42 Jct10. Chapel House is in the market square beside the church.**

BAKEWELL (Rowsley)

EAST LODGE COUNTRY HOUSE HOTEL

ROWSLEY, NR MATLOCK, DERBYSHIRE DE4 2EF
TEL: 01629 734474 FAX: 01629 733949

OWNERS: Joan and David Hardman
CHEF: Mark Allday

S: £68
D: from £90

This graceful 17th century lodge on the edge of the Peak District was originally built as the East Lodge to Haddon Hall, the Derbyshire seat of the Duke of Rutland. Converted to a hotel in the 1980's, East Lodge is now owned and run by Joan and David Hardman and their attentive staff. The lodge has won many accolades including AA 3 star.

The attractive lounge with log fire, charming restaurant and spacious hall offers high levels of comfort combined with a warm and relaxed atmosphere. The 15 en suite bedrooms are tastefully furnished, each having its own distinctive character. Imaginative lunches and dinners are served daily in the excellent AA Rosetted restaurant with lighter meals available in the lounge. A wide selection of fine wines is on offer.

Set in 10 acres of attractive gardens and surrounded by rolling Derbyshire countryside, East Lodge provides a tranquil setting for relaxing breaks, conferences and corporate activity/team building events.

Places of interest nearby: Peak District National Park, which boasts some of the country's most spectacular walks. The famous stately homes, Chatsworth House and Haddon Hall, are within two miles. Bakewell, Buxton, Matlock and Crich are a short drive away. **Directions: Set back from the A6 in Rowsley village, three miles from Bakewell. The hotel entrance is adjacent to the B6012 junction to Sheffield/Chatsworth.**

THE PEACOCK HOTEL AT ROWSLEY

ROWSLEY, NR MATLOCK, DERBYSHIRE DE4 2EB
TEL: 01629 733518 FAX: 01629 732671

OWNERS: Jarvis Hotels plc
MANAGER: Roger Hudson
CHEF: Ashleigh Hooten

S: £85–£100
D: £145–£160
(including dinner)

Once the Dower House to Haddon Hall, this superb 17th century country house is now a marvellous hotel with gardens leading down to the River Derwent.

When first a hotel in 1820 it attracted bathers who plunged into the nearby River Wye! Fishermen are spoilt here. There are 12 rods on the River Wye and two on the Derwent. Tickets are available and the Head Keeper offers advice and tuition. Fish caught will be cooked by the hotel or put in the freezer. The dedicated can enjoy the Angler's Picnic, brought to the riverside. Walkers get a delicious picnic in a thermally insulated knapsack.

The hotel is beautifully furnished throughout, with antiques and flowers in abundance. The bedrooms are extremely comfortable and thoughtfully equipped.

Resident and non-resident diners can enjoy an apéritif in the delightful bar or lounge before dining in one of the three rooms, two of which feature furniture by "Mousey" Thompson. Both lunch and dinner are served in traditional style and smoking during food service is discouraged. A special diet can be catered for with prior notice. Special rates may be available on weekdays at certain times of the year. There are excellent facilities for small meetings in a delightfully furnished room.

Places of interest nearby: Haddon Hall, Chatsworth, Crich Tram Museum. **Directions: M1/exit 28, head for A6. Rowsley is midway between Matlock and Bakewell.**

BAMBURGH

WAREN HOUSE HOTEL

WAREN MILL, BAMBURGH, NORTHUMBERLAND NE70 7EE
TEL: 01668 214581 FAX: 01668 214484 E-MAIL: enquiries@warenhousehotel.co.uk

OWNERS: Peter and Anita Laverack
CHEFS: Jean Francois Perocheau and Paul Tindle

S: £57.50–£67.50
D: £115–£135
Suite: £155–£185

"To visit the North East and not to stay here, would be foolish indeed". So says one entry in a visitors book that is filled with generous and justified praise for this delightful traditional country house which lives up to all its promises and expectations and beyond. The hotel is set in six acres of gardens and woodland on the edge of Budle Bay Bird Sanctuary overlooking Holy Island and two miles from the majestic Bamburgh Castle.

The owners, Anita and Peter, do not cater for children under 14, so they are able to offer a rare commodity of peace and tranquillity even during the busy summer months. Throughout the hotel, the antique furnishings and the immaculate and well-chosen décor evoke a warm, friendly and charming ambience.

Seated in the candlelit dining room, surrounded by family pictures and portraits, guests can select dishes from the daily changing menu and wines from over 250 bins. There is a boardroom for executive meetings. Dogs by prior arrangement. Special short breaks available all year.

Places of interest nearby: The Farne Islands are just a boat trip away, while Bamburgh, Alnwick and Dunstanburgh Castles along with Holy Island are nearby. Waren House is open all year. **Directions: There are advance warning signs on the A1 both north and south. Take B1342 to Waren Mill. Hotel (floodlit at night) is on south-west corner of Budle Bay just two miles from Bamburgh.**

DOWNREW HOUSE HOTEL

BISHOPS TAWTON, BARNSTAPLE, DEVON EX32 0DY
TEL: 01271 342497 FAX: 01271 323947 E-MAIL: downrew@globalnet.co.uk

OWNERS: Patrick and Fiona Byrne
CHEF: David Tithecott

S: £55
D: £80–£130

Built in 1640 and enlarged in the early years of the 18th century, this Queen Anne-style house is surrounded by 12 acres of attractive meadowland and gardens and lies 500ft above sea level facing the slopes of Codden Hill.

Inside, the elegant air of an English country house blends harmoniously with a relaxed ambience making this an ideal escape from the pressures of a hectic lifestyle. The six bedrooms in the main house are well-appointed with en suite facilities whilst those in the coach house are furnished in a more practical manner. A cottage within the grounds provides self-catering accommodation.

The comfortable drawing room is ideal for reclining before sampling dishes made with fine local produce in the restaurant. The daily changing menu includes choices such as honey-baked ham with Cumberland sauce and mignon of beef fillet with potato rosti and a Madeira jus.

Places of interest nearby: Popular day trips include visits to the Maritime Museum at Appledore or exploring the many National Trust properties and gardens within the area, such as Tapeley Park, Rosemoor and Arlington Court. Walkers may follow the Tarka Trail or one of the many wonderful coastal paths. **Directions: From M5, exit at junction 27, and join A361 to Barnstaple. Then take A39 towards Bideford and at the next roundabout join A337. Follow through Bishops Tawton and at the garage on the right, join the lane directly opposite.**

APSLEY HOUSE

141 NEWBRIDGE HILL, SOMERSET BA1 3PT
TEL: 01225 336966 FAX: 01225 425462 E-MAIL: apsleyhouse@easynet.co.uk

OWNERS: David and Annie Lanz

S: £50–£75
D: £70–£110

One mile from the centre of Bath, this elegant Georgian house was reputedly built for the Duke of Wellington in 1830 and is set in a delightful garden.

The hosts, David and Annie Lanz, greet guests with a warm welcome into their home, with its magnificently proportioned reception rooms which have been refurbished in great style and comfort including the addition of two new rooms opening onto the garden. A quite delicious breakfast is the only meal served, although drinks are available. David and Annie will recommend local restaurants and inns which visitors will enjoy.

The bedrooms are invitingly romantic with lovely drapery and delightful en suite bathrooms. Televisions almost seem to intrude in this timeless décor. Private parking available.

Places of interest nearby: There is so much to see and do in Bath, the centre of which is just a 25 minutes stroll from Apsley House. The magnificent architecture includes the Assembly Rooms, mentioned so often in Jane Austen's and in Georgette Heyer's historical novels, the Royal Crescent and the Roman Baths. Fascinating museums, the thriving theatre and excellent shopping all add to ones enjoyment of this lovely city. The Cotswolds, Mendip Hills, Stourhead, Stonehenge, Avebery and Longleat are within driving distance. **Directions: The hotel lies one mile west of the centre of Bath, on the A431 which branches off A4, the Upper Bristol Road.**

BATH LODGE HOTEL

NORTON ST PHILIP, BATH, SOMERSET BA3 6NH
TEL: 01225 723040 FAX: 01225 723737 E-MAIL: walker@bathlodge.demon.co.uk

OWNERS: Graham and Nicola Walker

  S: from £45
D: £65–£95

The Bath Lodge Hotel, originally called Castle Lodge, was built between 1806 and 1813 as one of six lodges added to a former gentleman's residence known as Farleigh House. This splendid building, with its towers, battlements, portcullis and heraldic shields, is redolent of Arthurian romance and offers guests a delightful setting in which to escape the stresses and strains of modern life.

The rooms, which are superbly decorated and furnished, are beautifully located and have many castellated features within them. Three rooms overlook the magnificent natural gardens with their cascading stream and the adjacent deer forest. The main entrance hall, lounge and conservatory all contain oak beamed ceilings, natural masonry and large log burning fireplaces. All the rooms are furnished in keeping with this unique building.

An excellent breakfast is served at the hotel. A five course dinner is available Friday and Saturday evenings. Alternatively there are many restaurants locally and in Bath. The hotel has a no-smoking policy, but guests may smoke in the conservatory area.

Places of interest nearby: Stonehenge and Longleat. Bath Lodge is an ideal location for enjoying the tourist attractions of the World Heritage City of Bath itself. Wells and Bristol are also both within easy reach. **Directions: From Bath take the A36 Warminster road. Bath Lodge is on your left after approximately seven miles.**

BLOOMFIELD HOUSE

146 BLOOMFIELD ROAD, BATH, SOMERSET BA2 2AS
TEL: 01225 420105 FAX: 01225 481958 E-MAIL: bloomfieldhouse@compuserve.com

OWNERS: Bridget and Malcolm Cox

  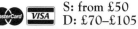

S: from £50
D: £70–£105

This elegant country house, Grade II listed, was commissioned in 1800 by a notable Mr Henshaw, later to become Lord Mayor of Bath. It nestles in a tranquil location in grounds that afford magnificent views over the city.

Bloomfield House is one of the most comfortable and relaxing country houses in the area and is furnished with handsome antiques, hand-woven silk curtains and French chandeliers.

The main bedrooms feature canopied or four-poster beds, including "The principal bedroom of the Mayor and Mayoress of Bath (1902/3)". Remote control colour television, direct dial telephone and tea/coffee making facilities are available in all bedrooms. There is ample parking.

A comprehensive list of restaurants and menus is available at Bloomfield House from which guests may choose their evening meals. Bloomfield House is a strictly non-smoking house.

Riding, golf, swimming, sauna and leisure facilities are available locally by arrangement.

Places of interest nearby: The Cotswolds, Castle Combe, Stourhead, Stonehenge and Longleat. **Directions: From the centre of Bath take the A367 Wells road for ¼ mile towards Exeter. Fork right after The Bear Pub; Bloomfield House is on the right before the third road junction.**

DUKES' HOTEL

GREAT PULTENEY STREET, BATH, SOMERSET BA2 4DN
TEL: 01225 463 512 FAX: 01225 483733

OWNERS: Caparo Hotels Ltd
MANAGER: Theresa Vickery

24 rms | 24 ens | SMALL HOTEL

S: £55–£70
D: £70–£100

Set just a few minutes' stroll from the city centre of Bath, Dukes' Hotel is a late 18th century Grade I listed building which has been extensively restored. It stands in Great Pulteney Street, Europe's most elegant Georgian boulevard. Mouldings, cornices and many other original features of the time have been retained as a mark of its architectural importance.

Internal refurbishment and modernisation has created elegant and comfortable accommodation throughout. The bedrooms have been carefully furnished to a high standard and include every modern comfort.

Breakfast is a generous meal, served in the hotel's restaurant. The dinner menu changes daily with the chef preparing sumptuous homemade meals using local produce. The hotel is fully licenced and guests may relax in either the cosy bar or the comfortable lounge. A good selection of wines have been chosen to complement any meal.

Places of interest nearby: Among the many places to visit in the city are the Roman Baths, Pump Room, Assembly Rooms and a number of museums. **Directions: From M4, junction 18, take A46 to Bath. Turn right into London Road, left at lights, over Bathwick Bridge, then right into Great Pulteney Street.**

EAGLE HOUSE

CHURCH STREET, BATHFORD, BATH, SOMERSET BA1 7RS
TEL: 01225 859946 FAX: 01225 859430 E-MAIL: jonap@eagleho.demon.co.uk

OWNERS: John and Rosamund Napier

 S: £38–£48
D: £48–£78

Three miles from Bath lies the charming conservation village of Bathford. Behind a high stone wall, wrought-iron gates and elegant façade, this Georgian home, designed by John Wood, stands in 1½ acres of grounds, giving far-reaching views of the surrounding countryside.

The eight bedrooms, including some large family rooms, all have private facilities, colour television, hairdryers and tea and coffee-making facilities. Cots and extra beds can be provided upon request. There is a spacious drawing room, where meetings for up to 12 people can be held, and a second, smaller lounge. Although dinner is not served at Eagle House, the owners, John and Rosamund Napier are always glad to help with reservations for tables in one of Bath's many good restaurants. For exercise there is a new lawn tennis court.

Set in a walled garden adjacent to the main house is a cottage with two bedrooms, two bathrooms, sitting room and kitchen, which can be occupied for stays of two nights or more. It offers complete privacy with views across the valley.

Places of interest nearby: The beautiful city of Bath, Castle Combe, the National Trust village of Lacock, the Cotswolds, Longleat House, Avebury and Stonehenge.
Directions: From the A4 take the A363 towards Bradford-on-Avon. After 150 yards, veer left up Bathford Hill. Take first right into Church Street; Eagle House is 200 yards on the right.

THE OLD PRIORY HOTEL

CHURCH SQUARE, MIDSOMER NORTON, BATH, SOMERSET BA3 2HX
TEL: 01761 416784 FAX: 01761 417851 E-MAIL: reservations@theoldpriory.com

OWNERS: Terri Knight
CHEF: Andy Jenner

S: £47.50–67.50
D: £67.50–£97.50

The Old Priory, circa 1152, sits in the quiet town of Midsomer Norton. The décor is Jacobean in style and the house was home to an order of monks who founded Christ College, Oxford and was owned by the college until 1712.

The welcoming owner, Terri Knight, searched throughout the UK for her 'dream hotel' and after many inspections, she happened across this country house. The charm and character of bygone times have been preserved with large Inglenook fireplaces, flagstone floors and oak beams, featured throughout the property.

The six bedrooms are all en suite and offer a range of modern comforts. Each room is individual in character, reflecting the age and uniqueness of this listed property. Fresh, local produce is used to prepare the fine cuisine, served in the attractive dining room.

Places of interest nearby: These include the Roman Baths at Bath, Cheddar Gorge and Caves, Wookey Hole and Glastonbury. The area is a delight for heritage enthusiasts as Longleat House and Safari Park, Stourhead House and Gardens, Castle Combe and Wells Cathedral are all within easy reach. **Directions: From M4, exit at junction 18 onto A46 to Bath. Join A367 towards Exeter and at Radstock turn right to Midsomer Norton.**

OLDFIELDS

102 WELLS ROAD, BATH, SOMERSET BA2 3AL
TEL: 01225 317984 FAX: 01225 444471 E-MAIL: info@oldfields.co.uk

OWNERS: Berkeley and Moira Gaunt

S: £55–£65
D: £60–£85

Oldfields is a large, elegant Victorian house built of the honey-coloured stone for which the city of Bath is famous. Superbly positioned just 10 minutes walk from the city centre, it has a private car park for the use of guests.

Although the house is equipped with every modern feature to ensure that visitors experience maximum comfort and convenience, it retains many of the elaborate cornices and artistry of its original character.

The bedrooms are beautifully furnished with rich fabrics and antiques and offer a full range of amenities. Ideal for the less mobile, two rooms are situated on the ground floor with level entry. Oldfields is a totally non smoking hotel.

Guests can choose between a traditional English breakfast or the lighter continental alternative offered by an extensive buffet. Unlimited supplies of tea and coffee are available and newspapers are provided for those with time to linger. Bath is full of excellent restaurants, many within a fifteen minute walk of Oldfields. Outdoor pursuits such as hot-air ballooning, golf and horse-riding can be arranged.

Places of interest nearby: Within Bath itself are the famous Roman baths and pump room, the Book Museum and No 1 Royal Crescent. The city is also the perfect centre from which to explore the Cotswolds, Glastonbury and Wells Cathedral, east to Stonehenge and Salisbury, west to Bristol and South Wales. **Directions: From the M4 junction 18 follow the signs to Bath city centre, then take the A367 Wells Road.**

PARADISE HOUSE

HOLLOWAY, BATH, SOMERSET BA2 4PX
TEL: 01225 317723 FAX: 01225 482005 E-MAIL: paradise@aspleyhouse.easynet.co.uk

OWNERS: David and Annie Lanz

S: £50–£75
D: £65–£115

In the peaceful grounds of this early 18th century mansion house, guests could be forgiven for forgetting that they are only seven minutes' walk from the Roman Baths, Pump Room and Abbey in the centre of the beautiful Georgian city of Bath.

Situated in a quiet cul-de-sac, Paradise House has been carefully modernised and restored to a high standard to enhance its classical elegance. Ornate plaster ceilings and a marble fireplace adorn the public rooms; where the décor is essentially a fusion of antique and contemporary furniture and soft pastel fabrics. The new garden room is glorious, featuring a sumptuous four-poster bed. The large walled garden, with its fish pond and rose covered pergola, is a delightful sun-trap affording a panoramic vista of the city and surrounding landscape, where guests may enjoy a game of boules .

The new owners, David and Annie, extend a friendly welcome to all their guests and are on hand to offer advice on the many nearby attractions. Although neither lunch nor dinner is served, details of over 85 local restaurants are provided. Garage parking is available.

Places of interest nearby: Wells, Glastonbury and Stonehenge are within easy reach. The city is also notable as a fashionable shopping centre and home of the arts. **Directions: Enter Bath on A4 London Road. Turn left onto A36. Take first left after viaduct onto A367 Exeter Road. Go left at Day and Pierce and down hill into Holloway cul-de-sac.**

VILLA MAGDALA

HENRIETTA ROAD, BATH, SOMERSET BA2 6LX
TEL: 01225 466329 FAX: 01225 483207 E-MAIL: jsvilla@villamagdala.co.uk

OWNERS: Mr and Mrs Roy Thwaites

S: £65–£85
D: £80–£120

Built in 1868, the Villa Magdala is steeped in a most interesting history. The property takes its name from one of Sir Charles Napier's victories in Ethiopia as Sir Charles himself was a resident in the road at the time of construction. All the attractions of Bath are within easy reach, making the house an ideal choice for those wishing to discover the city.

The 18 bedrooms are well-appointed and feature an array of modern conveniences from colour televisions and hairdryers to refreshment trays. All are en suite. The airy dining room provides a most convivial ambience in which to enjoy a traditional English breakfast whilst at dinnertime, the attentive owners are pleased to recommend some of the many nearby restaurants and brasseries.

Places of interest nearby: Pulteney Bridge, the Roman Baths and Pump Room are only a five minute walk away whilst keen shoppers will be pleased with the variety of individual and specialist shops in the centre of Bath. The National Trust village of Lacock is worth a visit and the area abounds with many stately homes and museums. There are delighful canalside walks along the Kennet and Avon canal. **Directions: From M4, junction 18, take the A46 to Bath. Turn right into London Road, left at lights, over Cleveland Bridge and second turning left into Henrietta Road.**

WIDBROOK GRANGE

TROWBRIDGE ROAD, BRADFORD-ON-AVON, WILTSHIRE BA15 1UH
TEL: 01225 864750/863173 FAX: 01225 862890

OWNERS: John and Pauline Price

S: £65–£95
D: £95–£115

According to the ancient rent books, Widbrook Grange was built as a model farm in the 18th century amid eleven acres of idyllic grounds, traversed by a stream. No longer a farm, Widbrook still reflects its agricultural heritage. Together resident owners John and Pauline Price have converted the Grange with skill and care to combine contemporary comforts with a traditional ambience.

All of the bedrooms, whether a spacious four-poster room or one that is petite and cosy, are well appointed with facilities and antique furnishings. Some of the bedrooms are in the recently converted 200-year old stone barn which forms the courtyard. Evening dinner is available Monday to Thursday in the spacious antique furnished dining room and there are also many excellent restaurants locally about which your hosts can advise you. The Manvers suite, with its oak table and carver chairs has been designed for board meetings, seminars and private functions.

Widbrook boasts a superb indoor heated swimming pool and gymnasium. There is an arrangement with nearby Kingsdown Golf Club. Riding and fishing can also be arranged.

Places of interest nearby: Longleat House and Safari Park, Bath, Avebury and Stonehenge. **Directions: From Bradford-on-Avon take the A363 Trowbridge Road, the Grange is on the right after the canal bridge.**

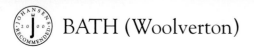

WOOLVERTON HOUSE

WOOLVERTON, NR BATH, SOMERSET BA3 6QS
TEL: 01373 830415 FAX: 01373 831243

OWNERS: Noel and Marina Terry

   SMALL HOTEL

S: £44–£55
D: £55–£80

This early 19th century house, built originally as a rectory for the 'United Parishes of Woolverton & Rode', has been sympathetically converted and restored to become an elegant English country house. It is set in over 2½ acres of grounds and commands scenic views over the 'glebe lands' on which the parson traditionally had grazing rights.

Today Woolverton House has been developed by its present-day hospitable owners into a retreat where the emphasis is on heritage, history and nature. The gardens are full of colour and also include a narrow gauge steam railway.

All the bedrooms are pleasantly decorated and furnished with private bathrooms en suite. They are fully equipped with colour television, direct dial telephone, hospitality tray, trouser press, hairdryer and minibar. Both the dining room and drawing room have log fires in the cooler months and the conservatory bar is pleasant all year.

The restaurant is beautifully furnished in excellent taste with food and wines to match and has been awarded an AA Rosette.

Places of interest nearby: There is plenty to explore in the historical and agricultural history of this area – most within a 20 mile radius. Major attractions include Bath, Longleat, East Somerset steam railway, Cheddar Caves, Wookey Hole and Rode Tropical Bird Gardens. **Directions: From M4 exit 17 take A350 and then A361 for Woolverton – or on A36 halfway between Bath and Warminster.**

DANNAH FARM COUNTRY HOUSE

BOWMAN'S LANE, SHOTTLE, NR BELPER, DERBYSHIRE DE56 2DR
TEL: 01773 550273/630 FAX: 01773 550590 E-MAIL: reservations@dannah.demon.co.uk

OWNERS: Joan and Martin Slack
CHEF: Joan Slack

S: £45–£55
D: £70–£110

Set amid undulating countryside high above the Ecclesbourne Valley, Dannah Farm is part of the Chatsworth Estates on the edge of the Peak District. This is an exceptional farmhouse conversion, so it is not surprising that in addition to obtaining 5 AA Diamonds, Dannah Farm has won National Awards for Excellence and Tourism in the region. As the Georgian farmhouse is still part of a 128 acre working farm, guests will discover plenty of activity within the grounds.

Rooms are beautifully furnished with antiques and old pine, and four-poster suites, twin-bedded, double and single rooms are offered, all overlooking rolling pastures and large, pretty gardens. The restaurant has rapidly earned a fine reputation.

Aromas of freshly baked bread, home-made soups and piquant sauces escaping from the kitchen whet the appetite for dinner, which is served with good wines in relaxed surroundings and is by arrangement. **Places of interest nearby:** The countryside is criss-crossed with footpaths with walks in all directions. Dannah Farm is optimally placed to enjoy the many attractions of the area – Chatsworth, Haddon Hall, Dovedale and water sports at Carsington. **Directions: From Derby take the A6 Matlock road. At Duffield turn left onto the B5023 towards Wirksworth. At the traffic lights at Cowers Lane turn right onto the A517 towards Belper, then take the first left to Shottle. Bowman's Lane is 100 yards past the crossroads in the village.**

THE MANOR HOUSE

NORTHLANDS, WALKINGTON, EAST YORKSHIRE HU17 8RT
TEL: 01482 881645 FAX: 01482 866501 E-MAIL: the manor-house-hotel@compuserve.com

OWNERS: Derek and Lee Baugh
CHEF: Derek Baugh

S: £70–£84
D: £85–£120

This delightful, 19th century house with decorated chimneys soaring majestically skywards stands serenely on the wooded flanks of the rolling Yorkshire Wolds. Surrounded by three acres of tree-lined grounds which overlook paddocks and parkland it is the perfect retreat for those seeking relaxation, comfort and excellent food. The house has been the RAC small hotel of the North on two occasions.

The seven spacious, en suite bedrooms – one in an adjoining cottage – provide superb views over the countryside. Each is individually furnished and decorated to the highest standard and guests will find themselves pampered with unexpected and useful personal comforts.

Chef-patron Derek Baugh, formerly of The Dorchester, provides a distinctive, imaginative style of cuisine, awarded two AA Rosettes. All meals are served with flair and the wine list is extensive. On summer evenings, diners can enjoy their evening meal in the cool elegance of the conservatory which overlooks the south facing terrace and lawns.

Places of interest nearby: Horse riding, clay pigeon shooting, rambling, hunting and golf are close by while Beverley, York and Doncaster racecourses are within easy reach. North Yorkshire Moors, the rugged coastline, the walled city of York with its magnificent Minster, enchanting villages and numerous stately homes. **Directions: From Walkington on B1230, turn left at the traffic lights (following the brown hotel signs), then left and left again for the hotel.**

BIBURY COURT

BIBURY COURT, BIBURY, GLOUCESTERSHIRE GL7 5NT
TEL: 01285 740337 FAX: 01285 740660 E-MAIL: aj@biburycourt.co.uk

OWNERS: Jane Collier, Andrew and Anne Johnston
MANAGER: Simon Gould

S: from £75
D: from £100
Suite: £150

Past visitors to Bibury Court are reputed to have included Charles II and during the reign of George III, the Prince Regent. This gracious mansion dates from Tudor times, but the main part was built in 1633 by Sir Thomas Sackville, an illegitimate son of the 1st Earl of Dorset. After generations of illustrious owners, it became a hotel in 1968.

The great house is set on the outskirts of Bibury, which William Morris called "the most beautiful village in England". As a hotel, it is run on country house lines with one of the main objectives being the provision of good food and wine in informal and pleasurable surroundings. Log fires during the cooler months add to the comfort of guests.

There are some lovely panelled rooms in the house, many containing antique furniture. Many of the bedrooms have four posters, all have private bathrooms and for those who like greater privacy there is the Sackville suite.

Trout fishing is available in the Coln, which forms the southern boundary of the hotel's six acres of grounds and there are golf courses at Burford and Cirencester. Water sports and riding are available nearby. The hotel is closed at Christmas.

Places of interest nearby: Bibury Court is ideally placed for touring the Cotswolds, while Stratford, Oxford, Cheltenham and Bath are all within easy reach.
Directions: Bibury is on the B4425, seven miles from Burford and seven miles from Cirencester.

BIGNELL PARK HOTEL

CHESTERTON, NR BICESTER, OXFORDSHIRE OX6 8UE
TEL: 01869 241444 FAX: 01869 241192

OWNERS: Eirling Sorenson
CHEF: Paul Franklin

S: £75–£85
D: £95–£105
Four-poster: £125

Set in a quiet village location, this small country hotel was built in 1740 and is surrounded by two and a half acres of informal gardens and an orchard. Bignell Park Hotel is an ideal choice for those seeking a country break as inside, the ambience of traditional old world Cotswold charm blends harmoniously with modern comforts.

The 14 bedrooms are beautifully appointed with soft fabrics and fine furnishings. All are en suite and feature an array of the latest facilities. Eight additional rooms are currently under construction.

Guests sip a drink in the oak beamed cocktail bar before dining in the attractive restaurant enhanced by wooden beams, a glowing open fire and a minstrels gallery. The outstanding cuisine, recently awarded an AA Rosette, is a fusion of English and continental flavours, complemented by a good list of fine wines. The delicate pastry dishes are highly recommended.

Places of interest nearby: Bignell Park is set in the heart of the Cotswolds and a plethora of historic sites are within easy reach such as Blenheim Palace, the ancestral home of the Dukes of Marlborough. The regency city of Bath, the university town of Oxford and Shakespeare's Stratford upon Avon are all nearby. **Directions: Bignell Park is only 2 miles away from Jct9 off the London to Birmingham M40 motorway and is served by the Bicester to London Marylebone railway line.**

YEOLDON HOUSE HOTEL

DURRANT LANE, NORTHAM, NR BIDEFORD, DEVON EX39 2RL
TEL: 01237 474400 FAX: 01237 476618

OWNERS: Kevin and Sue Jelley
CHEF: Kevin Jelley

10 rms · 10 ens · SMALL HOTEL

S: £45–£60
D: £75–£100

Kevin and Sue Jelley have achieved a special quality at Yeoldon, a distinguished and attractive country house standing in beautiful grounds in the village of Northam, birthplace of J.H.Taylor, England's only winner of 5 Opens. Visitors are charmed by the hotel's refreshingly casual atmosphere and its blend of Victorian grandeur with today's comforts.

A rich green and terracotta colour theme enhances the Yeoldon's relaxing ambience. Deep, soft sofas and armchairs in the inviting lounge are so comfortable that guests may find it difficult to leave them for pursuit of the hotel's surrounding charms. The bedrooms are beautifully decorated in country style and have panoramic views over the expansive lawned gardens which slope gently down to the River Torridge and the estuary beyond.

A wide choice of cuisine is served in the elegant restaurant where chef Kevin Jelley takes pride in his à la carte dinner menus. He uses local produce whenever possible and bakes his own bread and biscuits daily.

Places of interest nearby: Bideford, Arlington Court, Rosemoor Gardens, Tapeley Park, Lundy Island and the picturesque village of Clovelly. **Directions: From the M5, exit at junction 27 and follow the A361 to Barnstaple and then the A39 to Bideford. At Torridge Bridge roundabout turn right onto the A386 towards Northam and then take the third turning on the right.**

BIGGIN HALL

BIGGIN-BY-HARTINGTON, BUXTON, DERBYSHIRE SK17 0DH
TEL: 01298 84451 FAX: 01298 84681 E-MAIL: Bigginhall@compuserve.com

OWNER: James Moffett

 S: £40–£55
D: £50–£75

Centrally situated in the Peak District National Park, Biggin Hall is a 17th century, Grade II* listed property set in eight acres of grounds. Situated 1,000 feet above sea level, the air may particularly benefit insomnia and asthma sufferers. Visitors come here for the peace and quiet and to enjoy the landscape with its dry-stone walling, deep wooded valleys, heather-clad moorlands and historic market towns and villages. Walkers will appreciate the many uncrowded footpaths nearby.

The rooms of this house feature massive oak timbers and antiques, with one containing a superb four-poster bed. One of the sitting rooms has an open log fire where guests can enjoy a convivial atmosphere. A recently converted 18th century stone building, comprising four self-contained studio apartments and two-roomed suites, each with a private bathroom, is situated 30 yards from the main house. The traditional farmhouse cooking puts emphasis on free-range produce, wholefoods and natural flavours. Dogs are accommodated in the apartments only. **Places of interest nearby:** Chatsworth, Bolsover Castle, Kedleston Hall, Alton Towers, Crich Tramway Museum, Buxton, Ashbourne and Bakewell. **Directions: This country house is situated at the end of Biggin Village, which is off the A515, nine miles from Ashbourne and ten miles from Buxton.**

LOWER BROOK HOUSE

BLOCKLEY, NR MORETON-IN-MARSH, GLOUCESTERSHIRE GL56 9DS
TEL/FAX: 01386 700286 E-MAIL: Lowerbrookhouse@compuserve.com

OWNER: Marie Mosedale–Cooper

 D: £80–£96

Lower Brook House has been skilfully created from a well-built detached property dating back to the 17th century and it epitomises the traditional Cotswold stone house of its period. Winner of the Times 1999 Golden Pillow Award, it is quietly situated in the village of Blockley, famous in the 1700s for its silk trade.

The hostess takes great care to ensure that guests' requirements are swiftly attended to. The five en suite bedrooms have antique furnishings and plenty of interesting bric-à-brac. One of the rooms has a four-poster bed and all have tea and coffee facilities, a colour television, hairdryer and fluffy towelling robes, fresh fruit and flowers, chocolates and mineral water are also provided.

Memorable breakfasts are enjoyed along with unlimited amounts of fresh and cooked fruits. The award-winning restaurant offers a daily-changing menu for fine dining and fresh local produce is used from the kitchen garden. A cellar of choice wines, with a selection of 36 to choose from, is available to complement your meal.

Places of interest nearby: Blockley is a short drive from Cheltenham, Oxford and Stratford-upon-Avon. As well as being a good base for exploring other picturesque local villages, Blockley is the perfect location to peruse the Moreton market every Tuesday. **Directions: As you enter the village from Moreton-in-Marsh, Lower Brook House can be found on your right.**

 BOLTON (Edgworth)

PELTON FOLD FARM

BURY ROAD, EDGWORTH, BOLTON, LANCASHIRE BL7 0BS
TEL: 01204 852207 FAX: 01204 852207

OWNERS: Christine Collins

| 2 rms | 2 ens | |

S: £35–£40
D: £55–£60

Pelton Fold Farm is set in four acres of farmland and gardens. The 16th century house overlooks the old Russia Fishing Lake and has views of the surrounding countryside and two church spires. The original oak beams, stone mullions, flag floors and fireplaces have all been preserved, giving the house a wonderfully rustic feel.

The sitting room and dining room look out onto the walled garden and both have wood burning stoves. Dinners comprise a set meal of traditional English fare made with fresh local produce and seasonal vegetables from the farm's garden. The house is unlicenced and guests are invited to bring their own wine. There are a number of charming traditional pubs in the nearby village of Edgworth, within a five minute walk.

Both of the double bedrooms are en suite and feature soft fabrics and modern amenities. Guests can observe the variety of wildlife in the grounds and other country pursuits such as fishing and horse-riding are in easy reach.
Places of interest nearby: Pelton is ideally located for Manchester, Bury, Bolton and Blackburn. Turton Tower, Jumbles Country Park and The East Lancashire Railway are all worth a visit. Directions: From Bolton take A676 towards Burnley. After 2 miles, left at lights into Bradshaw Road and after 1½ miles turn left at crossroads into Bury Road. Follow the road along, Pelton Fold Farm is on the left opposite 333 Bury Road.

QUARLTON MANOR FARM

PLANTATION ROAD, EDGWORTH, TURTON, BOLTON, LANCASHIRE BL7 0DD
TEL: 01204 852277 FAX: 01204 852286

OWNERS: Pauline and Philip Davies
CHEF: Pauline Davies

S: £40–£80
D: £69–£95

Standing in its own 20 acres at the heart of rural Lancashire's hill country this sprawling 17th century stone-built farmhouse is the essence of peace and tranquillity. It is ideally suited to those seeking the friendliness and warmth of homely, family accommodation. It has built up an excellent local reputation for its food. Huge open fireplaces, heavy oak beams, antique furnishings and wholesome farmhouse cooking add to the hotel's charm.

Guests enjoy sumptuous five-course set dinners around a large table in the galleried dining hall or in the conservatory with its panoramic views over the countryside and hills. Business meetings are welcome. Two double-bedded rooms and a twin share two bathrooms. The main bedroom is en suite and has a huge four-poster bed. With another four-poster in the three room en suite ground floor family suite which can sleep six in total. All bedrooms are non-smoking. Original member of the Green Globe Sustainable Tourism initiative.

Places of interest nearby: Manchester, The East Lancashire Railway, Jumbles Country Park and Turton Tower. **Directions: From Bolton take A676 (A56) towards Burnley. After two miles turn left at traffic lights into Bradshaw Road and after one-and-a-half miles turn left at crossroads. Turn right at the Edgworth crossroads into Broadhead Road, then turn right again into Plantation Road and then 1 mile to the end.**

CROSS LANE HOUSE HOTEL

CROSS LANE HEAD, BRIDGNORTH, SHROPSHIRE WV16 4SJ
TEL: 01746 764887 FAX: 01746 768667 E-MAIL: m.hobbs@virgin.net

OWNERS: Ann and Mike Hobbs
CHEF: Ann Hobbs

S: £42.50
D: £60

Situated just a mile from the heart of the historic town of Bridgnorth, this delightful 17th century house, under the hospitable ownership of Ann and Mike Hobbs, is a haven of peace, quiet and comfort amidst the beauty of Shropshire's open countryside.

The hotel is surrounded by two acres of mature gardens from these and from the windows of the house there are stunning views over the Severn Valley.

Although ancient in origin, with an ornate William IV tiled entrance hall, impressive inglenook fireplace and exposed beams throughout, Cross Lane House offers every modern comfort for the discerning guest.

All bedrooms are en suite and most have roll topped Victorian cast iron baths with overhead showers. The restaurant is small and intimate with Ann serving up excellent wholesome traditional dishes complemented by a carefully chosen wine list. Diets can be catered for. Golf, riding, fishing and shooting facilities are a short drive away. Smoking is not permitted within the hotel.

Places of interest nearby: Ironbridge, the birthplace of the industrial revolution, Shrewsbury, the Coalport China Museum, the Severn Valley Railway, the Midland Motor Museum and the Aerospace Museum at Cosford.
Directions: Cross Lane House is on the B4373 Bridgnorth-Broseley road, one mile north of Bridgnorth.

THE GRANVILLE

124 KINGS ROAD, BRIGHTON BN1 2FA
TEL: 01273 326302 FAX: 01273 728294 E-MAIL: granville@brighton.co.uk

OWNERS: Mick and Sue Paskins
CHEF: Alison Lynch

24 rms	24 ens	SMALL HOTEL

 S: £55–£85
D: £85–£155

You only have to take one step through the front door to realise, and appreciate, that this Regency sea front property is a place for the style aware. Proprietor Sue Paskins believes that a hotel stay should be memorable and has furnished The Granville with flair and elegance to offer guests something unique. Situated in the heart of Brighton overlooking the sea and the splendid Edwardian West Pier, her creation is both lavish and original in its furnishings, decor and outlook and has been awarded 3 Stars by the English Tourist Board.

The majority of the 24 en suite bedrooms are not large but they are quite distinctive and have sumptuous bathrooms. Many have fabulous sea views. Among them is the romantic, pale pink and white Brighton Rock Room, the opulent Noel Coward Room with its art-deco bathroom, the huge late-Victorian four-poster bed and marble fireplaces of the Balcony Room and the Marina Room with a water bed.

Apart from breakfast, the cuisine served in Trogs Restaurant is vegetarian, comprising imaginative and substantial dishes. Meals are complemented by an excellent range of organic wines. The atmosphere is convivial with beautifully laid tables. **Places of interest nearby:** The delights of Brighton, including the Royal Pavilion, the famous Lanes, theatres and cinemas. Glyndebourne, Arundel, Chichester and Lewes are within easy reach. **Directions: The Granville is on the north side of Kings Road opposite the West Pier.**

THE BROADWAY HOTEL

THE GREEN, BROADWAY, WORCESTERSHIRE WR12 7AA
TEL: 01386 852401 FAX: 01386 853879 E-MAIL: bookings@cotswold–inns–hotels.co.uk

OWNERS: Cotswold Inns and Hotels Ltd
MANAGER: Noel Linington
CHEF: Vernon Crowther

20 rms 20 ens

S: £68.50–£75
D: £110–£125

The delightful Broadway Hotel stands proudly in the centre of the picturesque Cotswold village of Broadway where every stone evokes memories of Elizabethan England. Once used by the Abbots of Pershore, the hotel was formerly a 16th century house, as can be seen by its architecture which combines the half timbers of the Vale of Evesham with the distinctive honey-coloured and grey stone of the Cotswolds. It epitomises a true combination of old world charm and modern day amenities with friendly efficient service. All of the bedrooms provide a television, telephone and tea and coffee making facilities. Traditional English dishes and a peaceful ambience are offered in the beamed Courtyard Restaurant. There is an impressive variety of à la carte dishes complemented by a good wine list. The cosy and congenial Jockey Club bar is a pleasant place to relax and enjoy a drink. The inn overlooks the village green at the bottom of the main street where guests can browse through shops offering an array of fine antiques. On a clear day, 13 counties of England and Wales can be viewed from Broadway Tower.

Places of interest nearby: Snowhill, Burford, Chipping Campden, Bourton-on-the-Water, Stow-on-the-Wold and Winchcombe as well as larger Cheltenham, Worcester and Stratford are within easy reach. **Directions: From London M40 to Oxford, A40 to Burford, A429 through Stow-on-the-Wold, then A44 to Broadway.**

COLLIN HOUSE HOTEL

COLLIN LANE, BROADWAY, WORCESTERSHIRE WR12 7PB
TEL: 01386 858354 FAX: 01386 858697 E-MAIL: collin.house@virginnet

OWNERS: Tricia and Keith Ferguson
CHEF: Antony Icke

  S: from £69
D: from £92

Believed to have formerly been the home of a wealthy wool merchant, Collin House is a 16th century Cotswold stone house standing in 2 acres of grounds, encompassing gardens, meadows and orchards set amid rolling countryside. It has been carefully restored to retain its original character, with oak beams, inglenook fireplaces where log fires burn on cool evenings, antique paintings and furnishings.

Each of the bedrooms is individual in style and is decorated and furnished to a high standard. All rooms have private bathrooms and two have four-poster beds. Collin House has long held a reputation for good English cooking served with flair and the candlelit restaurant, with its exposed timbers, mullioned windows and views over the gardens, provides the perfect setting. A balanced choice of delicious dishes is offered by the à la carte menu while an exceptional variety of imaginative bar and garden meals is served at lunchtime. Recommended by many accommodation and good eating guides. Closed for five days at Christmas.

Places of interest nearby: The Cotswolds, renowned for its picturesque villages and National Trust properties. Stratford-upon-Avon and Cheltenham are also within easy reach.

Directions: Collin House is 1 mile north-west of Broadway on the A44; turn right at the roundabout into Collin Lane.

BROADWAY (Willersey)

THE OLD RECTORY

CHURCH STREET, WILLERSEY, BROADWAY, GLOUCESTERSHIRE WR12 7PN
TEL: 01386 853729 FAX: 01386 858061 E-MAIL: beauvoisin@btinternet.com

OWNERS: Liz and Chris Beauvoisin

S: £55–£85
D: £75–£110

Built of mellow Cotswold stone, the 17th century Old Rectory at Willersey is quietly tucked away at the end of a lane, opposite the 11th century church. With a backdrop of the Cotswold hills and a dry stone wall surrounding the delightful garden, this is truly an idyllic spot. A mulberry tree, reputed to have been planted in the reign of Elizabeth I, is laden with fruit and often supplies the breakfast table.

A superb breakfast is served in the elegant dining room, with log fires in winter. The immaculate bedrooms feature attractive bathrooms, each subtly stencilled and colour washed. Amenities include colour television, radio alarms, hairdryers and Crabtree and Evelyn toiletries. The combination of four poster beds and tranquillity make this an ideal place for honeymooners. A self-catering holiday cottage is also available alongside the non-smoking house.

The Bell Inn for lunch or dinner and many other fine restaurants are only minutes away. An ideal base from which to tour the Cotswolds with walks straight from the house and maps and picnics provided. Horse riding and bicycle hire locally. Broadway golf course is only 1 mile away.

Places of interest nearby: Cheltenham, Stratford, Warwick Castle. Blenheim Palace, Snowshill Manor, Hidcote Gardens.
Directions: From Broadway take B4632 (Stratford Road) for 1¹/₂ miles. At Willersey turn right (opposite duck pond) into Church Street, the Rectory is at end of road. The private car park is at the rear of property.

THATCHED COTTAGE HOTEL & RESTAURANT

16 BROOKLEY ROAD, BROCKENHURST, HAMPSHIRE SO42 7RR
TEL: 01590 623090 FAX: 01590 623479 E-MAIL: ThatchedCottageHotel@email.msn.com

OWNERS: The Matysik Family

5 rms	5 ens	SMALL HOTEL

S: From £70
D: £90–£145
Suite: £135–£155

This enchanting thatched cottage was built in 1627 and only became a hotel in 1991. The Matysik family has over 111 years of hotel experience between them and this is reflected in the careful transformation that has taken place.

Set in one of the prettiest villages in the heart of the New Forest, modernisation for the comfort of guests has not detracted from its original charm. The individually decorated double bedrooms each have a special feature for example, a four-poster bed, Turkish steam shower or open hearth gas fireplace. A cosy beamed lounge is idyllic for pre/after-dinner drinks. An elegant tea garden is presented with lace table cloths and sun parasols. Memorable services include a superb late breakfast, Champagne cream tea and gourmet wicker hampers. In the evening, exquisite culinary delights are freshly prepared by the culinary team on show in their open country kitchen. The table d'hôte menu offers luxurious ingredients harmoniously combined with flair and imagination. "A dining experience difficult to surpass" set in a unique and relaxing ambience by romantic candlelight. An authentic Japanese celebration menu can be prearranged.

Places of interest nearby: Home of Lord Montagu and his National Motor Museum, Rothschild's Exbury Gardens and the yachting town of Lymington. Activities include wild mushroom hunting, riding, sailing and golf. **Directions: M27, Jct1, drive south on A337 through Lyndhurst, in Brockenhurst turn right before level crossing.**

WHITLEY RIDGE COUNTRY HOUSE HOTEL

BEAULIEU ROAD, BROCKENHURST, NEW FOREST, HAMPSHIRE SO42 7QL
TEL: 01590 622354 FAX: 01590 622856 E-MAIL: whitleyridge@brockenhurst.co.uk

OWNERS: Rennie and Sue Law
CHEF: Gary Moore

S: £60–£80
D: £96–£106
Suite: £120

Whitley Ridge, once a royal hunting lodge, was built in Georgian style in the late 18th century. In more recent years the house has undergone extensive refurbishment, enhancing the appeal of its original Georgian features.

The bedrooms are individually decorated and most have lovely views over open Forest. The public rooms are elegantly furnished with and log fires burning on cooler evenings.

The Restaurant has two AA Rosettes for good food, offering a table d'hôte menu, which changes daily, together with a high standard of à la carte choices, plus a well balanced and imaginative vegetarian menu. The wine selection includes those wines from traditional areas and also interesting choices from further afield.

You are invited to relax in the grounds or enjoy a game of tennis. In addition, some of the best woodland walks in the country are directly accessible from the gardens. Whichever pastime you choose, Whitley Ridge is the perfect setting for a restful holiday. Your hosts Rennie and Sue Law welcome guests for a very pleasant stay.

Places of interest nearby: A number of stately homes, including Broadlands and Wilton House, are within easy reach. Lord Montagu's Motor Museum, Buckler's Hard and historic Stonehenge are also within driving distance. **Directions: M27 junction 1. Situated on the B3055, Brockenhurst – Beaulieu.**

NEW HOUSE FARM

LORTON, COCKERMOUTH, CUMBRIA CA13 9UU
TEL: 01900 85404 FAX: 01900 85404

OWNERS: Hazel Hatch

4 rms 4 ens

S: £40–£53
D: £76–£80

Set in 15 acres of lovely gardens and grounds, New House Farm is located in the beautiful Lorton Vale between the villages of Lorton and Loweswater. The name of the house is something of a misnomer as it is neither "new" nor a "farm"!. In fact, the property dates back to the 17th century. Recent and careful renovation revealed many of its original features, such as oak beams and rafters, stone fireplaces and flagged floors.

The spacious, comfortable bedrooms all offer en suite facilities and spectacular views of the surrounding fells. Two separate lounges, both with open fireplaces, provide the ideal environment in which to enjoy the scenery.

In the afternoon, teas with home-made scones and preserves can be enjoyed in the garden, after which guests may like to explore the adjoining fields and woodlands. Hazel produces a fine range of five-course traditional English dinners, including roast pheasant and duckling, Derwent salmon and local trout. AA 5 Diamonds. The Which? hotel guide 1994 Cumbrian Hotel of the Year.

Places of interest nearby: This is a wonderful location for guests who enjoy walking, ponytrekking, fishing and golf. It is also an ideal base from which to tour the quieter Western lakes. **Directions: From M6 Junction 40 take A66 past Keswick. Turn left onto B5292 to Lorton over the Whinlatter Pass. New House Farm is one mile from Lorton on the left in the middle of the Lorton Vale.**

MELBOURN BURY

MELBOURN, CAMBRIDGESHIRE, NR ROYSTON SG8 6DE
TEL: 01763 261151 FAX: 01763 262375 E-MAIL: mazecare@aol.com

OWNERS: Anthony and Sylvia Hopkinson

S: £60
D: £90

Set in extensive grounds with a lake and wildfowl, Melbourn Bury is an elegant manor house. It has had only two ownerships since the 1500s. The first owners were the monks of Ely and then in 1850, the property was purchased by the ancestors of Sylvia Hopkinson.

Gracious reception rooms are furnished with antiques and fine paintings, while the en suite bedrooms are comfortable and have charming views of the gardens. Fresh flowers and log fires are extra touches which guests will appreciate. Adjoining the library is a 19th century billiard room with a full-size table.

Delicious home cooking encompasses traditional English recipes and continental dishes prepared in cordon bleu style. Dinner is by prior arrangement.

Lunches and dinners for up to 22 persons seated; more can be accommodated buffet-style – small conferences, receptions and exhibitions. Closed at Christmas and Easter.

Places of interest nearby: Cambridge, Duxford Air Museum, Audley End, Ely, Wimpole Hall and Hatfield House. **Directions: Off A10, 10 miles south of Cambridge, 3rd turning on left to Melbourn; 2 miles north of Royston, 1st turning on right to Melbourn. Entrance is 300 yards on left after the turning. Look for the white gate posts and lodge cottage.**

CROSBY LODGE COUNTRY HOUSE HOTEL

HIGH CROSBY, CROSBY-ON-EDEN, CARLISLE, CUMBRIA CA6 4QZ
TEL: 01228 573618 FAX: 01228 573428 E-MAIL: crosbylodge@crosby–eden.demon.co.uk

OWNERS: Michael, Patricia and James Sedgwick
CHEF: James Sedgwick

S: £78–£90
D: £100–£140

Crosby Lodge is a romantic country mansion that has been converted into a quiet efficient hotel without spoiling any of its original charm. Grade II listed, it stands amid pastoral countryside close to the Scottish Lowlands and the Lake District.

Spacious interiors are elegantly furnished and appointed to provide the maximum of comfort. The personal attention of Michael and Patricia Sedgwick ensures that a high standard of service is maintained. All of the bedrooms are beautifully equipped, most with antique beds and half-testers. Two bedrooms are situated in the converted courtyard stables overlooking the walled garden and in these rooms guests are welcome to bring their pet dogs.

In the restaurant, extensive menus offer a wide and varied choice of dishes. Traditional English recipes are prepared along with continental cuisine. Tables are set with cut glass and gleaming silver cutlery and in keeping with the gracious surroundings, gentlemen are requested to wear a jacket and tie for dinner. Crosby Lodge, with its spacious grounds, is a superb setting for weddings, parties, business and social events. Closed 24 December to 20 January.

Places of interest nearby: Hadrian's Wall, Carlisle Cathedral and Castle and six miles from Lanercost Priory, the Scottish Borders. **Directions: From M6 junction 44 take A689 Brampton road for three miles; turn right through Low Crosby. Crosby Lodge is on the right at High Crosby.**

AYNSOME MANOR HOTEL

CARTMEL, GRANGE-OVER-SANDS, CUMBRIA LA11 6HH
TEL: 015395 36653 FAX: 015395 36016

OWNERS: Tony, Margaret, Chris and Andrea Varley
CHEF: Victor Sharratt

| 12 rms | 12 ens | 🌲 SMALL HOTEL |

MasterCard   VISA   AMERICAN EXPRESS

S: £58–£66
D: £97–£116
(including dinner)

In the beautiful Vale of Cartmel, with views of the priory and beyond to the village of Cartmel itself, stands Aynsome Manor, once the home of Wiliam Marshall, Earl of Pembroke. It is an ideal retreat for anyone seeking peace and quiet. Guests can stroll around the grounds or, in cooler months, relax by log fires in the lounges.

The elegant candlelit dining room is the perfect setting in which to enjoy a five-course dinner. The restaurant has an excellent reputation for its home cooking, from delicious home-made soups such as apple, celery and tomato, to main courses such as roast breast of pheasant with smoked bacon and an orange and chestnut sauce. Fresh, local produce is used wherever possible. A high tea is provided for children under five as they are regrettably not allowed in the restaurant for dinner. There are 12 bedrooms, two of which are in Aynsome Cottage, across the courtyard.

Places of interest nearby: Aynsome Manor is a perfect base for touring the Lake District. Lake Windermere is 4 miles away. In summer, Holker Hall organises ballooning and vintage car rallies. There is horseracing in Cartmel on Whitsun and August bank holidays and 5 golf courses nearby. Closed January. **Directions: Leave M6 at junction 36 and take the A590 signposted Barrow-in-Furness. At end of dual carriageway (12 miles) turn left into Cartmel. The hotel is on the right.**

BOND'S - BISTRO WITH ROOMS

ANSFORD HILL, CASTLE CARY, SOMERSET BA7 7JP
TEL/FAX: 01963 350464

OWNERS: Kevin and Yvonne Bond

 S: £50
D: £58

A warm and friendly informal atmosphere envelopes Bond's, a listed Georgian country house, formerly known as the 'Half Moon Inn'. In the late 18th century this was a favourite rest and refreshment stop for weary travellers coaching across the vast tract of peaceful mid-Somerset countryside. It is still a tranquil region scattered with dairy farms and noted for the milk used to make the original Cheddar cheese.

Polished wood floors and log fires enhance the public rooms, adding charm and character to the house. The attentive owners have created a relaxing haven and the seven en suite bedrooms are well-equipped with modern amenities such as telephones, television and tea and coffee making facilities.

The talented chef Yvonne prepares tempting dishes including carefully chosen daily specials. A typical choice may begin with duck and orange pie served with onion marmalade and green leaf salad, followed by herb-crusted roast of rack lamb served pink with field mushroom risotto. Traditional favourites such as sticky toffee pudding and butterscotch sauce comprise the dessert menu. The extensive wine list has been compiled with the flavours in mind.

Places of interest nearby: Sherborne, the house and garden of Longleat, the cathedral city of Wells and Wincanton races. **Directions: Castle Cary is signed from A303 at Sparkford and from A371 at Shepton Mallet.**

EASTON COURT HOTEL

EASTON CROSS, CHAGFORD, DEVON TQ13 8JL
TEL: 01647 433469 FAX: 01647 433654 E-MAIL: stay@easton.co.uk

OWNERS: Gordon and Judy Parker

S: from £70
D: £128–£138
(including dinner)

Easton Court is a 15th century, Grade II listed, thatched Tudor house with many historic connections, particularly literary ones. Both Evelyn Waugh – who wrote *Brideshead Revisited* here – and Patrick Leigh Fermor found inspiration in this rural setting amid the glorious Devon countryside. The sensitive restoration of the hotel has removed none of its old-world charm and period features such as exposed granite walls, oak beams and a great inglenook fireplace, complete with bread oven, have been retained. For those with a literary bent, there is a superb library housing a fascinating collection of old tomes.

The eight tastefully furnished bedrooms have lots of interesting nooks and crannies and offer wonderful rural and moorland views. The menus in the attractive restaurant vary with the seasons and special diets can be catered for by prior arrangement. Special breaks available. **Places of interest nearby:** Dartmoor's mystery and grandeur lie 'on the doorstep' of the hotel, offering an endless variety of breathtaking walks, while Exmoor, Lynton and the rugged North Devon coast are a short journey away. Castle Drogo, Fernworthy Reservoir and Exeter are among the many other local places of interest. Closed January. **Directions: From Exeter, take the A30. At the first roundabout take the A382 signposted Moretonhampstead.**

MILL END HOTEL

DARTMOOR NATIONAL PARK, CHAGFORD, DEVON TQ13 8JN
TEL: 01647 432282 FAX: 01647 433106 E-MAIL: millendhotel@talk21.com

OWNER: Keith Green
CHEF: Alan Lane

 S: £56–£80
D: £75–£110

Formerly an eighteenth century floor mill, the Mill End Hotel offers a warm and friendly service in a most delectable setting. Situated on the banks of the River Teign and the Teign Gorge, the hotel has a uniquely tranquil situation. The gardens running down to the river feature a working water wheel, making this a beautiful spot to while away a sunny afternoon.

Inside, the many hidden corner nooks and walls covered in beautiful paintings and old photographs, imbue a feeling of comfort and seclusion and the smell of wood smoke and polished wood are omnipresent. The en suite bedrooms are furnished in a practical manner. Major upgrades are planned during autumn. The tasteful elegance of the dining room is matched by the delicious award-winning cuisine where the emphasis is on modern British cuisine using only the finest seasonal produce. Visitors should not neglect the cheese, all of which is produced in a county famed for its dairy produce.

Places of Interest nearby: The hotel is ideally placed for exploring Dartmoor, Devon and the West Country. An excellent 18-hole golf course is close at hand, and pony trekking, shooting and hunting trips are also available. Needless to say the area boasts many fine walks of varying difficulty. The hotel also has eight miles of fishing rights.
Directions: From M5, take exit 30 towards Okehampton. Exit at Merrymount roundabout and take A382 towards Moretonhampstead. The hotel is on the right.

CHARLTON KINGS HOTEL

CHARLTON KINGS, CHELTENHAM, GLOUCESTERSHIRE GL52 6UU
TEL: 01242 231061 FAX: 01242 241900

OWNER: Trevor Stuart
MANAGERS: Cassie Fuller and Aran Hayes
CHEF: Aran Hayes

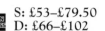

S: £53–£79.50
D: £66–£102

Surrounded by the Cotswold hills, on the outside of Cheltenham but just a few minutes by car to the heart of town stands Charlton Kings Hotel. If you seek instant peace and solitude follow the footpath running alongside the hotel into the beautiful Cotswold countryside. The famous 'Cotswold Way' escarpment walk passes just half a mile away.

The hotel is attractively furnished with an accent on light woods and pastel colouring. All rooms are en suite, some are reserved for non smokers. The Restaurant is fresh and inviting offering space and privacy for those all important business meetings or perhaps an intimate dinner for two? An à la carte menu is supplemented by a daily table d'hôte, using the finest fresh produce. The bar and conservatory are open throughout the day for snacks and refreshments. A full Sunday Roast Lunch is served 12–2. **Places of interest nearby:** Cheltenham Spa – famous for its architecture festivals and racing also has plenty to offer in the way of theatres, restaurants and a distinguished selection of shops. To the North, East and South lie charming Cotswold Villages, too numerous to mention, and to the West the Forest of Dean, Wye Valley, Malvern Hills and much more. **Directions: The hotel is the first property on the left coming into Cheltenham from Oxford on the A40 (the 'Welcome to Cheltenham' Boundary Sign is located in their front garden!).**

HALEWELL

HALEWELL CLOSE, WITHINGTON, NR CHELTENHAM, GLOUCESTERSHIRE GL54 4BN
TEL: 01242 890238 FAX: 01242 890332

OWNER: Mrs Elizabeth Carey-Wilson

S: £60–£70
D: £87
S: £150

This enchanting manor house is built of warm honey-coloured Cotswold stone. It is the home of Elizabeth Carey-Wilson who has made it a charming venue for guests seeking to stay within the ambience of a private house. The skillful restoration reflects both her affection for Halewell and consideration for those staying with her.

The guest rooms are individual. Two have adjoining rooms so families can be together and a ground floor room has been designed for disabled guests.

Breakfast is seldom before 9 o' clock and early children's meals are provided. Dinner is available for parties of eight or more. Lunches and more exotic meals can be found in the attractive pubs close by.

Guests use the Sitting Room which has a games table and can be shown her private drawing room upon request, The Solar, with its unusual vaulted ceiling. Within the grounds are delightful terraced gardens, a stretch of the River Colne and a large trout lake, in addition to an outdoor swimming pool.

Places of interest nearby: The Cotswolds offer fine walking and there is an old Roman villa within 2 miles walk. Cheltenham has its races and festivals and Blenheim and Sudeley are in easy reach. **Directions: Leave A40 South at Andoversford (A436). Take first left to Withington village, then second right and second entrance on the left.**

GREEN BOUGH HOTEL

60 HOOLE ROAD, CHESTER, CHESHIRE CH2 3NL
TEL: 01244 326241 FAX: 01244 326265 E-MAIL: greenboughhotel@cwcom.net

OWNERS: Philip and Janice Martin
CHEF: Philip Martin and Peter Howlett

18 rms   18 ens

S: £55–£80
D: £75–£110

A late Victorian town house, the Green Bough Hotel is conveniently placed, as its name suggests, on a leafy route into the ancient city of Chester. Bought three years ago by Philip and Janice Martin, it has been completely refurbished and now combines the convenience of modern facilities with the charm of period features and furnishings. Of its 18 bedrooms the majority have antique beds. Many of the original architectural features of the building and the adjoining Victorian Lodge bedroom wing remain intact.

The restaurant is presided over by Philip Martin who trained at the Savoy Hotel, working with the renowned Maitre Chef des Cuisine Silvino S Trompetto. The menu, served in the Fleur de Lys Restaurant, is complemented by a wine list of a range and quality that belies the relatively small size of the hotel.

The Green Bough provides an excellent base for exploring the city of Chester and hires bicycles for this purpose. It is also ideal for those venturing further afield into the beautiful Cheshire countryside and Snowdonia.

Places of interest nearby: The cathedral, river, racecourse and shops of the city of Chester. The Blue Planet Aquarium and the world class Chester Zoo. The castles of Cheshire. Snowdonia. **Directions: Leave the M53 at junction 12. Take the A56 into Chester for 1 mile. The Green Bough Hotel is on the right.**

60

CROUCHERS BOTTOM COUNTRY HOTEL

BIRDHAM ROAD, APULDRAM, NEAR CHICHESTER, WEST SUSSEX PO20 7EH
TEL: 01243 784995 FAX: 01243 539797

GENERAL MANAGER: Lloyd Van Rooyen
CHEF: Gavin Wilson

S: £45–£70
D: £65–£105

This former farmhouse, set just half a mile from the Yacht Basin and 2 miles from the centre of Chichester, has been transformed into a fine country hotel offering 16 opulent bedrooms, good food and a most attentive service.

Located in the converted coach house and barn, all the rooms are beautifully appointed with a full range of amenities, including telephone, colour television, hairdryer and tea and coffee-making facilities.

Free-range hens provide the eggs of a full English breakfast, which may be enjoyed whilst overlooking the attractive courtyard. Guests recline in the comfortable lounge or enjoy a preprandial drink in the bar before dining in the hotel restaurant, awarded three AA Stars and one Rosette. The freshly prepared dishes are the inspiration of the talented chef, Gavin Wilson, and only the finest of fresh ingredients are used. Crouchers Bottom Country Hotel will delight those wishing to merely relax and escape the pressures of a hectic lifestyle. In the summer months a tranquil ambience envelopes the courtyard as guests sip chilled drinks and laze in the sun whilst in winter the roaring log fires are truly inviting! **Places of interest nearby:** Chichester Cathedral, Marina, Museum, Art Gallery and Festival Theatre. The charming harbour village of Bosham with its Saxon church, Goodwood House and Arundel Castle. **Directions: From M27, junction 12, take A27 to Chichester and then A286 south towards The Witterings. Crouchers Bottom Hotel is on the left.**

 CHICHESTER (Charlton)

WOODSTOCK HOUSE HOTEL

CHARLTON, NEAR CHICHESTER, WEST SUSSEX PO18 0HU
TEL: 01243 811666 FAX: 01243 811666

OWNERS: Michael and Elizabeth McGovern

  SMALL HOTEL

S: £38.50–£55
D: £66–£92

Nestling below the heights of Charlton Forest in the middle of West Sussex downland, Woodstock House is a perfect example of the small country house hotel. In summer the sun shines all day on its secluded courtyard garden. It was built in the 18th century but the public rooms, which include a bar and two sitting rooms, enjoy a feeling of comfortable spaciousness.

The dining room, however, retains a traditional, atmosphere in which the high standard of cooking – set by Mrs McGovern – can be savoured to the full. The 11 bedrooms, all en suite, are comfortable and well-equipped with television and tea-making facilities. One bedroom offers a four-poster bed.

The hotel could not be better placed for offering outside interests from horse and motor racing at Goodwood, golf at Goodwood and Cowdray Park golf clubs, sailing at Itchenor, Bosham and Dell Quay and Chichester Sea School and yacht basin, bathing at East and West Wittering and the Chichester Festival Theatre.

Places of interest nearby: There are historic houses in the area: Goodwood, Petworth, Parham and Uppark and Arundel Castle. The gardens of Wakehurst Place and Sheffield Park are well worth a visit, also nature reserves at Kingsley Vale and Pagham Harbour. **Directions: From M27 take A27 north of the Goodwood Estate. Charlton can be approached from A285 or A286.**

STANTON MANOR

STANTON SAINT QUINTIN, NR CHIPPENHAM, WILTSHIRE SN14 6DQ
TEL: 01666 837552 FAX: 01666 837022 E-MAIL: stanton.manor@virgin.net

OWNERS: Duncan and Linda Hickling
CHEF: Tony Sargent

S: £75–£95
D: £95–£135

Rebuilt in 1840 and standing near to the M4 just off the beaten track in five acres of leafy gardens, there has been a habitation at Stanton Manor for over 900 years. The original house was listed in the Domesday Book and was later owned by the Lord Burghley, Elizabeth I's chief minister. The Elizabethan dovecote in the garden bears witness to that period, although the present building dates largely from the 19th century.

The bedrooms are furnished in a homely, country style and several offer views over Wiltshire farmland. Those in the new wing are extremely spacious and the new owners are carefully upgrading the entire hotel. In addition to the formal restaurant, serving an à la carte menu of traditional British cuisine, there is a cosy bar offering light snacks.

Proprietors Linda and Duncan Hickling are invariably on hand to ensure that a friendly, personal and attentive service is extended to all that arrive at Stanton Manor. **Places of interest nearby:** The Roman city of Cirencester, Chippenham and an array of pretty villages all invite exploration. **Directions: Leave the M4 at junction 17 and join the A429 towards Cirencester. After 200 yards, turn left to Stanton Saint Quintin; Stanton Manor is on the left in the village.**

THE MALT HOUSE

BROAD CAMPDEN, GLOUCESTERSHIRE GL55 6UU
TEL: 01386 840295 FAX: 01386 841334 E-MAIL: nick@the–malt–house.freeserve.co.uk

OWNERS: Nick and Jean Brown
CHEF: Julian Brown

S: £59.50–£89.50
D: £85–£115
Suites: £105–£125

Nick and Jean Brown have achieved a blend of warm, relaxed and yet professional service, welcoming guests as part of an extended family. The idyllic surroundings of The Malt House, a beautiful 17th century Cotswold home in the quiet village of Broad Campden, further enhance the congenial atmosphere.

Rooms, including residents' sitting rooms, combine comfortable furnishings with antiques and displays of fresh flowers. Most bedrooms overlook the wide lawns which lead to a small stream and orchard beyond. All of the recently refurbished rooms are individually decorated and have an en suite bathroom. The Windrush Suite has an 18th century four-poster bed and a family suite is also available.

Dinner is served five days a week. The proprietors' son Julian is a highly accomplished chef who uses many ingredients from the kitchen gardens to prepare a table d'hôte menu, accompanied by a choice selection of wines. The English breakfasts are equally good.

The Malt House has earned many awards for its standard of accommodation and meals including, most deservedly, 2 Rosettes for its food and Premier Select 5Q from the AA.
Places of interest nearby: Hidcote Manor Gardens (N.T), Chipping Camden Church, The Cotswolds, Cheltenham, Stratford-upon-Avon, Oxford and Bath. **Directions: The Malt House is in the centre of the village of Broad Campden which is just one mile from Chipping Campden.**

Mynd House Hotel & Restaurant

LITTLE STRETTON, CHURCH STRETTON, NR SHREWSBURY, SHROPSHIRE SY6 6RB
TEL: 01694 722212 FAX: 01694 724180 E-MAIL: myndhouse@go2.co.uk

OWNERS: Paul and Louise Oatham
CHEF: Stewart Blower

D: £55–£80
per person
(including dinner)

In the main street of the idyllic village of Little Stretton at the base of the NT Longmynd, this Edwardian village house is run by a husband and wife team and is the perfect retreat for those wishing to spend a few days or short break in the country.

Comfort is an important criterion in the two lounges and the intimate bar as guests often frequent these rooms and recline with a book during the afternoons or enjoy a pre-dinner drink in the evenings. The bedrooms, many with glorious views across the valley, are individually furnished and well-equipped. The hotel is entirely non-smoking except in the congenial bar.

Awarded an AA Rosette and an RAC Merit Award, the restaurant offers a fixed price four-course menu comprising traditional recipes and using the finest local produce. Guests may choose a wine to accompany their meal from a wide selection including an impressive list of full and half-bottles. Those wishing to explore the surrounding landscape can begin with the 6 well-described walks starting from the hotel.

Places of interest nearby: There are many distractions within easy reach such as Acton Scott Historic Farm museum, the Marches, the Ironbridge Gorge museum and the market town of Shrewsbury. Antique shops may be found in Ludlow and Bridgnorth whilst several music and arts festivals take place within the area. **Directions: Little Stretton is signposted off A49, 1½ miles south of Church Stretton.**

CLEARWELL (Forest of Dean)

TUDOR FARMHOUSE HOTEL & RESTAURANT

HIGH STREET, CLEARWELL, NR COLEFORD, GLOUCESTERSHIRE GL16 8JS
TEL: 01594 833046 FAX: 01594 837093 E-MAIL: reservations@tudorfarmhouse.u–net.com

OWNERS: Colin and Linda Gray
CHEF: Dean Wassell

S: £48.50
D: £60

Tudor Farmhouse is an idyllic haven away from the hustle and bustle of everyday life. A cosy, friendly 13th century stone-built hotel in the centre of the historic village of Clearwell on the peaceful fringe of the Forest of Dean. Clearwell's history dates from Roman times and the village is dominated by the huge ramparts of a fine Neo Gothic castle.

Owners Colin and Linda Gray take pride in the standard of comfort and hospitality at Tudor Farmhouse, whose features include massive oak beams and original panelling. There is a large, roughstone inglenook fireplace in the attractive lounge providing warmth and cheer in winter. A conservatory looks onto the landscaped garden and 14 acres of fields. The bedrooms have been refurbished in traditional style. Those in the house are reached by a wide, oak spiral staircase. Others are in converted stone cider makers' cottages quietly situated in the garden and include three family suites.

The candlelit restaurant, awarded a red Rosette, with its open stonework and exposed beams is the ideal setting in which to enjoy unhurried evening meals.

Places of interest nearby: The Forest of Dean and Wye Valley, Offa's Dyke, Tintern Abbey, Monmouth and Ross on Wye, spectacular Symonds Yat, Raglan and Chepstow Castles. **Directions: From M4 join M48 taking junction 2 to Chepstow then follow A48 and B4231.**

FOXDOWN MANOR

HORNS CROSS, NR CLOVELLY, NORTH DEVON EX39 5PJ
TEL: 01237 451325 FAX: 01237 451525

OWNER: Colonel Peter Williams

 S: from £50
D: from £100

Deep in the heart of the North Devon countryside the sixteen acres of woodlands and gardens that surround Foxdown Manor provide a most rare and peaceful setting.

The garden is a sun-trap. Along the western walls that house the pool, sauna and Jacuzzi, figs, vines and roses grow in abundance. Nearby are a Victorian walled garden, croquet lawns and putting greens alongside a free-running trout stream.

This idyllic setting is the home of Col. Peter Williams and is managed by his sister Brenda and her husband Tony Cathcart who provide every comfort for their guests in a traditional way. The day rooms, too, are traditional in style and comfort, the drawing rooms' bay and French windows affording wonderful views of the surrounding countryside.

All the bedrooms have private facilities, colour televisions, telephones, beverage trays and baby listening. Several have four-poster beds and a feature of the bridal suite is its 18th century full canopy four-poster with a barley twist oak frame. Fresh seasonal fare is prominent on the dinner menu: fish from the local market, supremes of free-range chicken and noisettes of Devon lamb.

Places of interest nearby: Beautiful countryside walks, Hartland Point, Clovelly Bay and Exmoor all lie within easy reach. **Directions: From junction 27 of the M5 (28 miles), Foxdown Manor is six miles west of Bideford on the A39.**

ABBOTS OAK

GREENHILL, COALVILLE LE67 4UY
TEL: 01530 832 328 FAX: 01530 832 328

OWNERS: Bill, Audrey and Carolyn White

4 rms 2 ens

S: £50–£60
D: £60–£85

This Grade II listed building is on the edge of Charnwood Forest, with 19 acres of gardens, woodland and unusual granite outcrops where guests can stroll or play croquet and tennis.

Inside is the most spectacular carved oak panelling and stained glass – indeed the staircase goes to the top of the tower from where it is possible to look out over five counties.

The house has four bedrooms available for the use of guests, two of which are en suite. There is a gorgeous drawing room and elegant dining room. Dinner is served en famille by candlelight. The menu is therefore not extensive and the wine list short but good. After dinner enjoy a game of snooker in the superb billiard room.

Places of interest nearby: Mid-week it is ideal for businessmen with meetings in Loughborough or Leicester. There is excellent golf nearby and shooting can be arranged. Further afield are Stratford-upon-Avon, Warwick Castle and Rutland Water. 15 minutes from Donington Park race circuit. **Directions: From the M1, take the A511 towards Coalville. At the first roundabout, take the third exit to Loughborough. At the traffic lights, turn left. Abbots Oak is 1¼ miles opposite the Bulls Head pub. From the A42, take the A511 towards Coalville. At the fourth roundabout turn left and take the second right, then right at T-junction. Abbots Oak is 50 yards on the right.**

ASHELFORD

ASHELFORD, EAST DOWN, NEAR BARNSTAPLE, NORTH DEVON EX31 4LU
TEL: 01271 850469 FAX: 01271 850862 E-MAIL: tom&erica@ashelford.co.uk

OWNERS: Tom and Erica McClenaghan
CHEF: Erica McClenaghan

S: £70
D: £80–£95

North Devon has over 850 square miles of heritage countryside and coast that are classified as one of the last remaining tranquil areas in England. Ashelford stands in over 70 acres of superb pasture and woodland facing south at the head of its own valley with views beyond the National Trust's Arlington Court to Exmoor.

Formerly a 17th century farmhouse, Ashelford has retained its sense of history with a wealth of oak beams, slate floors and log fires. Owners Tom and Erica McClenaghan offer peace, seclusion and cosy informality where a visitor's comfort is their greatest concern.

Privacy is enhanced by enchanting, warmly decorated and well-appointed bedrooms, each having en suite facilities and extras that include a refrigerator with fresh milk, orange juice and spring water. The lounge and dining room are comfortable and welcoming with superb meals prepared from local produce.

The 8 inch reflectory telescope will delight those wishing to observe the planets and stars. Golf, fishing, riding and carriage driving can be arranged. The residence has an outside bath with hot and cold water for well-behaved dogs after they have completed one of the many nearby walks with their owners!

Places of interest nearby: The R.H.S. Rosemoor Gardens, Dartington Glass, Arlington Court. **Directions: From Barnstaple take A39 towards Lynmouth. After Shirwell village take second turning on left and follow signs to Churchill. Ashelford is on the right.**

CREDITON (Coleford)

COOMBE HOUSE COUNTRY HOTEL

COLEFORD, CREDITON, DEVON EX17 5BY
TEL: 01363 84487 FAX: 01363 84722 E-MAIL: coombehs@eurobell.co.uk

OWNERS: David and Pat Jones
CHEF: Bill Denton

 S: £49.50–£59.50
D: £79–£99

This elegant Georgian manor is listed as a protected building of historic interest and certainly the Cellar Bar has over 700 years of history – reputedly it sheltered Cromwell's men in the Civil War. Now these elegant buildings which offer relaxation in lovely landscaped grounds are being thoughtfully refurbished and up-graded by their caring and welcoming owners.

There are 15 bedrooms in all, the spacious Superior rooms at the front of the house enjoying restful views over the grounds and surrounding countryside with well-equipped bathrooms en suite; the six Standard en suite rooms are equally pleasant but their differing quality is reflected in the price structure.

The AA Rosette restaurant was once a ballroom added on in Victorian times and it provides a gracious, elegant atmosphere in which to enjoy the daily-changed cuisine and wines from the informative list. The grounds provide facilities for those who wish to play tennis, or indulge in croquet. For the more adventurous golf, shooting and riding can all be arranged.

Places of interest nearby: The city of Exeter with its cathedral and university, the Taw and Torridge valleys, Dartmoor, Exmoor and a number of National Trust properties. **Directions: From Exeter join A377 and pass through Crediton. After approximately 1½ miles further on the hotel is signposted**

BEL ALP HOUSE

HAYTOR, NR BOVEY TRACEY, SOUTH DEVON TQ13 9XX
TEL: 01364 661217 FAX: 01364 661292

OWNERS: Jack, Mary and Rachael Twist

S: £65–£75
D: £130–£160

Peace and seclusion are guaranteed at the Bel Alp House with its spectacular outlook from the edge of Dartmoor across a rolling patchwork of fields and woodland to the sea, 20 miles away.

Built as an Edwardian country mansion and owned in the 1920s by millionairess Dame Violet Wills, Bel Alp has been lovingly restored and the proprietors' personal attention ensures their guests' enjoyment and comfort in the atmosphere of a private home.

The set dinner is changed nightly, using only the best local produce and the meals are accompanied by a well-chosen and comprehensive wine list.

Of the eight en suite bedrooms, two still have their original Edwardian basins and baths mounted on marble plinths and all bedrooms have views over the gardens.

An abundance of house plants, open log fires and restful colours complements the family antiques and pictures to create the perfect environment in which to relax. Awarded an AA Rosette.

Places of interest nearby: Bel Alp is ideally situated for exploring Devon and parts of Cornwall. Plymouth, famed for Drake and the Pilgrim Fathers, Exeter with its Norman cathedral and National Trust properties Castle Drogo and Cotehele Manor House are all within an hour's drive. **Directions: Bel Alp House is off the B3387 Haytor road, 2½ miles from Bovey Tracey.**

CHIPPENHALL HALL

FRESSINGFIELD, EYE, SUFFOLK IP21 5TD
TEL: 01379 588180/586733 FAX: 01379 586272

OWNERS: Barbara and Jakes Sargent

5 rms	5 ens

S: £70–£74
D: £76–£80

The present manor is a listed Tudor building, although its origins date from Saxon times and is referred to in the *Domesday Book* as Cybenhalla. Secluded at the end of a long leafy drive, the hall enjoys a setting of rural tranquillity amid seven acres of lawns, trees, ponds and gardens.

Every evening, by arrangement, a superb candlelit dinner is prepared by the hostess and served in convivial surroundings. Proprietors Barbara and Jakes Sargent pride themselves in offering a fine choice of reasonably priced wines from the cellar to complement your meal. A seat beside the copper-canopied inglenook fire in the Shallow End bar room is the ideal place to enjoy pre-dinner drinks.

The house is heavily-beamed throughout, including the en suite bedrooms which are named after relevant historical associations. During the summer, guests can relax by the heated outdoor swimming pool which is set in the rose-covered courtyard. With attentive service, good food and wine, it is not surprising to learn that Chippenhall Hall won the Johansens 1998 Country Houses and Small Hotels Award and is ETB Highly Commended and AA Premier Selected.

Places of interest nearby: Snape Maltings, Minsmere Bird Sanctuary, the Otter Trust at Earsham and the towns of Bury St Edmunds and Norwich. **Directions: One mile outside Fressingfield on the B1116 to Framlingham.**

STARSTON HALL

STARSTON, HARLESTUN, NORFOLK IP20 9PU
TEL: 01379 854252 FAX: 01379 852966 E-MAIL: starstonh@aol.com

OWNER: Christina Baxter
CHEF: Warren Van Der Eb

S: £50
D: £70

Starston Hall, a magnificent Listed house of Elizabethan origins partly surrounded by a moat, stands regally in five acres of lovingly tended landscaped gardens on the Norfolk/Suffolk borders south of Norwich. It has recently been extensively renovated with many of the original features being sympathetically restored. There are delightful beamed rooms filled with antiques, gilt framed oil paints and prints, rich fabrics and furnishings, large open fireplaces and vases and vases of fresh, colourful flowers.

The Hall's owner, Christina Baxter, is fluent in French, German and Italian and takes pleasure in ensuring that guests live in the lap of luxury while staying with her. The three en suite bedrooms are spacious, extremely attractive, have every home-from-home comfort and offer panoramic views over the gardens. Christina's son, Warren, is a talented chef and produces delicious and varied menus using organic produce, drug free meat and fresh local fish delivered daily.

Places of interest nearby: Norwich, Southwold, Bressingham Hall Gardens, Sandringham and Blickling Hall. **Directions: From London take M11, A11 to Bury St. Edmunds, A143 to Diss and Great Yarmouth, take 1st exit at roundabout to Harleston (B1134), slip road to Starston, over cross roads to T junction. Cross bridge go north up Church Hill for 1.2 miles and entrance to Starston Hall is on your right, follow lane up to the house. From Norwich travel south on A140 to junction with B1134 to Pulham Market and Harleston.**

HAMILTON'S RESTAURANT & HOTEL

CARR HOUSE ROAD, DONCASTER, SOUTH YORKSHIRE DN4 5HP
TEL: 01302 760770 FAX: 01302 768101 E-MAIL: ham760770@aol.com

OWNER: Andrew Roberts
CHEF: Christopher Randle-Bissell

5 rms	5 ens	SMALL HOTEL

S: £70
D: £90
Suite: £150

Standing in two acres of walled gardens just 200 yards from Doncaster Racecourse this former home of Lord and Lady Hamilton combines the welcoming ambience of a country residence with the comforts of an elegant, modern hotel. Built in 1856, the lavish refurbishment has resulted in five spacious bedrooms, each individually designed and named after a famous opera.

'Cooking is the art, dining is the experience' is the mission statement at Hamilton's and at meal times, this aim is clearly evident. Talented chef Christopher Randle-Bissell is dedicated to Old English and European cooking and his extensive menus will please the most discerning visitor in the warm ambience of the attractively furnished restaurant. His starter of roasted sea scallops with a sweet ratatouille of vegetables, drizzled with truffle essence, followed by a daube of braised beef wrapped in a crepinette with a new potato mash, roasted shallots and morrel mushrooms is not to be missed. The dining experience is complemented by a well chosen wine list and enhanced by classical service. The private dining room has an atmosphere of grandeur and caters for a maximum of 24 guests.

Places of interest nearby: Brodsworth Hall, Conisbrough Castle, the Dome leisure complex and the Earth Centre are all nearby. **Directions: From M18 and A1 follow signs for Doncaster Race Course and Exhibition Centre. Hamilton's in on the left of the dual carriageway, 200 yards before the racecourse roundabout.**

YALBURY COTTAGE HOTEL

LOWER BOCKHAMPTON, DORCHESTER, DORSET DT2 8PZ
TEL: 01305 262382 FAX: 01305 266412 E-MAIL: yalbury.cottage@virgin.net

OWNERS: Heather and Derek Furminger
CHEF: Russell Brown

S: £51
D: £78

Yalbury Cottage Hotel is a lovely thatched property dating back about 300 years. Family run, it offers guests a warm welcome and a friendly, personal service in an atmosphere of peace, relaxation and informality.

The eight spacious bedrooms are attractively decorated and furnished, all having well appointed bathrooms en suite. Each offers a full range of desirable extras, including colour television, hairdryer and tea and coffee making facilities.

A comfortable lounge, complete with large inglenook fireplace and low, beamed ceilings, is the perfect place to relax before dinner. The proprietors pride themselves on the high standard of cuisine served in the attractive dining room. A good variety of imaginative dishes is always available, for example, oven-baked fillet of hake with a lime and coriander salsa, pastry case filled with ratatouille topped with a herb crust served with mushroom sauce, lamb cutlets topped with a tarragon mousse with red wine jus. Yalbury cottage has been awarded two AA Rosettes for outstanding cuisine. A selection of carefully chosen wines is available to complement any meal. **Places of interest nearby:** Thomas Hardy's birthplace, Athelhampton House, Parnham House, Abbotsbury Swannery, Corfe Castle and Sherborne Castle. Yalbury Cottage is an excellent centre from which to explore Dorset, with its superb walking country, pretty villages and magnificent coastline. **Directions: Lower Bockhampton is one mile south of A35 between Puddletown and Dorchester.**

THE GEORGE HOTEL

HIGH STREET, DORCHESTER-ON-THAMES, OXFORD OX10 7HH
TEL: 01865 340404 FAX: 01865 341620

OWNERS: Brian Griffin
MANAGER: Michael Pinder

18 rms   18 ens

S: £65
D: £85
Four Poster: £97

In the heart of the Thames Valley lies The George. Dating from the 15th century, it is one of the oldest inns in the country. In the days of the stage coach, it provided a welcome haven for many an aristocrat including the first Duchess of Marlborough, Sarah Churchill. However, more recent times have seen famous guests of a different hue such as author DH Lawrence. The buildings of the George Hotel have changed little since their heyday as a coaching inn. It retains all the beauty and charm of those days, whilst offering every modern amenity. All the rooms are en suite and furnished with fine antiques and the owners have created a décor which suits the requirements of modern times whilst maintaining the spirit of the past. The menu changes daily allowing the chef to ensure that only the freshest and finest produce reaches your table. The imaginative cuisine, awarded 2 AA Rosettes, is beautifully presented and delicious. The beamed dining room provides a delightful setting in which to enjoy an excellent meal, served by friendly, professional staff.

Places of interest nearby: Dorchester-on-Thames provides easy access to the Cotswolds, Blenheim Palace and Oxford. Stratford-upon-Avon, Henley, Windsor and an inexhaustible source of beautiful walks and cultural and sporting activities. Excellent meeting facilities for up to 36 in the Stable Suite and two smaller rooms each for up to 8 people. **Directions: On A4074, 9 miles south of Oxford.**

WALLETT'S COURT

WEST CLIFFE, ST MARGARET'S-AT-CLIFFE, DOVER, KENT CT15 6EW
TEL: 01304 852424 FAX: 01304 853430 E-MAIL: WallettsCourt@Compuserve.com

OWNERS: Chris, Lea and Gavin Oakley

S: £65–£110
D: £75–£130

This listed Grade II house, recorded in The Doomsday Book as 'The Manor of Westcliffe', was transformed by the Oakley family who discovered it in ruins in the late 70s. The result is a charming property, enveloped in a relaxing atmosphere and set in landscaped grounds near to Canterbury.

The beautifully appointed bedrooms are comfortable and well-equipped with an array of modern conveniences. They are located in either the main house or barn conversion, the most recent of which also features tan indoor swimming pool and leisure facilities. Fitness enthusiasts may use the steam room, sauna, spa pool, tennis courts and croquet lawn.

The attractive restaurant, awarded 3 AA Rosettes, offers an imaginative menu with a robust Kentish flavour. The dishes change every month to incorporate the fresh seasonal produce. Try the St. Margaret's Bay Lobster served with pilaaf rice and roasted vegetables, Dover Sole Meuniere or Romney Marsh Lamb. The extensive wine list includes a good selection of half-bottles, all acceptably priced. Breakfast is another feast, with farm eggs, sausages made by the nearby butcher and home-made preserves.

Places of interest nearby: Enjoy cliff top walks to St Margaret's Bay, exploring the Cinque Ports and playing golf on the championship courses. The city of Canterbury and the Cruise Terminal at Dover. **Directions: From A2 roundabout immediately north of Dover take A258 signposted Deal. After 1 mile turn right and the Court is on the right.**

DOVER (Temple Ewell)

THE WOODVILLE HALL

TEMPLE EWELL, DOVER, KENT CT16 3DJ
TEL: 01304 825256 FAX: 01304 825256

OWNER: Mr A.D.M. Allen
MANAGERS: Sue and Roger Westoby

 Suites: from £95

The owners justifiably boast that this is one of the most beautiful small hotels in England. One cannot believe that this magnificent residence, built in 1820 for Henry Colman (of mustard fame) and set in 25 acres of secluded parkland, is just a short drive from Dover and the Channel Tunnel.

The accommodation is superb, three spectacular suites which are all furnished most luxuriously in the greatest detail. Awarded 'Best Small Hotel' by the Welcome to Kent Scheme.

The ambience throughout the entire house reflects the gracious Georgian era, with silver and highly polished antiques, oil paintings and marvellous flowers. Welcoming and friendly hospitality is of the highest standard. Guests enjoy immaculate service and fine food beautifully presented with interesting wines and champagnes. Dinner is served either in the dining room or in the suites.

Places of interest nearby: When not enjoying the extensive grounds with its ancient woodland. Guests can visit nearby nature reserves, Dover Castle and Hellfire Corner, the Battle of Britain Museum, the Old Town Gaol, the White Cliffs Experience and Walmer Castle, or, further afield, Canterbury Cathedral. **Directions: Take A2 from Dover and at the second roundabout turn left. At the bottom of the hill turn right towards Lydden. Continue for one mile and Woodville Hall is on your right just before the "Z" bend.**

ASHWICK COUNTRY HOUSE HOTEL

DULVERTON, SOMERSET TA22 9QD
TEL: 01398 323868 FAX: 01398 323868 E-MAIL: ashwickhouse@talk21.com

OWNER: Richard Sherwood
CHEF: Richard Sherwood

S: £78–£84
D: £136–£148
(including dinner)

This small, charming AA Red Star Edwardian Country House stands in six acres of beautiful grounds above the picturesque valley of the River Barle within Exmoor National Park. Sweeping lawns lead to large water gardens where guests can relax in summer shade and breathe in sweet floral scents. Ashwick House offers old world hospitality. Its atmosphere is sunny with flowers in summer and elegantly cosy with candlelight and log fires in winter.

The baronial style hall with its long, broad gallery and cheerful log fire, the restaurant opening onto a terrace where breakfast is served and the comfortably furnished lounge offer a peaceful sanctuary not easily found in today's busy world. All bedrooms are spacious and pleasantly decorated, finished with many thoughtful personal touches.

Chef-patron Richard Sherwood presents quality cuisine using fresh local produce. Shooting and riding facilities are close by.

Places of interest nearby: Dunster's Norman Castle and 17th century Yarm Market, Exmoor Forest, many National Trust houses and gardens. **Directions: From the M5, exit at junction 27 onto the A361 to Tiverton. Take the A396 north until joining the B3222 to Dulverton and then the B3223 signposted Lynton and Exford. After a steep climb drive over a second cattle grid and turn left to Ashwick House.**

OAK LODGE HOTEL

80 VILLAGE ROAD, BUSH HILL PARK, ENFIELD, MIDDLESEX EN1 2EU
TEL: 020 8360 7082

OWNERS: John and Yvonne Brown

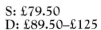

S: £79.50
D: £89.50–£125

Oak Lodge is just nine miles from central London with excellent road and rail connections and conveniently placed for each of the capital's five airports. The hotel is small but it offers a very generous welcome which encompasses charm, courtesy and old-fashioned hospitality.

Each en suite bedroom is highly individual, imaginatively furnished, and with all the facilities found in larger rooms. A superb new mini executive suite is now available.

Traditional English cuisine complemented by an exceptionally good wine list, is served in the intimate restaurant, awarded an AA Rosette, which overlooks and opens out onto a delightful evergreen garden. For after-dinner relaxation a pianist regularly entertains guests in a romantic Noel Coward style in the hotel's elegant lounge.

Enfield has excellent shopping facilities and preserves the atmosphere of the country town it once was. There are many fine old houses, particularly in Gentlemen's Row, where the 19th century author Charles Lamb lived.

Places of interest nearby: Forty Hall, built in 1632 for Sir Nicholas Raynton, Lord Mayor of London, now a cultural centre and museum, Capel Manor, St Albans cathedral and the ruins of a Roman amphitheatre. **Directions: From M25, exit at Jct25 onto A10 south. Turn right at 11th set of traffic lights into Church Street, then right again at next traffic lights into Village Road. Oak Lodge is 200yards on the right.**

CHALK LANE HOTEL

CHALK LANE, EPSOM, SURREY KT18 7BB
TEL; 01372 721179 FAX: 01372 727878 E-MAIL: chalklane@compuserve.com

OWNER: Steven McGregor
CHEFS: Daniel Bartholomew and Phillip Mathews

   S: £60–£75
D: £65–£115

This delightful country house is hidden away from the hustle and bustle of modern life in the conservation area that is old Epsom. With a total refurbishment programme nearing completion it repays handsomely any effort of locating it. The newly decorated bedrooms and bathrooms are presented to an impressive standard.

Discerning gastronomes will be delighted by the imaginative and beautifully-presented cuisine on offer. A good range of starters includes such irresistible offerings as hot roasted red pepper and goats cheese tart, Provençal-style vegetable and seared lamb fillet terrine and hot smoked Scottish salmon on a potato pancake with lemon on dill. A choice of nearly a dozen main courses includes mouth-watering dishes like Thai style monkfish curry with bok choi and jasmine rice, Scotch rib eye steak with crunchy leeks, French fries and port wine sauce and roasted salmon fillet with a red wine risotto scented with thyme and served with green asparagus. Vegetarians are also superbly catered for.

Places of interest nearby: This is an ideal location for horse-racing enthusiasts – the course at Epsom Downs is just minutes' away. Wisley, Hampton Court and Richmond. **Directions: M25, junction 9. Take A24 Dorking Road, turn right into Woodcote Road, left into Avenue Road and right into Worple Road. Take a left into Chalk Lane – the hotel is situated on the right.**

RECTORY HOUSE

FORE STREET, EVERSHOT, DORSET DT2 0JW
TEL: 01935 83273 FAX: 01935 83273

OWNERS: Denis and Angela Carpenter
CHEF: Angela Carpenter

5 rms   5 ens

S: from £50
D: £70–£100

Rectory House is a charming, 18th century listed building standing serenely in a quiet, unspoilt village surrounded by an area of natural beauty made famous by the novels of Thomas Hardy. Denis and Angela Carpenter give all their guests a genuinely friendly welcome, encouraging them to relax as if in their own home. On warm summer days and evenings the colourful garden with its huge beech tree for shade is popular with visitors seeking a secluded spot for a coffee, a cool drink or a quiet read.

Antique furniture, deep pile rugs and vases of fresh flowers abound throughout the house. Three of the five bedrooms are situated by the garden. All are en suite, tastefully decorated and furnished and have every comfort.

The cuisine is highly regarded with chef Angela Carpenter using fresh local produce to create a distinctive brand of international cooking.

The unspoilt countryside and its coastline, 12 miles south, make for limitless exploration and bring to life the setting of the Hardy novels. Golf is available at Chedington Court and there is fishing, riding and sailing at Sutton Bingham. Closed December–January.

Places of interest nearby: Sherborne Castle, the Cerne Giant, Parnham House, Yeovilton Air Museum and the gardens at Mapperton House, Kingston Maurward, Hooke Park and Forde Abbey. **Directions: Leave the A37 for Evershot halfway between Dorchester and Yeovil.**

THE MILL AT HARVINGTON

ANCHOR LANE, HARVINGTON, EVESHAM, WORCESTERSHIRE WR11 5NR
TEL: 01386 870688 FAX: 01386 870688

OWNERS: Simon and Jane Greenhalgh

S: £64
D: £99

From the first glimpse of Simon and Jane Greenhalgh's elegant brochure one is aware that The Mill at Harvington is going to be very special. This delightful small country house hotel set on the bank of the Avon is in the heart of England with easy access to the West, The Cotswolds, Wales and, of course, Shakespeare country.

From inside the welcoming and graceful reception rooms, which are brightened by big open fires in the winter, there are views over the extensive gardens and the river.

The high standards of hospitality and service are evident. The en suite bedrooms whether in the main building or the superb recent annexe extension are beautifully furnished with all the modern comforts including hairdryers, mineral water, colour television, tea and coffee facilities.

A modestly priced but excellent wine list accompanies the appetising menu which makes maximum use of local and seasonal produce, fish and game (there are also light lunches on the Terrace), reflecting the owners' belief that dining well must be high on the agenda for a successful visit. Guests take away memories of spectacular countryside, superb meals, immaculate service, charming surroundings and perfect hosts. **Directions: The Mill can be reached by a roadbridge over A46 opposite Harvington village, off the Evesham to Bidford road.**

THE CROWN HOTEL

EXFORD, EXMOOR NATIONAL PARK, SOMERSET TA24 7PP
TEL: 01643 831554/5 FAX: 01643 831665 E-MAIL: bradleyhotelsexmoor@easynet.co.uk

OWNERS: Mike Bradley and John Atkin
CHEF: Eric Bouchet

17 rms | 17 ens | SMALL HOTEL

S: £47.50–£75
D: £80–£116

This coaching inn, almost three hundred years old, in the Exmoor National Park is surrounded by wonderful countryside, from coastline to valleys, streams and moorland, populated with red deer, ponies, amazing birdlife and salmon.

The hotel has been completely refurbished, to the highest standards of elegance and comfort. Guests can enjoy its comfort in every season – its coolness in summer, its warmth in winter.

The bedrooms, all en suite, have been beautifully decorated and are well-equipped with modern necessities.

There is a lively bar, patronised by the locals, for drinks or informal meals ordered from the extensive menu, or guests may prefer an apéritif in the lounge before entering the delightful 2 Rosettes dining room for a beautifully presented evening meal from the seasonal menu. Good wines complement the meal. After dinner guests may wish to stroll in the water garden. Special breaks available throughout the year.

Places of interest nearby: Wild life Land-Rover safaris. Riding over the moor and clay pigeon shooting can be arranged. Order a packed lunch and walk the moor or visit Lynmouth and Porlock. **Directions: Exit M5, junction 27. Drive eight miles down the A361, then take the A396 to Wheddon Cross, where Exford is signposted.**

THE BEACON COUNTRY HOUSE HOTEL

BEACON ROAD, MINEHEAD, SOMERSET TA24 5SD
TEL: 01643 703476 FAX: 01643 707007 E-MAIL: Beacon@globalnet.co.uk

OWNERS: David and Gina Twist

S: £58–£98
D: £86–£96
suite: £136

An elegant Edwardian country house hotel perched high above the coastline, embraced by its own 20 acres of land, gardens, orchard, livery and home farm, nestling peacefully amid the rolling countryside, the hotel has direct access onto Exmoor and the Coastal Path, yet is only minutes from Minehead town centre.

All bedrooms are en suite, individually decorated, some with sea view and all overlooking the landscaped gardens and countryside beyond. There are two attractive lounges with open fireplaces, a domed glass conservatory and a stylish restaurant and bar serving superb food and drink. Riding, golfing, hiking, cycling, fishing, sailing, sightseeing and shopping are all close by. The hotel is

highly reputed for its friendly staff and thoughtful personal service.

Places of interest nearby: The Beacon Country House Hotel is an ideal base for touring Exmoor and the West Country. **Directions: From M5, turn off to Bridgewater at Jct23 then take A39 to Minehead. At Minehead follow signs into the Town Centre. Turn right at T-junction onto The Parade, take second left into Blenheim Road, then first left into Martlet Road. Proceed uphill and turn straight across at the memorial into Burgundy Road. Carry on round the hairpin bend and follow Beacon Road to the end. The hotel is on the right with its own car park.**

FALMOUTH (Mawnan Smith)

TRELAWNE HOTEL – THE HUTCHES RESTAURANT

MAWNAN SMITH, NR FALMOUTH, CORNWALL TR115HS
TEL: 01326 250226 FAX: 01326 250909

OWNERS: Paul and Linda Gibbons
CHEF: Nigel Woodland

12 rms   12 ens   SMALL HOTEL

S: £58–£80
D: £95–£155
(including 4 course dinner)

A very friendly welcome awaits guests, who will be enchanted by the beautiful location of Trelawne Hotel, on the coast between the Rivers Fal and Helford. Large picture windows in the public rooms, including the attractively decorated, spacious lounge/bar, ensure that guests take full advantage of the panoramic vistas of the ever-changing coastline.

The bedrooms are charming, many with views of the sea. The soft colours of the décor, the discreet lighting and attention to detail provide a restful atmosphere, in harmony with the Wedgwood, fresh flowers and sparkling crystal in The Hutches Restaurant, which has been awarded 2 AA Rosettes.

The menu changes daily and offers a variety of inspired dishes, including local seafood, game and fresh vegetables. Recreational facilities include an indoor heated swimming pool and a games room. Trelawne Hotel offers its own golf package at no less than ten fine courses. 'Slip Away Anyday' spring, autumn and winter breaks. Closed January.
Places of interest nearby: The Royal Duchy of Cornwall is an area of outstanding beauty, with many National Trust and English Heritage properties to visit and a range of leisure pursuits to enjoy. **Directions: From Truro follow A39 towards Falmouth, turn right at Hillhead roundabout, take exit signposted Maenporth. Carry on for 3 miles and Trelawne is at the top overlooking Falmouth bay.**

86

WHITE WINGS

QUAKER CLOSE, FENNY DRAYTON, NR NUNEATON, LEICESTERSHIRE CV13 6BS
TEL: 01827 716100 FAX: 01827 717191 E-MAIL: lloyd@whitewings.freeserve.co.uk

OWNERS: Ernest and Josephine Lloyd

**S: £60
D: £80**

This lovely family home provides peaceful and informal accommodation with spacious and traditionally furnished rooms. The well appointed bedrooms all offer private facilities, colour television and views of the luxuriant garden.

Breakfast and dinner are served on some of the finest collections of china and crystal, in fact Josephine's collection is so vast that you could quite easily not see the same china twice during your stay and all this is in the elegant dining room overlooking the garden. Afterwards, guests are invited to relax in the library or the conservatory and to enjoy the use of the Steinway grand piano or go through to the billiard room and play on a full sized billiard table.

The surrounding villages and towns offer plenty of entertainment including music, opera, ballet, theatre and exhibitions. For the active, there are golf courses and opportunities for fishing, canal trips and indoor skiing. **Places of interest nearby:** Fenny Drayton is an excellent centre from which to visit Stratford-upon-Avon, Warwick, Kenilworth and Leicester, with their ancient castles, historic houses, museums and art galleries. Close by is the village of Twycross with its zoo housing a famous collection of primates. **Directions: On the A444 from Nuneaton, turn left into George Fox Lane (becoming Old Forge Road) and right into Quaker Close.**

GATWICK (Charlwood)

STANHILL COURT HOTEL

STAN HILL ROAD, CHARLWOOD, NR HORLEY, SURREY RH6 0EP
TEL: 01293 862166 FAX: 01293 862773 E-MAIL: stanhillct@aol.com

OWNERS: Antonio and Kathryn Colas

S: from £95
D: £110–£150

Built in 1881 in the Scottish Baronial style, Stanhill Court Hotel is set in 35 acres of ancient wooded countryside and offers spectacular views over the North Downs. It boasts an original Victorian walled garden and amphitheatre available for concerts or corporate presentations and events.

The hotel is traditionally furnished to provide an intimate, warm and comfortable atmosphere, with rich pitch pine panelling evident throughout the hall, minstrels gallery and barrel roof. There is a wide choice of bedrooms, all decorated and furnished to the same high standards and offering a full range of facilities. A superb à la carte restaurant offers a menu which is international in flavour and complemented by an excellent range of regional and vintage wines. A choice of vegetarian dishes is always included and old style, personal service is guaranteed.

Versatile conference facilities include small meetings rooms and five function rooms. Stanhill Court is also a fine venue for wedding receptions, family celebrations and social gatherings and was voted Hotel of the Year 1998 by the South East England Tourist Board and Most Romantic Hotel by the AA. **Places of interest nearby:** Leonardslee, High Beeches, Nymans and Wakehurst Place. **Directions: Charlwood is north west of the airport and reached off the M23/A23 via Hookwood or Lowfield Heath. Go through Charlwood and follow signs towards Newdigate.**

THE CORMORANT HOTEL

GOLANT BY FOWEY, CORNWALL PL23 1LL
TEL: 01726 833426 FAX: 01726 833426 E-MAIL: cormorant@eclipse.co.uk

OWNERS: George and Estelle Elworthy

11 rms | 11 ens | SMALL HOTEL

S: £38–£58.50
D: £76–£92

The Cormorant Hotel stands high above the beautiful Fowey Estuary with magnificent views over the shimmering waters and the Cornish countryside. A warm, friendly and inviting atmosphere pervades the hotel which is enjoying gradual artistic refurbishment.

There are 11 entirely individual bedrooms, all en suite and with colour television, radio, direct dial telephone and extensive views over the estuary and creeks. Guests can relax in an extremely comfortable lounge which has full length picture windows and a log fire in winter. The bar is small and welcoming. Guests can also enjoy lounging on the terrace near the hotel's heated swimming pool which has a sliding roof for opening on hot summer days.

This corner of Cornwall is a living larder of wholesome produce all made use of by enthusiastic chef-patron George Elworthy and served in a pretty candlelit restaurant. A choice of long and imaginative menus is offered.

Places of interest nearby: Miles of walking along the coastline, quaint fishing villages, Lanhydrock House and gardens, Trelissick garden and many National Trust properties. Fishing, riding and golf can be arranged locally. **Directions: From Exeter, take A30 towards Bodmin and then B3269 towards Fowey. After six miles turn left at a staggered junction to Golant. Bear right as you approach the estuary and continue along the water's edge. The hotel is on the right.**

WHITE MOSS HOUSE

RYDAL WATER, GRASMERE, CUMBRIA LA22 9SE
TEL: 015394 35295 FAX: 015394 35516 E-MAIL: dixon@whitemoss.demon.co.uk

OWNERS: Peter and Susan Dixon

8 rms	8 ens	SMALL HOTEL

S: £80–£95
D: £130–£190
(including 5-course dinner)

Set in a fragrant garden of roses and lavender, White Moss House was once owned by Wordsworth, who often rested in the porch here between his wanderings. Built in 1730, it overlooks beautiful Rydal Water. Many famous and interesting walks through fells and lakeland start from the front door. Guests have free use of the local leisure club and swimming pool and free fishing on local rivers and lakes.

It has been described by a German gourmet magazine as 'probably the smallest, most splendid hotel in the world'. Proprietors Peter and Susan Dixon have created an intimate family atmosphere with a marvellous degree of comfort and attention to detail.

The seven bedrooms in the main house and the two in the Brockstone Cottage Suite are individually furnished, and most have lake views. Chef Peter Dixon has won international acclaim for his culinary skills including 2 AA Rosettes and a Red Star. The restaurant is deservedly famous for food prepared with imagination and style – 'the best English food in Britain', said *The Times* – and offers an extensive wine list of over 300 bins. Special breaks available. Closed December, January and February.

Places of interest nearby: Dove Cottage and Rydal Mount (Wordsworth's houses) are both one mile away. **Directions: White Moss House is off the A591 between Rydal Water and Grasmere, on the right as you drive north to Grasmere.**

THE OLD RECTORY

BARSHAM ROAD, GREAT SNORING, NORFOLK NR21 OHP
TEL: 01328 820597 FAX: 01328 820048 E-MAIL: greatsnoringoldrectory@compuserve.com

OWNERS: Rosamund and William Scoles

 S: £69.50–£75
D: £91–£95

The Old Rectory, a former manor house, stands in 1½ acres of walled gardens amid the unspoilt countryside of North Norfolk. The house, believed to date back to 1490, when it was the seat of Sir Ralph Shelton, was originally hexagonal. Two towers now remain with an intricate south east façade showing stone mullion windows bordered with frieze designs in terracotta tiles. The timeless tradition of the decor and furnishings creates an ambiance of bygone days. This secluded haven promises the discerning traveller old fashioned charm with a homely warmth and friendliness. The ideal base from which to explore this special part of Norfolk.

Established since 1978, The Old Rectory has also become a popular venue for group entertaining where 10–12 guests can enjoy the exclusive use of the house.

For those who like to be cosseted, but who relish the idea of independence, The Sheltons, self contained cottages in the grounds, are available. These are serviced daily and provide complete privacy in delightful surroundings. The house is closed from 24–27 December.
Places of interest nearby: Heritage coast, nature reserves, Sandringham and Walsingham. **Directions: Great Snoring is 3 miles north-east of Fakenham from the A148. The Old Rectory is on the Barsham Road, behind the church.**

CHASE LODGE

10 PARK ROAD, HAMPTON WICK, KINGSTON-UPON-THAMES, SURREY KT1 4AS
TEL: 0181 943 1862 FAX: 0181 943 9363

OWNERS: Nigel and Denise Stafford-Haworth

| 11 rms | 11 ens | SMALL HOTEL |

S: from £65
D: from £71

Chase Lodge is situated in Hampton Wick, adjacent to Bushy Park, in a conservation area of outstanding architectural and historical merit. Indeed, it is an ideal touring centre for places of historical interest such as Kew Gardens, Hampton Court Palace, Richmond Theatre and Royal Windsor.

Its proximity to so many major events makes Chase Lodge a popular choice for good accommodation. The Wimbledon Tournament, the Oxford and Cambridge Boat Race, racing at Kempton, Epsom, Ascot and Sandown, rugby at Twickenham and summer regattas at Kingston and Richmond are among the attractions within easy reach.

Originally built in 1870, Chase Lodge is a very successful small hotel, run with style and personality by proprietors Nigel and Denise Stafford-Haworth. The interiors have been designed to a high standard with well-chosen items of furniture and striking fabrics. The bedrooms, although not large, are beautifully appointed.

Private parties and functions can be accommodated. **Places of interest nearby:** Hampton Court, Windsor Castle and Richmond Park. **Directions: From the centre of Kingston take the A308 towards Hampton Court. Just after Kingston bridge is the Hampton Wick roundabout; take the White Hart exit into High Street (A310), the left at The Forresters into Park Road.**

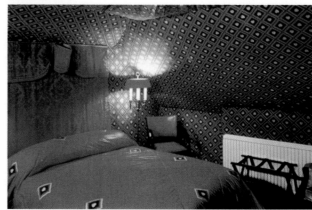

GROVE HOUSE

HAMSTERLEY FOREST, NR BISHOP AUCKLAND, CO DURHAM DL13 3NL
TEL: 01388 488203 FAX: 01388 488174 E-MAIL: X0V47@dial.pipex.com

OWNERS: Helene Close

S: £44–£58
D: £86–£96
(including 5 course dinner)

Grove House nestles at the heart of a beautiful garden in the middle of glorious Hamsterley Forest. Two small rivers run, on each side of the property, through 5,000 acres of old oaks and moors. It is an idyllic situation. Peaceful, quiet and historical, the house was built in 1830 as an aristocrat's shooting box and it exudes grandeur. There are fine furnishings and fabrics, stylish décor and open fires. The bedrooms, two doubles with en suite bathroom, a twin with en suite shower and toilet – have full facilities and are extremely comfortable. This is a non smoking house.

Helene prepares five-course evening meals from the best fresh ingredients. Often on the set menu are venison and pheasant direct from the forest. Grove House is unlicensed so guests are invited to take their own wine.

Those requiring total seclusion can stay at the adjoining, fully fitted, three-bedroomed Grove Cottage which has a large patio and a hillside rock garden.

Places of interest nearby: Bowes Museum, Raby Castle, High Force waterfall, Killhope Wheel, Beamish Open Air Museum and Durham Cathedral. **Directions: From A1(M) turn off onto A68 and just over two miles after Toft Hill turn left, through Hamsterley Village until the sign for "The Grove". Follow road to right, then left and after ½ a mile turn right to Hamsterley Forest and Grove House. Grove House is three miles further on.**

THE WHITE HOUSE

10 PARK PARADE, HARROGATE, NORTH YORKSHIRE HG1 5AH
TEL: 01423 501388 FAX: 01423 527973 E-MAIL: whitehouse–hotel@demon.co.uk

OWNER: Jennie Forster

 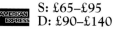

S: £65–£95
D: £90–£140

The White House enjoys a splendid location overlooking the Stray, 200 acres of parkland just a few minutes from the town centre. You will discover a unique residence in which luxury and comfort have blended with informality creating a relaxed atmosphere. The en suite bedrooms are individually furnished with designer fabrics and antiques together with full facilities.

The Venetian Room Restaurant offers a wide variety of exquisite and original dishes, with a very fine wine list and has held two AA Rosettes for many years.

Some of the many awards the hotel has achieved recently are 'Which?' County Hotel of the Year, A.C.E. Best Small Hotel, RAC Restaurant and Hospitality awards.

A perfect hotel for a private house party or wedding, where attention to detail is a foregone conclusion. Special mini breaks, available all year round.

Places of interest nearby: Harrogate is a spa town with its own Turkish bath, beautiful parks and gardens and numerous shops including antiques. Other attractions include Fountains Abbey, Harewood House and the Yorkshire Dales. **Directions: The White House is situated on The Stray and is set back from the A59. Request a map when booking for detailed directions.**

ROOKHURST COUNTRY HOUSE HOTEL

WEST END, GAYLE, HAWES, NORTH YORKSHIRE DL8 3RT
TEL: 01969 667454 FAX: 01969 667128 E-MAIL: rookhurst@lineone.net

OWNER: Richard and Judith Hynds

S: £70
D: £110–£130
(including dinner)

Nestling in the midst of Wensleydale, the front gate of this part-Georgian, part-Victorian country house opens onto the 250 mile-long Pennine Way. The cosy oak-beamed Georgian bedrooms are well-appointed and the more spacious Victorian bedrooms are furnished with four-poster beds whilst the rustic Bridal Suite is particularly ornate, featuring a half-tester bed. This is a non smoking house.

Judith specialises in traditional home-cooked English dishes, made with fresh mostly locally produced ingredients and bakes the bread for Breakfast. A wood-burning stove creates a snug atmosphere in the sitting room and bar, where guests can relax with a drink and enjoy the views over the garden and fields to the fells. Special break rates available.

Places of interest nearby: Rookhurst makes an ideal base for exploring Herriot country – the Yorkshire Dales are a delight for both serious walkers and strollers. Nearby is the Carlisle to Settle railway and you can be collected from Garsdale Station. Just round the corner is the Wensleydale Creamery, and in Hawes the Upper Dales folk museum. **Directions: Take A684 Sedbergh–Bedale road. At Hawes take Gayle Lane to Gayle. At the top of the lane turn right and the hotel is 300 yards further on the right.**

SAWREY HOUSE COUNTRY HOTEL

NR SAWREY, HAWKSHEAD, AMBLESIDE, CUMBRIA LA22 0LF
TEL: 015394 36387 FAX: 015394 36010 E-MAIL: Enquires@Sawrey–house.com

OWNERS: Shirley and Colin Whiteside
CHEF: Nigel Skinkis

S: £45–£65
D: £90–£120

Marooned in three acres of sculpted gardens designed for lazy indolence, Sawrey House Country Hotel is a quintessentially English rural hideaway. Built in the 1830s with slate from the local quarry, it is one of the prettiest buildings in the pristine conservation hamlet of Near Sawrey. Next door is 'Hilltop' once the home of Beatrix Potter, and visitors to Near Sawrey cannot fail to be captivated by the village's quaint tranquillity which so inspired her writings.

Owners Shirley and Colin Whiteside are justifiably proud of their Chef's award-winning dinners and their comfortable dining room, which has spectacular views over Esthwaite water and the lush forests beyond. Guests can take afternoon tea in the spacious lounge, while the bar offers guests some of the finest locally-brewed ales. The whole area is surrounded by National Trust land and is idyllic for walking. The hotel is centrally situated with the Windermere ferry only minutes from the House and Hawkshead, Ambleside and Coniston only a few minutes drive away. For the more energetic, Sawrey House will organise horse riding, fishing, sailing and even hot-air ballooning.

Places of interest nearby: Langdale and the Grizedale Forest are amongst the many natural attractions in the near vicinity.
Directions: Take junction 36 off M6, and follow A591 in the direction of Windermere, and continue to Ambleside. Take sign B5286, then the B5285 to Near Sawrey. Sawrey House in on the right.

NANSLOE MANOR

MENEAGE ROAD, HELSTON, CORNWALL TR13 0SB
TEL: 01326 574691 FAX: 01326 564680

OWNERS: The Ridden Family

S: £45–£59
D: £75–£120

This enchanting Georgian manor stands in romantic Daphne du Maurier country and guests are instantly aware they are coming to somewhere very special, as they approach the house along the tree lined drive.

Discovering Nansloe is serendipity – peaceful, surrounded by verdant, rural countryside, the hotel is owned (and managed) by the Ridden family, who have personally added so much to its warm ambience.

The bedrooms have lovely views across the Loe Valley. Each differs from the next, all are spacious and luxurious, with curtains and covers in gorgeous fabrics.

The drawing room has a fine Victorian fireplace, a welcome sight on cool evenings. It is charmingly furnished, big bowls of fresh flowers adding colour; the overall effect is relaxing – the ideal spot for a traditional Cornish tea or apéritif, in summer enjoyed alfresco on the croquet lawn.

The two AA Rosette restaurant is famed for its inspired menus, featuring local specialities including fish fresh from the sea, and the cellar contains excellent wines.

Places of interest nearby: Helston, Falmouth, St Ives and many gardens. Golf and sailing. Special breaks are available. **Directions: The Manor is situated the end of a well signed drive some 800 yards from junction of A394 from Falmouth and A3083 to the Lizard.**

THE BOWENS COUNTRY HOUSE

FOWNHOPE, HEREFORDSHIRE HR1 4PS
TEL: 01432 860430 FAX: 01432 860430

OWNERS: Carol and Tony Hart

S: £38
D: £65

Surrounded by 1½ acres of mature garden and the outstanding natural beauty of the peaceful Wye Valley, this stone-built 17th century renovated farmhouse provides every modern comfort while retaining its bygone charm and character. It stands on the eastern edge of the village of Fownhope, nestling beneath wooded slopes, once the sites of Iron Age hill forts, of which there are many in the area. The fish filled River Wye meanders through meadows south of the village.

The hotel's cosy lounge opens onto the garden and features a magnificent inglenook, discovered during recent alterations. The en suite bedrooms, including four on the ground floor, offer every up-to-date facility and superb views over the garden and the village's 11th century church.

Traditional English cuisine is served in the compact dining room. Tucked away in the garden are a putting green and grass tennis court. Golf, riding, canoeing, fishing and horse racing are within easy reach. Half-board breaks are available all year round.

Places of interest nearby: Hereford, Ross-on-Wye and the beauties and attractions of the Wye Valley, the Malverns, Brecon Beacons and The Marches.
Directions: From the M50, exit at junction 4 and join the A449 towards Ledbury. After approximately 2½ miles turn onto the B4224 to Fownhope.

THE STEPPES

ULLINGSWICK, NR HEREFORD, HEREFORDSHIRE HR1 3JG
TEL: 01432 820424 FAX: 01432 820042

OWNERS: Henry and Tricia Howland

S: from £45
D: from £80

A Grade II listed 17th century yeoman's house, The Steppes is located in Ullingswick, a *Domesday Book* hamlet set in the Wye Valley. The gleaming whitewashed exterior conceals a host of original features. Cobble and flag-flooring, massive oak timbers and an inglenook fireplace were part of the ancient dairy and cider-making cellars, which form the splendid cellar bar and lounge.

Winner of the Johansens 1996 "Value for Money Award", the ambience of this non–smoking house has been applauded by *The Sunday Telegraph*, *The Guardian* and *The Independent* newspapers – all of which praise the enthusiasm and hospitality of owners Henry and Tricia Howland and, in particular, Tricia's cooking. The candlelit dinners are compiled from medieval recipes, revived local dishes, Mediterranean delicacies and French cuisine. The interesting breakfast menu is complemented by generous service. Exceptionally high standard en suite accommodation is provided in either the Tudor Barn or Courtyard Cottage, both located within the grounds. Closed for two weeks before Christmas and three weeks after New Year.

Places of interest nearby: River Wye (salmon fishing), Black Mountains, Malvern Hills (Elgar's birthplace), Welsh Marches, Gloucester and Worcester. Riding can be arranged. **Directions: A mile off A417 Gloucester–Leominster, signed Ullingswick.**

FELBRIGG LODGE

AYLMERTON, NORTH NORFOLK NR11 8RA
TEL: 01263 837588 FAX: 01263 838012 E-MAIL: info@felbrigglodge.co.uk

OWNERS: Jill and Ian Gillam

S: £65
D: £90
Suite: £110

Jill and Ian Gillam have created this charming Lodge with the aim of providing the highest possible standards of accommodation in North Norfolk in a setting of total quiet and relaxation. Evoking an informal and welcoming ambience, the Lodge provides complete freedom for guests to mix with others or to seek solitude. Here time has stood still. Nothing disturbs over 70 different species of birds and other wildlife amongst rolling lawns and specimen trees and shrubs.

Felbrigg Lodge enjoys an unrivalled position just outside the Felbrigg Hall estate, a 17th century house owned by the National Trust. Approached by a long drive, the eight acres of grounds are totally secluded. The rooms, which are all at ground level, are situated around the gardens to take the greatest advantage of the view and landscape. All are sumptuously decorated with flair and imagination and have luxurious en suite bathrooms. Full English breakfasts and candlelit dinners are served in the converted stables. Jill is an enthusiastic cook and uses the best local produce.

Guests may relax in the privacy of their own rooms, wander at leisure through the gardens, play croquet, take afternoon tea in the summer house or swim in the heated indoor pool. A small, well-equipped gym is provided for the more energetic. **Places of interest nearby:** Felbrigg Hall, Blickling Hall and Holkham Hall. The cathedral city of Norwich is worth a visit whilst the North Norfolk coast is just 2km away. **Directions: Please ring the Lodge for detailed directions and brochure.**

THE OLD RECTORY

CRICKET MALHERBIE, ILMINSTER, SOMERSET TA19 0PW
TEL: 01460 54364 FAX: 01460 57374 E-MAIL: malherbie@aol.com

OWNERS: Michael and Patricia Fry-Foley, Ruth Parker

 S: from £48
D: from £75

Set in the tiny hamlet of Cricket Malherbie, The Old Rectory is a delightful country house with Strawberry Hill Gothic windows, a thatched roof and weathered hamstone walls. The flagstoned hall leads guests through to the enchanting sitting room, adorned with exquisite carved oak beams and exuding a tranquil atmosphere.

The five bedrooms are peaceful and furnished in a very tasteful manner, some with Gothic windows and all overlooking the gardens. Well-equipped and offering every possible comfort, the rooms include en suite bathrooms and showers. This is a totally non-smoking property.

The dining room is beautifully presented with large shuttered windows affording views of the lawns on both sides of the house. Guests sit at the grand table in dinner-party fashion and indulge in the daily-changing four-course menu. Produce from the vegetable garden and local fish and game feature highly in the inspired dishes.

Places of interest: Those with an interest in architecture will be pleased with the location as Bath, Stonehenge, Wells and Glastonbury are ideal destinations for day trips. Montacute House, Barrington Court and Yeovilton Air Museum are all close by. **Directions: The nearest motorway is M5. Exit at junction 25, join A358 towards Chard at A303 roundabout take the Chard exit again onto A358. Drive through the village of Donyatt, turn left for Ilminster and then right for Cricket Malherbie.**

NEW ILSINGTON (Dartmoor)

ILSINGTON COUNTRY HOTEL

ILSINGTON, NEWTON ABBOT, DEVON TQ13 9RR
TEL: 01364 661452 FAX: 01364 661307 E-MAIL: hotel@ilsington.co.uk

OWNERS: Tim and Maura Hassell
CHEF: Mike O'Donnell

S: £80
D: £135

The Ilsington Hotel stands in ten acres of beautiful private grounds within the Dartmoor National Park. Run by friendly proprietors, Tim and Maura Hassell, the delightful furnishings and ambience offer a most comfortable environment in which to relax. Stylish bedrooms and suites all boast outstanding views across the rolling pastoral countryside and every comfort and convenience to make guests feel at home, including English toiletries. The distinctive candle-lit dining room is perfect for savouring the superb cuisine, awarded an AA rosette, created by talented chefs from fresh local produce. The library is ideal for an intimate dining party or celebration whilst the Victorian conservatory is the place for morning coffee or a Devon cream tea. There is a fully equipped purpose built gymnasium, heated indoor pool, sauna and spa – also experienced masseurs.

Places of interest nearby: Some of England's most idyllic and unspoilt scenery surrounds Ilsington, with the picturesque villages of Lustleigh and Widecombe-in-the-Moor close by. Footpaths lead from the hotel on to Dartmoor. Riding, fishing and many other country pursuits can be arranged. **Directions: From M5 join A38 at Exeter following Plymouth signs. After approximately 12 miles exit for Moretonhampstead and Newton Abbot. At roundabout follow signs for Ilsington.**

RYLSTONE MANOR

RYLSTONE GARDENS, SHANKLIN, ISLE OF WIGHT PO37 6RE
TEL: 01983 862806 FAX: 01983 862806 E-MAIL: rylstone@dialstart.net

OWNERS: Neil Graham and Alan Priddle
CHEF: Neil Graham

   S: from £36
D: from £72

Neil Graham and Alan Priddle are the proud owners of this hidden gem uniquely located in four and a half acres of tranquil gardens on the fringe of Shanklin. Just two minutes' walk away through the gardens are the promenade and beach and the manor enjoys stunning views out across Shanklin Bay.

An atmosphere of comfort and relaxation is engendered in the stylish day rooms where afternoon tea and a good book are just the thing on inclement days.

In the restaurant, Neil prepares a nightly table d'hôte menu with an eagle eye on the best available produce and an expert's touch in its preparation. Poached fillet of salmon, roast loin of lamb and breast of duck are served with imaginative, simple sauces.

Both the restaurant and bedrooms are designated non-smoking; no children under 16 are taken; and dogs are not permitted. Rylstone Manor is truly a haven of peace, in a delightfully protected environment.

Places of interest nearby: For the more active, water sports, fishing, riding and golf can all be arranged. In addition to being a walkers' paradise, the island has many other manor houses and gardens to visit. Nearby are the thatched cottages of Shanklin Old Village, Queen Victoria's Osborne House, Carisbrook Castle and Rylstone Gardens Countryside Centre.

Directions: Just off the A3055 Sandown to Ventnor road in Shanklin Old Village, follow signs directly into Rylstone Gardens.

KESWICK (Lake Thirlmere)

DALE HEAD HALL LAKESIDE HOTEL

THIRLMERE, KESWICK, CUMBRIA CA12 4TN
TEL: 017687 72478 FAX: 017687 71070 E-MAIL: stay@dale–head–hall.co.uk

OWNERS: Alan and Shirley Lowe and family

S: £82–£99
D: £105–£170
(including 5 course dinner)

On the edge of Thirlmere, "the lake in the hollow", with only the sound of the birds breaking the silence stands Dale Head Hall. It is a truly scenic gem. At the foot of Helvellyn, almost completely surrounded by lush woodlands, this glorious 16th century house reigns alone on the shores of the lake and must surely command one of the most tranquil settings in the Lake District. Hosts Alan and Shirley Lowe and family, having restored the 16th century authenticity of the house, now offer exceptional accommodation and service. The hotel was deservedly runner-up for the Johansens 1995 Most Excellent Country House Hotel.

Bar and lounge are both delightful, sharing views over lake and mountains. The oak panelled dining room is the ideal place to enjoy the hotel's superb cuisine (Michelin; Good Food Guide; 2 AA Red Rosettes; RAC Restaurant Award). The bedrooms are extremely welcoming, warm and spacious and have all the things that you will expect to find, plus those little extras that make your stay so very special. Dale Head is one of those wonderful secrets which you would like to keep for yourself.

Places of interest nearby: All the splendours of the Lake District: Helvellyn is on the doorstep and Borrowdale is close by. **Directions: On the A591, halfway between Keswick and Grasmere. The hotel is situated along a private driveway overlooking Lake Thirlmere.**

SWINSIDE LODGE HOTEL

GRANGE ROAD, NEWLANDS, KESWICK, CUMBRIA CA12 5UE
TEL/FAX: 017687 72948

OWNER: Graham Taylor

S: £77–£90
D: £128–£170
(including dinner)

Swinside Lodge, situated at the foot of Catbells, is a Victorian lakeland house, surrounded by hills, valleys and woodland, and close to the shores of Derwentwater.

The house has seven attractive en suite bedrooms, each offering a high degree of comfort and equipped with colour TV, radio, hairdryer, tea making facilities plus a wealth of extras. Begin your day with a hearty Cumbrian breakfast and later return to the comfort of the charming sitting rooms before enjoying your four-course dinner in the intimate candle-lit dining room. Menus change daily and a typical meal could include fillet of cod on a bed of salad of crushed potatoes with a dill vinagrette, a delicious soup with home-baked rolls followed by pan-fried breast and stuffed leg of guinea fowl with a red wine and shallot sauce with freshly cooked vegetables. A choice of puddings or a variety of British farmhouse cheeses is followed by coffee.

An AA Red Star hotel with 2 Rosettes for food, RAC Blue Ribbon Award and ETB 3 Crown De Luxe, Swinside Lodge is non-smoking and unlicensed but guests are welcome to bring wine of their own choice. Closed December to January. **Places of interest nearby:** Keswick Pencil Museum, Castlerigg Stone Circle, Wordsworth's birthplace, excellent walks from the house. **Directions: M6 junction 40 take the A66 bypassing Keswick – over main roundabout – take second left. Go through Portinscale towards Grange; hotel is two miles further on the right.**

HIPPING HALL

COWAN BRIDGE, KIRKBY LONSDALE, CUMBRIA LA6 2JJ
TEL: 015242 71187 FAX: 015242 72452 E-MAIL: hippinghal@aol.com

OWNERS: Ian and Jocelyn Bryant

7 rms	7 ens

S: £72–£84
D: £88–£110

Hipping Hall is a 17th century country house set in three acres of walled gardens on the Cumbria/North Yorkshire borders, so an ideal centre from which to tour both the Lake District and Yorkshire Dales. Having just five double rooms and two cottage suites, this is an especially suitable venue for small groups wanting a place to themselves – families or friends celebrating an anniversary, golfing parties, corporate entertaining etc – and these house parties (available throughout the year) are a feature of Hipping Hall's success.

But from March to November it is mostly individual guests who enjoy the comfort and informality of staying with Ian and Jocelyn. The well-equipped bedrooms are largely furnished with antiques and all have attractive bathrooms. Guests help themselves to drinks from a sideboard in the conservatory before dining together at a large table in the Great Hall in a very informal dinner party style. Dinner is a set four course menu (including vegetarian dishes by prior request), served with three wines (optional) selected by Ian for that particular menu. All dishes are freshly prepared by Jocelyn, whose AA Rosette cooking draws so many people back to Hipping Hall.

Places of interest nearby: The Lake District, The Yorkshire Dales, The Settle to Carlisle Railway, Brontë country, Sizergh Castle. **Directions: Hipping Hall lies on the A65, two miles east of Kirkby Lonsdale towards Settle & Skipton, eight miles from M6 junction 36.**

LAVENHAM PRIORY

WATER STREET, LAVENHAM, SUFFOLK CO10 9RW
TEL: 01787 247404 FAX: 01787 248472 E-MAIL: tim.pitt@btinternet.com

OWNERS: Tim and Gilli Pitt

S: £59–£69
D: £78–£98

The magnificent timber-framed Priory was originally a 13th century hall house and the home of Benedictine monks. Over succeeding centuries it passed through a number of illustrious families, including the Earls of Oxford. Although considerable alterations have been made through the ages, The Priory retains many original features. Ceilings are high and mullioned windows, exposed beams and oak boarded floors abound.

The Priory stands as a historical and intriguing bridge between past and present, a comfortable family home with modern furnishings and amenities. At its heart is the heavily beamed Great Hall with a massive Tudor inglenook fireplace and a solid Jacobean staircase leading to the principal bedchambers decorated with Elizabethan wall-paintings. The bedrooms are spacious and comfortably furnished.

Guests can enjoy summer breakfast or a quiet drink in the sheltered herb garden surrounded by three acres of grounds. Dinner is by arrangement. The Priory received the AA Guest Accommodation of the Year Award for 1999 and recently acquired the grading of five Diamonds with a Gold Award.
Places of interest nearby: Medieval Lavenham, the market town of Sudbury, birthplace of painter Thomas Gainsborough and many National Trust properties. **Directions: From Bury St Edmunds join A134 towards Sudbury then A1141 to Lavenham. From Colchester join A134 signed Sudbury. Take by-pass, signed Long Melford, right onto B1115 which becomes B1071 to Lavenham.**

LOWER BACHE HOUSE

KIMBOLTON, NR LEOMINSTER, HEREFORDSHIRE HR6 OER
TEL & FAX: 01568 750304

OWNERS: Rose and Leslie Wiles

S: £34.50
D: £59

A Johansens award winner 4 miles from historic Leominster, Lower Bache is an oasis for nature lovers in 14 acres of a gentle Herefordshire valley. This substantial 17th century stone farmhouse has been restored by Rose and Leslie Wiles. While retaining its exposed stone walls, wealth of oak beams and flagstone flooring, it incorporates all the comforts of modern living. An annexe of three en suite bedrooms is furnished in a charming cottage style. Each bedroom has its own private sitting room. Water colours, original prints, plants, books and ornaments create an atmosphere of quality and comfort. With its vaulted ceiling and original cider mill, the dining room is unique. Rose and Leslie are acclaimed gourmet cooks: their set menus are superb value. Bread, ice-cream and preserves are all home-made; fish, game and poultry are smoked on the premises and most of the vegetables are grown organically in the garden. The breakfast menu offers an exceptional choice including laverbread, kedgeree, sautie bannocks, floddies and scrambled eggs with smoked salmon. Organic wines are also available.

Places of interest nearby: The Marches, Ludlow, Hereford, Worcester and Hay-on-Wye. 13 golf courses and 3 race courses are situated within 25 miles. **Directions: Kimbolton village is 2 miles north-east of Leominster (which is off the A49). Lower Bache is signposted at the top of the hill on the Leysters road A4112.**

THE THATCHED COTTAGE
COUNTRY HOTEL AND RESTAURANT

SPRYTOWN, LIFTON, DEVON PL16 0AY
TEL: 01566 784224 FAX: 01566 784334 E-MAIL: victoria@thatchedcott.u-net.com

OWNERS: Garth and Rita Willing and Victoria Bryant and Janet Purr

S: £46.75–£61
D: £93.50–£122

Nestling on the edge of Dartmoor in 2¹/₂ acres of landscaped gardens, The Thatched Cottage Country Hotel & Restaurant is just 1 mile from the Saxon village of Lifton. The bedrooms are situated in a converted coach house a few yards from the main thatched house. All rooms are decorated in a charming cottage style and have lovely views of the surrounding countryside.

The 16th century thatched cottage houses the restaurant, where a leisurely breakfast is served until 10am. The restaurant has been awarded two stars and a rosette by the AA and RAC for food and service. The menu which changes regularly plus an extensive wine list offers a varied and imaginative choice for the gourmet.

The lounge, with its inglenook fireplace, comfortable armchairs and cosy atmosphere, is the ideal place to enjoy apéritifs, after-dinner coffee, liqueurs and petits fours.

The premises are unsuitable for very young children.

Places of interest nearby: Well-placed for exploring Exmoor, Bodmin Moor and Dartmoor. This is an area rich in sites of historical, architectural and archeological interest. **Directions: From Exeter, follow the A30 for about 35 miles. Leave the A30 at Stowford Cross. At the top of the slip road at the T-junction turn left (the hotel is signposted) and travel to Sprytown Cross, straight across, the hotel drive is 100 yards on right.**

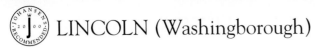
WASHINGBOROUGH HALL

CHURCH HILL, WASHINGBOROUGH, LINCOLN LN4 1BE
TEL: 01522 790340 FAX: 01522 792936 E-MAIL: washingborough.hall@btinternet.com

OWNERS: David Hill and Margaret Broddle
EXECUTIVE CHEF: David Hill

14 rms | 14 ens | SMALL HOTEL

S: £65–£80
D: £85–£125

This listed Georgian Manor House is set in four acres of secluded grounds, containing many mature trees and wonderful colourful borders. During the summer months, its main lawns are an ideal place for relaxing with a drink or playing croquet whilst in winter, guests can recline in the lounge in front of a roaring fire. The bedrooms are individually styled and furnished to a very high standard with en suite bathrooms, tea and coffee making facilities, hairdryer, trouser press and many other amenities. There is also a Computer Lounge with a high specification computer with complimentary Internet access and other software.

Overlooking the gardens, the Lounge Bar and Restaurant offer the highest quality of fresh local produce, prepared to the highest standards, complemented by an extensive wine list and well-stocked bar. The Wedgwood Dining Rooms were awarded two AA Rosettes this year for the second year running for its outstanding cuisine. The Washingborough is happy to arrange golf at Blakeney and Canwick Golf Clubs as well as a host of other activities including tennis and riding.

Places of interest nearby: The city of Lincoln with its magnificent 11th century cathedral and castle. Aircraft buffs should visit The Battle of Britain Memorial Flight and The Aviation Heritage Centre. **Directions: From Lincoln take B1188 towards Branston and turn left onto B1190 towards Bardney. Turn right (approx 2 miles) opposite telephone box. The Hall is 200 yards on the left.**

COOMBE FARM

WIDEGATES, NR LOOE, CORNWALL PL13 1QN
TEL: 01503 240223 FAX: 01503 240895

OWNERS: Martin and Sylvia Eades
MANAGER/CHEF: Sally Low

         S: £28–£36
D: £56–£72

Coombe Farm was originally part of a large estate and the house was built in 1928 for a nephew of the landowner. It enjoys magnificent views down an unspoilt wooded valley to the sea and is set in 10½ acres of lawns, meadows, woods, streams and ponds.

A warm, friendly and relaxed atmosphere pervades the house, which has been carefully furnished with antiques and paintings. Open log fires in the winter months add to the sense of comfort and cosiness. All the bedrooms offer lovely country views and are cheerfully decorated and centrally heated.

A full English breakfast is served at Coombe Farm and in the evening a four-course dinner is available in the lovely candlelit dining room. The traditional menu is changed daily and vegetarians are well catered for.

There are over three acres of lawns where guests are invited to soak up the sun, play croquet or swim in the heated outdoor swimming pool and there is a snug stone outhouse for snooker and table tennis. The farm is closed to guests from 1 November to 1 March.

Places of interest nearby: Coombe Farm is ideal for visiting all parts of Cornwall and most of Devon – The Coastal Path, fishing villages, old smuggling coves and beaches. Dartmoor and Bodmin Moor, many superb National Trust houses and gardens. **Directions: B3253 just south of Widegates village, 3½ miles east of Looe.**

 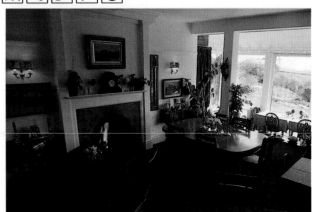

WINDER HALL

LOW LORTON, NR COCKERMOUTH, CUMBRIA CA13 9UP
TEL: 01900 85107 FAX: 01900 85107 E-MAIL: winderhall@lowlorton.freeserve.co.uk

OWNERS: Derek & Mary Denman

 S: £35–£50
D: £60–£74

With its grey-stone walls, tall chimneys, stone-mullioned windows and diamond patterned leaded-lights this historic old manor house is one of the most attractive hotels in Lakeland. It stands majestically on the River Cocker in a peaceful little village surrounded by the rugged charm of the Lake District National Park and close to Loweswater, Crummock and Buttermere Lakes. Grade II listed, the Hall is named after the Winder family who owned the estate and built the Hall between 1397 and 1699.

Despite renovations and refurbishments over the years Winder Hall retains many original features which combine gracefully with the comforts required by today's discerning guests. Six en suite bedrooms are luxurious and charmingly decorated and furnished with antiques in keeping with the elegance of the Hall. All offer panoramic views over Lorton Fells and welcoming fresh flowers and Cumbrian handmade chocolates on arrival. Chef proprietor Derek Denman provides superb, full Cumbrian breakfasts and four-course dinners in the oak panelled dining room which overlooks the formal walled garden.

Places of interest nearby: William Wordsworth's birthplace at Cockermouth, the market town's ruined 12th century castle. **Directions: From Keswick take A66 west to Braithwaite and then follow B5292 to the T-junction with B5289. Turn left through Low Lorton and Winder Hall is on the right.**

THE OLD MANOR HOTEL

11-14 SPARROW HILL, LOUGHBOROUGH, LEICESTERSHIRE LE11 1BT
TEL: 01509 211228 FAX: 01509 211128 E-MAIL: bookings@oldmanor.com

OWNER: Roger Burdell

| 7 rms | 7 ens | SMALL HOTEL |

MasterCard VISA

S: £65–£85
D: £75–£140

Overlooking the ancient churchyard of All Saints parish church at the heart of old Loughborough, the Old Manor Hotel is a treasure trove of history. It was rebuilt in the 1480s and later remodelled by Edward, First Lord Hastings of Loughborough, Lord Chamberlain to Queen Mary Tudor. Today it is a lovely hotel, full of interesting furnishings and superb fabrics. Alongside many antiques, some of the fine furniture has been beautifully made by the owner.

The Old Manor has undergone many alterations and renovations over the centuries. Today it has all modern comforts but retains a number of original features. These include extensive exposed beams and timberwork. The décor is individual, rich and earthy throughout with an emphasis on comfort and an atmosphere of total friendliness. The Old Manor is an entirely non-smoking house.

Although recently developed into a hotel the building has been a restaurant in the ownership of Roger Burdell for more than 15 years. His menus are thoughtfully planned. The food is simple but innovative with an Italian influenced style.

Places of interest nearby: Charnwood Forest, Donnington Park Motor Racing Circuit, Rutland Water, Nottingham Castle, National Watersports Centre at Holme. **Directions: From A6 South. At traffic lights past Jarvis Hotel, (Kings Head), turn right onto Baxter Gate. At traffic lights by Flan O'Brien pub turn left onto Sparrow Hill. The Old Manor Hotel is the first main building on the right hand side.**

DELBURY HALL

DIDDLEBURY, CRAVEN ARMS, SHROPSHIRE SY7 9DH
TEL: 01584 841267 FAX: 01584 841441 E-MAIL: wrigley@delbury.com

OWNERS: Patrick and Lucinda Wrigley

S: £55
D: £90–£100

| 3 rms | 1 ens | 🌳 |

Delbury, built in 1753 and probably Shropshire's most beautiful Georgian mansion, faces south across water meadows to medieval Ludlow, with a backdrop of the Clee Hills and the Wenlock Edge. Approached through 80 acres of landscaped parkland, the house is in a tranquil setting, surrounded by flower-filled gardens and overlooking a lake with ornamental ducks.

Delbury is a family house, complete with two children, two dogs and a cat! There are bedrooms available for guests, one with a four-poster, one with a half-tester, all with private bathrooms (one en suite) and all recently restored to a high standard. The large entrance hall has the original oak staircase, leading up to a first floor gallery on three sides and there is a large drawing room and sitting rooms for guests' use.

Guests dine at one large table in the dining room, where Patrick, an enthusiastic cook, serves the finest home produced food; smoked salmon and duck from the house smoker, home cured prosciutto and bresaola, fresh vegetables from the walled garden and free range eggs. **Places of interest nearby:** Ludlow Castle. Offa's Dyke (built centuries ago to fend off the Welsh), Stokesay Castle, a 13th century manor house five miles away and the Severn Valley Steam Railway. **Directions: On the B4368 between Craven Arms and Much Wenlock.**

OVERTON GRANGE HOTEL

OVERTON, LUDLOW, SHROPSHIRE SY8 4AD
TEL: 01584 873500 FAX: 01584 873524

OWNERS: Christine Ward
MANAGER: Ignacio Gonzalez
CHEF: Claude Bosi

S: £57
D: £88–£120

The setting of Overton Grange Hotel, which stands in 2½ acres of peaceful gardens overlooking the scenic Shropshire countryside, would be hard to rival for guests seeking to relax and refresh their spirits. A genuinely friendly and courteous staff delivers a first class personal service.

Most of the generously sized and elegant bedrooms offer excellent views over the landscape and have been individually designed with the highest standards of comfort in mind. Similar attention to detail has been paid in the spacious and attractive public rooms. For a quiet drink there is a choice of location – the cosy cocktail bar or the conservatory, which opens out onto the gardens and patio.

A comfortable oak-panelled restaurant is the setting in which to enjoy the gastronomic delights of Claude Bosi's cuisine. Awarded a Michelin star in 1999, his dishes might include Cornish lobster roasted with salted butter and fresh peas à la Francaise and avocado soufflé with homemade chocolate ice cream.

Sporting facilities such as tennis, swimming, fishing, golf and riding are all available within the local area.

Places of interest nearby: The hotel is only 1½ miles from the centre of the country town of Ludlow with its impressive castle and interesting museum. Stokesay Castle and Berrington Hall are also within easy reach. **Directions: From A49, exit 2 miles South of Ludlow, take B4361 Ludlow-Richard Castle road. The hotel is about ¼ mile along this road.**

LUTON (Little Offley)

LITTLE OFFLEY

HITCHIN, HERTFORDSHIRE SG5 3BU
TEL: 01462 768243 FAX: 01462 768243

OWNERS: Martin and Lady Rosemary French

3 rms | 3 ens

S: £55
D: £70

Set in 650 acres of farmland in the Chiltern Hills, Little Offley, not a hotel but a beautiful 17th century country house, affords wonderful views over the garden and surrounding countryside. One complete wing of the house has been set aside for guests and it provides a quiet haven comprising a large drawing room with a listed carved fireplace, dining room and 3 double bedrooms with bathrooms. The rooms are spacious and comfortable and there is an outdoor swimming pool available for guests' use in summer.

Accommodation is offered on a bed-and-breakfast basis. Lunch and dinner for larger groups can be provided, as can exclusive house parties, meetings, small exhibitions and receptions.

Alternatively, there are 4 pubs – all of them with excellent restaurants – in the nearby village of Great Offley, 1¹/₂ miles away. Guests may leave their car at the house when flying from Luton Airport. No children under 12.

Places of interest nearby: Little Offley is an ideal touring base from which to visit Hatfield House, Luton Hoo, Whipsnade Zoo, Woburn Abbey and Cambridge. The nearest town is Hitchin, which has large open-air markets on Tuesdays and Saturdays. London is 30 minutes by train. **Directions: Take A505 Luton–Hitchin road. At Great Offley, turn off for Little Offley.**

MOOR VIEW HOUSE

VALE DOWN, LYDFORD, DEVON EX20 4BB
TEL: 01822 820220 FAX: 01822 820220

OWNERS: David and Wendy Sharples
CHEF: Wendy Sharples

S: from £65
D: from £110
(including dinner)

This small Victorian country house has offered hospitality to the traveller throughout its life. The four double bedrooms make it ideal for small groups who want exclusive use of a house for special occasions or simply to relax with friends and enjoy good food and friendly service. Christmas and New Year parties are very popular and from spring to autumn, it is mainly individual guests who stay with the charming owners. The property faces Dartmoor from the front, while to the west are wonderful vistas of the landscape are lit by the setting sun.

Always putting their guests' comfort first, David and Wendy Sharples have created a friendly hotel with a genuinely relaxing ambience. Awarded AA and RAC 5 Diamonds. The reception rooms reflect the cheery glow of open fires and tasteful furnishings are a feature throughout. A Victorian decorative theme characterises the well-appointed bedrooms.

Sparkling crystal, bone china and gleaming silver in the dining room ensure that each meal is a special occasion. The daily four-course dinner menu embodies traditional country-style recipes using the finest local seasonal meat, fish and game, complemented by sound, sensibly priced wines. Awarded the new RAC Dining Award. **Places of interest nearby:** Lydford Gorge and Castle, Tavistock, Clovelly and Exeter. **Directions: From Exeter take A30 Okehampton bypass to Sourton Cross. Then take A386 signposted to Tavistock; Moor View's drive is situated four miles along on the right.**

THATCH LODGE HOTEL

THE STREET, CHARMOUTH, NR LYME REGIS, DORSET DT6 6PQ
TEL: 01297 560407 FAX: 01297 560407

OWNERS: Christopher and Andrea Worsfold
CHEF: Andrea Ashton-Worsfold

D: £78–£92
Four Poster/Half-Tester: £100
Suite: £120

A former 14th century Monks Retreat for nearby Forde Abbey. Charmouth is internationally renowned for its Jurassic fossil-strewn beach. To the east is Golden Cap, the highest cliff on the south coast rising 617ft high, and to the west Lyme Regis, with its romantic Cobb which featured both in 'The French Lieutenant's Woman' and Jane Austen's 'Persuasion'.

Thatch Lodge itself makes its own unique contribution to an Area of Outstanding Natural Beauty – thatched roof, pink cobb walls, hanging baskets, oak beams, antiques, walled garden and a 200 year old vine. Each of the bedrooms has its own character, some have four poster and half tester beds. Luxury toiletries, crisp sheets, courtesy tray, television and thoughtful extras add to your comfort. AA 2 Star 76%.

Awarded The Sunday Times Golden Pillow '99.

An outstanding feature of the 'Thatch' is the dining. Andrea, a qualified chef, cooks to order, using the freshest seasonal produce, resulting in a meal that will delight the eye and the palate. The Daily Mail comments "I have never tasted a soufflé as good/delicious/perfect". Awarded two AA Rosettes for outstanding cuisine. Totally non-smoking.

Places of interest nearby: Dorset Heritage Coast, Thomas Hardy Trail, Abbotsbury Swannery and subtropical gardens, Forde Abbey. Devon's Beer and Branscombe. Golf, tennis, riding, fishing, bird-watching and walking. **Directions: Charmouth is off the A35, two miles east of Lyme Regis.**

HOTEL GORDLETON MILL

SILVER STREET, HORDLE, NR LYMINGTON, NEW FOREST, HAMPSHIRE SO41 6DJ
TEL: 01590 682219 FAX: 01590 683073 E-MAIL: bookings@gordleton–mill.co.uk

OWNERS: William Stone
CHEF: Allan Dann

S: £76
D: £76–£144
Suite: £150–£180

Hidden in the countryside between the New Forest National Park and the sea lies an ivy-clad 17th century Water Mill, now privately owned and sympathetically renovated to make a most luxurious hotel. It is set in 5½ acres of landscaped, natural garden, with woods, fields, millpond, sluice gates, rustic bridges and a lily pond creating a perfect riverside retreat.

Gordleton Mill is renowned too for the gastronomic delights of its nationally acclaimed 'Provence Restaurant', which has won a star from Egon Ronay, two Red Stars and four Rosettes from the AA for its excellent food. Also rated 'Restaurant of the Year' in the Good Food Guide 1997.

This idyllic hotel boasts eight exquisitely furnished bedrooms some including whirlpool baths and showers along with luxury towelling robes, flowers, bottled water, fruit and a half bottle of Joseph Perrier champagne to greet guests on their arrival. Five of the bedrooms are exclusively reserved for non-smokers. Prices include continental breakfast and unlimited tea and coffee throughout a guest's stay.

Places of interest nearby: include Beaulieu, Bucklers Hard, Exbury Gardens, Romsey and Broadlands.
Directions: M27, junction 1. A337 south for 11 miles near Lymington after the railway bridge and mini roundabout turn sharp right before Toll House Inn, head towards Hordle and hotel is on right in about 1½ miles.

ROSEFIELD HOUSE

SWAY ROAD, LYMINGTON, NEW FOREST, HAMPSHIRE SO41 8LR
TEL: 01590 671526 FAX: 01590 689007

OWNERS: Keith and Vanessa Gibbs
CHEF: Keith Gibbs

    D: £70–£80

Encompassed by two acres of mature garden, this is a delightful, luxury house ideally situated for guests wishing to enjoy the nearby sailing delights of Lymington, the nature walks of the New Forest or the invigorating sea air of Bournemouth and Poole. Standing in the shadows of overlooking trees, Rosefield House is excellent value for money with amenities comparable with many four-star hotels.

The first-floor bedrooms have stylish en suite facilities and are furnished to the highest standard with king-size beds and refrigerator in which guests find welcoming chocolates. A cosy library provides a quiet retreat and an elegant lounge with log fire, is idyllic for relaxing, following an energetic day's outing.

Guests can enjoy breakfasting on the famous New Forest sausages, traditional afternoon cream and chocolate cake teas and superb four-course dinners prepared by chef patron Keith Gibbs. Diners should try his wonderful crab ramekins, gourmet steak Diane and speciality Banana Flambé. The dining room is intimate and charming and the table settings of gold underplates and coasters and glittering cutlery truly luxurious. Dinner is served four nights a week by arrangement.
Places of interest nearby: Exbury Gardens, Broadlands, Beaulieu Abbey and Lord Montague's National Motor Museum, the cathedral cities of Salisbury and Winchester.
Directions: Exit M27 at junction 1, drive south on A337 through Lyndhurst and Brockenhurst. At Lymington, cross the mini roundabout and take first right into Sway Road.

HEWITT'S HOTEL

NORTH WALK, LYNTON, DEVON EX35 6HJ
TEL: 01598 752293 FAX: 01598 752489

OWNERS: Angelika and Tito Spaldi

 S: £50–£80
D: from £100

Once the home of a distinguished Victorian, Sir Thomas Hewitt, this elegant and secluded 19th century country house hotel stands high on the cliffs overlooking the sea to Wales. Its 27 acres of woodland and gardens are a haven for wildlife and visitors can enjoy glorious vistas as they stroll down through the grounds to Lynmouth Harbour, 500 feet below.

Hewitt's is just minutes from the centre of Lynton and behind the hotel's grey stone walls there is only the Coastal Path, which meanders for miles through Exmoor. Although having every modern facility, the Victorian character of the house has been beautifully retained. A sweeping oak staircase leads from the imposing reception area past a superb stained glass window by Burne-Jones. The ornate fireplaces and panelling in the lounges and bar provide a warm and friendly ambience. The bedrooms, some of which have balconies, are well-furnished and all face seawards. A 3 bedroomed apartment is also available.

The hotel's terrace, where afternoon tea is served, affords magnificent views. International cuisine of a Cordon Bleu standard may be savoured in the intimate dining room. The beautifully presented dishes are the creations of Italian chef patron, Tito Spaldi. Ample parking. Dogs by arrangement.
Places of interest nearby: Valley of the Rocks, Watersmeet, Arlington Court, Barnstaple and numerous National Trust properties. **Directions: Leave the M5 at junction 23, signposted Minehead, follow the A39 to Lynton.**

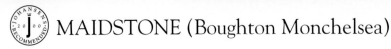

MAIDSTONE (Boughton Monchelsea)
TANYARD

WIERTON HILL, BOUGHTON MONCHELSEA, NR MAIDSTONE, KENT ME17 4JT
TEL: 01622 744705 FAX: 01622 741998

OWNER: J.M.Davies

S: from £65–£90
D: from £115–£155

Standing within its own ten acres of garden with gently flowing stream, Tanyard is situated in the heart of rural Kent, with far-reaching views across the Kentish Weald. The features and ambience of this medieval farmhouse have been extremely well preserved – exposed beams and inglenook fireplaces abound.

The interiors have been decorated and furnished in a style sympathetic to the age and character of the house. Antique accoutrements are combined with up-to-date facilities to ensure guests' comfort. As well as the five bedrooms, a heavily beamed suite complete with spa bath is available. Occupying the whole top floor of the house, this suite affords particularly fine views.

Dating from about 1350AD the restaurant is the oldest part of the building previously used as a tannery. An imaginative menu is offered for dinner on seven evenings a week.

Winner of the Johansens Recommended Country Houses Award 1993.

Places of interest nearby: Optimally located for touring the 'Garden of England', Leeds Castle and Sissinghurst. The Channel ports, tunnel and Gatwick Airport are within an hour's drive. **Directions:** From the B2163 at Boughton Monchelsea turn opposite The Cock into Park Lane, right into Wierton Road, right again for Tanyard.

NEWSTEAD GRANGE

NORTON-ON-DERWENT, MALTON, NORTH YORKSHIRE YO17 9PJ
TEL: 01653 692502 FAX: 01653 696951

OWNERS: Pat and Paul Williams

S: £45–£50
D: £72–£85

Enclosed in 2¹/₂ acres of gardens and grounds, Newstead Grange is an elegant Georgian country house with wonderful views of the Wolds and Moors. Resident owners Paul and Pat Williams extend a warm welcome to their guests, who are assured of personal attention.

The Grange maintains the quality and style of a country house restored. It has antique furniture and original features including working shutters and fine fireplaces. Open fires are lit in cooler months in one or both of the lounges. Bedrooms, all individual in character, have period furniture, paintings and prints. The Celebration Room contains an antique mahogany half-tester bed. Menus are prepared from the extensive organic kitchen garden and the best local produce. Wines are selected to complement the food. Special diets are catered for.

Newstead Grange is an entirely non-smoking house. English Tourism Council 5 diamonds. Closed mid October to mid March. Special break rates available.

Places of interest nearby: The ancient market town of Malton, York, the North York Moors National Park and the East Coast. Stately homes (including Castle Howard), abbeys, scenic walks and drives. **Directions: Follow signs out of Malton and Norton-on-Derwent to Beverley. Newstead Grange is on the left, ¹/₂ mile beyond the last houses and at the junction with the Settrington Road**

ABBEY HOUSE AND COACH HOUSE

WEST END ROAD, MAXEY, CAMBRIDGESHIRE PE6 9ES
TEL: 01778 344642 FAX: 01778 342706 E-MAIL: abbeyhouse@maxeyl.freeserve.co.uk

OWNERS: Freda and Brian Fitton

S: £35
D: £59

Abbey House stands tall and proud in the peaceful conservation village of Maxey whose surroundings are famed for having the greatest recorded concentration of prehistoric cursuses and circles in the country. Like Maxey, this solidly built hotel, encompassed by fine gardens, is steeped in history. Built in the late 12th century it was renovated in 1454 by the Almoner of Peterborough Abbey and in 1540 passed into the hands of the Dean and Chapter of Peterborough Cathedral.

Over the succeeding decades the house has been renovated, many original features restored and facilities extended and modernised to satisfy the most discerning visitor. The interior is bright and welcoming and the en suite bedrooms are delightfully decorated and furnished. They offer every home-from-home facility and most have beautiful garden views. A comfortable lounge is a fine venue in which to relax for a chat or quite read. Delicious breakfasts are served in the intimate dining room whose windows look out over the garden.

The personal attention of Freda and Brian Fitton ensures a high standard of service and they are happy to make dining reservations at the excellent restaurants and pubs in the area. **Places of interest nearby:** Stamford, Peterborough Cathedral, Belvoir Castle, Rutland Water, Geoff Hamilton's Barnsdale Gardens and Burghley House. **Directions: From Stamford take A16 towards Market Deeping, then turn south onto A15. Turn right into Maxey, 1st right into Castle End, 1st left into West End. Hotel is 400yards on the left.**

PERITON PARK HOTEL

MIDDLECOMBE, NR MINEHEAD, SOMERSET TA24 8SN
TEL: 01643 706885 FAX: 01643 706885

OWNERS: Richard and Angela Hunt

S: £65
D: £99

As you climb the winding drive through the woods, rhododendrons and azaleas to this Victorian country house hotel on the edge of the Exmoor National Park, it is not hard to see why Periton Park is described as a place "where time stands still". Richard and Angela Hunt run the hotel in an efficient and friendly way ensuring that, while their guests are staying with them, they will be carefully looked after. All the rooms are spacious and well proportioned, enlivened with warm autumn colours to create a restful atmosphere.

The wood panelled restaurant, with its double aspect views over the grounds, is the perfect place to enjoy some of the finest food on Exmoor. Menus change with the seasons to reflect the best of West Country produce – fresh fish, local game, delicately cooked vegetables, local cheeses and Somerset wine.

Exmoor is for country lovers with miles of varied, unspoilt, breathtaking landscape. A perfect retreat from the trials of everyday life. Riding is available from stables next to the hotel. Website: http://www.smoothhound.co.uk/hotels/periton.html

Places of interest nearby: Dunster Castle and Gardens, Knightshayes, Rosemoor, Selworthy, Arlington Court and Exmoor. **Directions: Exit M5 junction 24. Take the A39 towards Minehead. Follow signs to Porlock and Lynmouth. Hotel is on the left hand side.**

MIDDLEHAM (Wensleydale)

MILLERS HOUSE HOTEL

MIDDLEHAM, WENSLEYDALE, NORTH YORKSHIRE DL8 4NR
TEL: 01969 622630 FAX: 01969 623570 E-MAIL: hotel@millershouse.demon.co.uk

OWNERS: James and Ann Lundie

7 rms	6 ens	SMALL HOTEL

S: £42–£78
D: £84–£98

The peaceful village of Middleham nestles in the heart of the Yorkshire Dales and the Millers House Hotel is a perfect base from which to explore James Herriot country. This elegant Georgian house has been decorated in period style, including a magnificent, fully canopied four-poster bedroom. A recent addition is an attractive conservatory. Voted Hotel of the Year runner up in the Yorkshire and Humberside Tourist Board White Rose Awards.

The restaurant has won an AA Red Rosette for the last few years. Extensive use is made of fresh local produce, complemented by a fine selection of sensibly priced wines. Especially popular are the gourmet wine-tasting weekends.

Close by is Middleham Castle, once the seat of Richard III. The village is now better known as a racehorse training centre and guests can combine enjoyment of the glorious views across Wensleydale and Coverdale with watching racehorses exercising on the moorland gallops. Racing breaks with a day at the races and a visit to a training yard are also popular. Millers House is open for Christmas and New Year breaks and is available for house parties.

Places of interest nearby: Bolton and Richmond Castles, Fountains and Jervaulx Abbies, Aysgarth Falls, York and Harrogate. **Directions: Approaching from A1 take the A684 to Bedale and Leyburn; the left turning immediately before Leyburn takes you to Middleham. Millers House Hotel is in the centre of the village.**

WATERFORD HOUSE

19 KIRKGATE, MIDDLEHAM, NORTH YORKSHIRE DL8 4PG
TEL: 01969 622090 FAX: 01969 624020

OWNERS: Everyl and Brian Madell

4 rms	4 ens

S: £50–£60
D: £70–£90

Overlooking the main square of Middleham, an unsullied village typical of the county, the Waterford House is an enchanting Georgian style small private hotel that styles itself as a 'restaurant with rooms'. On entering, visitors are struck by the charming décor and friendly ambience.

However, it is the award-winning restaurant, holder of two AA Rosettes and listed in the Good Food Guide, that attracts visitors from afar with its eclectic cuisine and outstanding collection of wines. Crafted by the inspired chef, Everyl Madell, the menus comprise English-style dishes with European influences such as fresh asparagus, parma ham and parmesan and gambas a la plancha. Those with a more traditional palate will favour the roast duck served with a spiced plum and fig sauce. Featuring nearly 1000 bins, the impressive wine list is one of the best in the country and recently won the Wine by the Glass Award. With over 200 Burgundies, a vintage dating back to 1934 and a superb Spanish list, the restaurant is an oenologist's delight! After dinner guests can relax by a log fire in the drawing room, which is crammed with antiques and other memorabilia.

Places of interest nearby: Dating from the 12th century Middleham Castle was once considered the court of England. Fountains Abbey is one of the most archaeologically significant ruins in Europe. **Directions: From the north, take A1 south, turn right onto A684 to Leyburn. Take A6108 to Middleham. From the south, take B6267 via Masham.**

 MINCHINHAMPTON

BURLEIGH COURT

MINCHINHAMPTON, GLOUCESTERSHIRE GL5 2PF
TEL: 01453 883804 FAX: 01453 886870

OWNERS: Ian and Fiona Hall

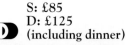

S: £85
D: £125
(including dinner)

Burleigh Court is a very special hotel, where a warmth reminiscence of an era long forgotten greets all guests from the moment they arrive at this beautiful 18th century Gentleman's Manor House. Situated amidst 3.5 acres of lovingly restored landscape gardens with terrace, pool and hidden pathways, every visitor is beguiled into enjoying all the pleasures of a tranquil Cotswold life.

All of the 18 individually decorated bedrooms are full of character and recreate the atmosphere of staying in a family home with friends. Indeed the house is still owned and operated by a close-knit family. In the dining room the thoughtfully prepared dishes offer an ideal blend of traditional cooking, with simplicity, freshness and purity.

Many of the herbs and salad vegetables are home-grown.
Places of interest nearby: Burleigh Court's setting in an area of outstanding natural beauty near Minchinhampton and Rodborough Commons affords the ideal location for touring the Southern Cotswolds, the Regency Spa towns of Bath and Cheltenham a short distance away and the picture postcard Cotswold villages on the doorstep.
Directions: Leave Stroud on the A419, heading towards Cirencester. 2½ miles outside Stroud take a right turn, signposted Burleigh and Minchinhampton, about 500 yards along this road there is a sharp left turn signposted Burleigh Court, the house will be on your right after a further 400 yards.

WIGHAM

MORCHARD BISHOP, NR CREDITON, DEVON EX17 6RJ
TEL: 01363 877350 FAX: 01363 877350 E-MAIL: info@wigham.co.uk
FROM USA TOLL FREE: 1 800 805 8210

OWNERS: Stephen and Dawn Chilcott

S: £65.50–£100
D: £98–£150
(including dinner)

Wigham is set within its own 30 acre organic farm in a delightful secluded valley, Soil Association approved this year. The picturesque 16th century thatched longhouse has been restored, providing a high standard of accommodation.

Wigham uses all its own lamb, pork, beef and poultry and dairy produce: smoked bacon and sausages and vibrant yellow yolked eggs are a feature at breakfast time. Dinner is served en famille at the large table and comprises mostly organic and local produce. The cuisine is home-cooked freshly each day and complements the excellent wine list, creating a very enjoyable atmosphere.

Proprietors Stephen and Dawn Chilcott have created a warm and welcoming atmosphere at this charming retreat.

The interiors are characterised by low ceilings, exposed beams, massive fireplaces and original wall panelling. The bedrooms are individually furnished in cottage style and have pretty, co-ordinated fabrics. In the honeymoon suite there is a rustic four-poster bed. All the bedrooms are en suite and have a television and direct dial telephone. For further entertainment there is a snooker lounge with a 7-foot table, a heated outdoor pool with a barbecue and a well-equipped 'honour' bar.

Places of interest nearby: Exmoor, Dartmoor, Exeter, Tiverton and Barnstable. **Directions: From Morchard Bishop, take the road marked Chawleigh–Chumleigh, fork right after ¾ mile, and ¾ mile further on, on the right, is a small private road marked Wigham.**

ROMNEY BAY HOUSE

COAST ROAD, LITTLESTONE, NEW ROMNEY, KENT TN28 8QY
TEL: 01797 364747 FAX: 01797 367156

OWNERS: Jennifer and Helmut Gorlich

S: from £50
D: £75–£120

This spectacular house was built in the 1920s for the American actress and journalist, Hedda Hopper, by the distinguished architect, Sir Clough Williams-Ellis.

The gracious drawing room overlooks the English Channel, panoramically surveyed through the telescope in the first floor library. There is access to the beach, a tennis court, croquet lawn and golf course. A 5 minute drive to Lydd airport and you can fly to Le Touquet for lunch.

The owners have completed an impressive refurbishing programme. Upstairs, designated non-smoking, the charming en suite bedrooms are furnished with antiques.

Wonderful cream teas can be enjoyed on the terrace in the sun-lit sea air, a traditional four-course dinner is served most nights and guests will strongly approve of the short but excellent wine list. Less than 20 minutes drive from the Channel Tunnel Terminal

Places of interest nearby: There is so much history in Romney Marsh, renowned years ago for its smuggling. Caesar landed here in 55BC at Port Lympne and the famous Cinque Ports stretch along the coast. Canterbury Cathedral is a reasonable drive inland. Littlestone Golf Courses adjoin the hotel and windsurfing is popular.

Directions: From New Romney head for the coast by Station Road leading to Littlestone Road – pass the miniature railway station – at the sea, turn left and follow signs for Romney Bay House for about a mile.

BEECHWOOD HOTEL

CROMER ROAD, NORTH WALSHAM, NORFOLK NR28 0HD
TEL: 01692 403231 FAX: 01692 407284

OWNERS: Don Birch and Lindsay Spalding
CHEF: Steven Norgate

S: £50–£65
D: £70–£88

The combination of an elegant, spacious, ivy-clad house, surrounded by well laid-out gardens, dating back to 1800, with a lovely ambience generated by the proprietors' warm welcome and the attentive staff has created a very special country house hotel in East Anglia.

For many years residents in North Walsham knew it as the doctor's house, then it was extended and transformed to accommodate guests, including Agatha Christie, who visited regularly until the mid-60s when it was a private house.

The bedrooms are delightful, with big windows, individually decorated and filled with traditional and antique furniture. The comfortable drawing room is well supplied with books and magazines and residents enjoy the intimate bar. The atmosphere in the Dining Room reflects the contentment of diners appreciating a menu that includes classic English dishes and the Chef's personal suggestions, incorporating the excellent local produce available, together with fine wines, many from the New World, selected by the owners. Winner of the 1999 Johansens Most Excellent Value for Money Award.

Places of interest nearby: Sandringham, Blickling Hall and Holkham Hall. Bird-watchers head for Cley Marches and the Nature Reserves; others enjoy the Norfolk Broads or explore Norwich Cathedral. **Directions: Leave Norwich on B1150, driving 13 miles to North Walsham. Pass under the railway bridge, then left at the first traffic lights and right at the next set, finding the hotel 150m on the left.**

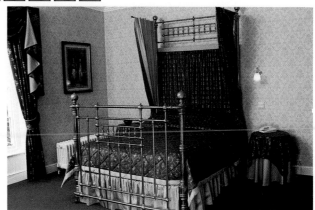

THE BEECHES HOTEL AND VICTORIAN GARDENS

2–6 EARLHAM ROAD, NORWICH, NORFOLK NR2 3DB
TEL: 01603 621167 FAX: 01603 620151 E-MAIL: reception@beeches.co.uk

OWNERS: Keith and Elisabeth Hill
CHEF: Simon Woodward

S: £54–£74
D: £70–£88

With three acres of English Heritage Victorian Gardens, this hotel offers discerning guests a warm welcome and exceptionally high standards of comfort in a relaxed, informal atmosphere. The three separate Grade II listed Victorian mansions have been beautifully restored, extended and attractively decorated and are collectively known as the Beeches.

When the houses were built in the mid-1800s, an idyllic Italianate garden was created in the deep hollow it overlooks. In 1980, this 'secret' garden, now known as The Plantation Garden, was rediscovered. It is being restored to its former glory and guests are free to wander through this enchanting and extraordinary reminder of our Victorian heritage with its ornate Gothic fountain and amazing terraces. All bedrooms feature charming individual décor, separate modern facilities and are non smoking.

A varied selection of tempting dishes is cooked to order and served in the Bistro Restaurant which overlooks a delightful patio garden. Residents and diners can enjoy a pre-dinner drink in the comfortable lounge bar.

Places of interest nearby: The city of Norwich, with its castle containing a famous collection of the Norwich school of painting and its fine cathedral, the Norfolk coast and Broads. **Directions: From the A11 take the ring road west and turn onto the B1108 (Earlham Road) to the city centre. The hotel is near the Roman Catholic cathedral.**

CATTON OLD HALL

LODGE LANE, CATTON, NORWICH, NORFOLK NR6 7HG
TEL: 01603 419379 FAX: 01603 400339 E-MAIL: enquires@catton–hall.co.uk

OWNERS: Roger and Anthea Cawdron

5 rms | 5 ens | SMALL HOTEL

S: £48
D: £66–£95

Catton Old Hall was built in 1632 and has been sympathetically restored to its former glory. It lies just $2^1/_2$ miles north east of Norwich city centre and within easy reach of the airport. The Hall, once a farmhouse, retains a wealth of oak beams and one of the largest inglenooks in Norwich. Now the family home of Roger and Anthea Cawdron, it provides luxurious accommodation for its guests. The en suite bedrooms are spacious, tastefully decorated and furnished to the highest standards. The dining room and lounge have a homely atmosphere and are ideal places in which to enjoy quiet comfort.

Full English breakfast is served at the Hall and evening meals are available if booked in advance. A typical evening meal might be a choice between breast of Barbary duck, cooked in blackberry and blueberry sauce laced with Crème de Mûre, or fillet of beef Wellington, a steak with a mushroom and onion farce wrapped in crisp pastry served with a rich port and thyme jus.

A full range of office facilities is available and arrangements can be made to visit local sporting events.
Places of interest nearby: The ancient cathedral city of Norwich, with its 12th century castle, fine museums and many other historic buildings. Also the Norfolk Broads and the long sandy beaches on the Norfolk coastline.
Directions: $2^1/_2$ miles north east of Norwich centre. Lodge Lane is just off Spixworth Road.

THE NORFOLK MEAD HOTEL

COLTISHALL, NORWICH, NORFOLK NR12 7DN
TEL: 01603 737531 FAX: 01603 737521

OWNERS: Don and Jill Flèming
RESIDENT BEAUTY THERAPIST: Nicki Fleming

S: £65–£85
D: £75–£99

This elegant Georgian manor house, dating back to 1740, sits on a quiet edge of the Norfolk Broads, standing in 12 acres of lovely gardens and rolling lawns which sweep down to the River Bure. Guests can stroll down to the water to catch a glimpse of a kingfisher or heron and enjoy the variety of birdlife. The owners Don and Jill Fleming have added a host of personal touches to create a homely atmosphere, the fragrance of fresh flowers pervades the hotel.

The delightful restaurant, overlooking the gardens and the river, offers a constantly changing menu thoughtfully selected by the chef to utilise the abundance of local produce, which includes fish caught off the Norfolk coast, game from the local estates, vegetables and herbs from the gardens. An extensive wine list has been carefully selected. Relax with a drink before dinner in the bar, where a log fire burns in winter and French windows open onto the old walled garden in the summer. Those wishing to be pampered will enjoy 'Nicki's Beauty Spot', the hotel's own salon offering a range of health and beauty treatments. Sport facilities include a well-stocked fishing lake, off-river mooring and a 60ft pool. Situated only 7 miles from the centre of Norwich and 12 miles from the coast, the Norfolk Mead is well-situated for both business and leisure. **Directions: On reaching Norwich take outer ring road to B1150 signposted North Walsham. After Horstead/ Coltishall bridge, bear right on the B1354, signposted Wroxham. Entrance signposted on right just before church.**

THE OLD RECTORY

103 YARMOUTH ROAD, THORPE ST ANDREW, NORWICH, NORFOLK NR7 OHF
TEL: 01603 700772 FAX: 01603 300772 E-MAIL: RectoryH@aol.com

OWNERS: Chris and Sally Entwistle

S: £59–£75
D: £78–£88

Chris and Sally Entwistle extend a warm and hospitable welcome and the promise of fine personal service to guests at the Old Rectory. Dating back to 1754, their delightful Grade II listed Georgian home, clad with Wisteria and Virginia Creeper, stands in an acre of mature gardens on the outskirts of Norwich overlooking the River Yare.

The spacious and well-furnished bedrooms, both in the hotel and the adjacent Coach House, offer quality, comfort and every modern amenity. After a busy day, guests may unwind over a pre-dinner drink in the elegant Drawing Room, enhanced by a roaring log fire during the winter and choose from a table d'hôte menu. The tempting dishes are changed daily and are freshly prepared to order.

The Wellingtonia Room and the Conservatory, overlooking the sun terrace and gardens, are excellent venues for business meetings and private luncheons or dinners.

Places of interest nearby: Within easy reach of the city centre and the Norfolk Broads, The Old Rectory is an ideal base from which to explore the historic city of Norwich, the beautiful Broadland countryside and the Norfolk coast.

Directions: Follow the A47 Norwich bypass towards Great Yarmouth. Take the A1042 exit and follow the road into Thorpe St Andrew. Bear left onto the A1242 and the hotel is approximately 50 yards on the right after the first set of traffic lights.

THE STOWER GRANGE

SCHOOL ROAD, DRAYTON, NORFOLK NR8 6EF
TEL: 01603 860210 FAX: 01603 860464

OWNERS: The McCoy Family
CHEF: Mark Smith

S: £52.50–£57.50
D: £67.50–£72.50
Four Poster: £87.50

The Stower Grange, built of mellow Norfolk bricks under Dutch pantiles, dates back to the 17th century. In former times it was a gracious rectory. Today it offers travellers a peaceful retreat – the gardens have fine lawns with inviting shade provided by the mature trees – yet the property is only 4½ miles from the commercial and historic centre of Norwich. Stower is owned by the McCoy family; the atmosphere is friendly and informal. In cooler months open fires add to the welcome. There are eight spacious individually-decorated bedrooms with en suite facilities, including one with a pine four-poster bed for those in a romantic mood. The Blue Restaurant, locally renowned as a 'special place' to dine, is supervised by the owners' daughter Kate and looks directly on to the gardens. The imaginative cooking of their son-in-law Mark ensures good eating from the individually priced menus. The restaurant closes on Sunday evenings, however, residents can enjoy a steak and salad in the Lounge Bar.

Places of interest nearby: Norwich, Norfolk Broads, Holkham Hall, Houghton Hall, Blickling Hall, Sandringham and the Norfolk Coast are all nearby.
Directions: From A11, turn left on to inner ring road and proceed to the ASDA junction with A1067 Norwich–Fakenham Road. Approximately two miles to Drayton turn right at the Red Lion public house. After 80 yards bear left. The Stower Grange is on the right.

COCKLIFFE COUNTRY HOUSE HOTEL

BURNT STUMP COUNTRY PARK, BURNT STUMP HILL, NOTTINGHAMSHIRE NG5 8PQ
TEL: 01159 680179 FAX: 01159 680623 E-MAIL: manager@cockliffehotel.freeserve.co.uk

OWNERS: Dane and Jane Clarke
CHEF: Nathan Measurers

S: from £95
D: from £105

This is Robin Hood country and Cockliffe is situated in the heart of it, six miles north of Nottingham. A lovely, unusually designed 17th century house with turreted-style corners it stands in two acres of colourful, mature gardens adjacent to the open spaces of Burnt Stump Country Park.

Dane and Jane Clarke rescued the house from disrepair five years ago and are proud of their renovations and refurbishments, many of which are in keeping with original features. Décor and furnishings throughout are elegant and tasteful and most rooms afford splendid views over the garden. The ten bedrooms are individually designed and comfortably appointed to reflect the needs of discerning guests. All are en suite, with thoughtful touches, period furniture and adorned with beautiful curtain fabrics carefully chosen by Jane Clarke.

Chef Nathan Measurers produces an excellent and imaginative menu using local fish and game when in season served in the attractive restaurant, adjoining the cocktail bar which is popular with guests for pre-meal drinks and after dinner coffee. A conference room with high-tech facilities is available. Golf, fishing, riding and fitness and leisure can be arranged locally.

Places of interest nearby: Nottingham and its castle, Sherwood Forest, 12th century Newstead Abbey and Southwell Minster with its medieval carvings, the earliest of their kind in England. **Directions: Exit M1 at junction 25 and take the A614 north from Nottingham.**

NOTTINGHAM (Ruddington)

THE COTTAGE COUNTRY HOUSE HOTEL

EASTHORPE STREET, RUDDINGTON, NOTTINGHAM NG11 6LA
TEL: 01159 846882 FAX: 01159 214721

OWNERS: Christina and Tim Ruffell
CHEF: Christina Ruffell

S: from £75
D: from £95
Suites: £115

Roses and honeysuckle ramble over the walls of The Cottage Country House Hotel, a unique restoration of 17th century cottages; it lies tucked away in the village of Ruddington, yet only a few minutes drive from the bustling city of Nottingham. It is the imaginative concept of the designer proprietors and with its private, gated courtyard and delightful walled garden it has won three major awards, including the Conservation Award for the best restoration of an old building in a village setting.

Christina and Tim Ruffell are proud of their attention to detail and they engaged local leading craftsmen to renovate and refurbish the hotel in keeping with its original features. Their aim was to provide quality, style and comfort in tranquil surroundings. They have succeeded in every way.

All the hotel's rooms are individually designed and furnished to reflect the needs of discerning guests. The bedrooms are all en suite, with thoughtful extra touches, and each room is individually named. The hotel offers two superb honeymoon suites. The excellent restaurant serves contemporary international cuisine and fine wines, there are two guest sitting rooms, one with an original inglenook fireplace. The terrace bar overlooks the enclosed courtyard and fountain, and there is a second terrace leading into the garden. Golf, tennis and water sports are within easy reach. **Directions: Ruddington is three miles south of Nottingham on the A60 Loughborough road. The hotel is situated at the heart of the village.**

L'AUBERGE

29 MAIN STREET, REDMILE, NOTTINGHAMSHIRE NG13 0GA
TEL: 01949 843086 FAX: 01949 843706

OWNERS: Alain and Sian Duval

S: £65
D: £85

A long gravelled drive edged by manicured lawns leads visitors to the welcoming door of this classic Georgian three-storey hotel and restaurant tucked away in rural splendour in the Vale of Belvoir, midway between Nottingham and Grantham. It is a charming, peaceful location providing complete relaxation from the stresses and strains of the modern world.

L'Auberge dates from about 1740 and was originally a farmhouse owned by the Duke of Rutland. It has been very tastefully restored by owners Alain and Sian Duval whose aim is to provide quality, style, comfort and a friendly atmosphere in tranquil surroundings. All the bedrooms are individually designed and furnished to reflect the needs of guests. Each is

en suite and offers colour television, telephone and modem points, tea and coffee making facilities.

Burgundian chef/proprietor Alain Duval produces delicious and imaginative à la carte menus in the cosy, beamed restaurant. Particularly delicious is his smoked gravalax with black and red roe, lemon and toast, followed by baked monkfish tails wrapped in bacon with a green peppercorn cream sauce, and a crème brulée with baked sugar crust.

Places of interest nearby: L'Auberge is an ideal base from which to visit Belvoir Castle, see first class cricket at Trent Bridge and to enjoy the delights of Robin Hood's Sherwood Forest. **Directions: Redmile is situated between A52 and A607 about 4 miles west of Grantham.**

LANGAR HALL

LANGAR, NOTTINGHAMSHIRE NG13 9HG
TEL: 01949 860559 FAX: 01949 861045 E-MAIL: langarhall–hotel@ndirect.co.uk

OWNER: Imogen Skirving

S: £75–£95
D: £95–£150
Suite: £175

Set in the Vale of Belvoir, mid-way between Nottingham and Grantham, Langar Hall is the family home of Imogen Skirving. Epitomising "excellence and diversity" it combines the standards of good hotel-keeping with the hospitality and style of country house living. Having received a warm welcome, guests can enjoy the atmosphere of a private home that is much loved and cared for.

The en suite bedrooms are individually designed and comfortably appointed. The public rooms feature fine furnishings and most rooms afford beautiful views of the garden, park and moat. Imogen and her kitchen team collaborate to produce an excellent, varied menu of modern British food. This is an ideal venue for exclusive 'House party' bookings and private dinner parties. The new children's adventure playground area will please younger visitors. Dogs can be accommodated by arrangement.

Places of interest nearby: Langar Hall is an ideal venue for small boardroom meetings. It is also an ideal base from which to visit Belvoir Castle, to see cricket at Trent Bridge, to visit students at Nottingham University and to see Robin Hood's Sherwood Forest. **Directions: Langar is accessible via Bingham on the A52, or via Cropwell Bishop from the A46 (both signposted). The house adjoins the church and is hidden behind it.**

THE HAUTBOY

OCKHAM LANE, OCKHAM, SURREY
TEL: 01483 225355 FAX: 01483 211176 E-MAIL: howardclare@hotmail.com

OWNERS: Richard and Mags Watney
CHEF: Darren Tidd

S: £98
D: £115–£125

More than 150 years of history, character and atmosphere are absorbed into the lovely interior of this warm, redbrick Gothic hotel ideally situated in the heart of the Surrey countryside midway between Heathrow and Gatwick airports. Family managed, The Hautboy is a magnificent hotel sympathetically refurbished and modernised but with many original features such as mullioned windows, steam bent wooden beams, vaulted ceilings and intimate corners.

The bedrooms are sumptuous, offering the grace and charisma of the past with the comfort and facilities of today. Each has its own fascinating architectural character, elegant furnishings and views over the garden, fields and woodlands.

Award winning chef Darren Tidd provides à la carte delights and six-course gastronomic menus to please every taste in the The Chapel restaurant, an opulent room of high vaulted ceilings and wonderful murals inspired by the owners' love of Tuscany. Less formal meals are served in the lively Oboe Bistro with its framed curios and garden access.

Places of interest nearby: Guildford cathedral, The Royal Horticultural Society's Wisley Gardens, Clandon Park, Loseley House, horse racing at Sandown Park, Esher. Epsom, Windsor and Ascot are within easy reach.

Directions: Exit M25 at Jct10 and join A3 towards Guildford. Turn left onto B2039 Ockham road, then left again at the war memorial. The Hautboy is 400 yards ahead.

PEN-Y-DYFFRYN COUNTRY HOTEL

RHYDYCROESAU, NR OSWESTRY, SHROPSHIRE SY10 7JD
TEL: 01691 653700 FAX: 01691 650066 E-MAIL: penydyffryn@go2.co.uk

OWNERS: Miles and Audrey Hunter
CHEFS: Paul Thomasson and Audrey Hunter

S: £55–£60
D: £80–£92

Pen-y-Dyffryn Country Hotel is a haven of peace and quiet, set in five acres of grounds in the unspoilt Shropshire hills, midway between Shrewsbury and Chester. And while civilisation is close at hand, buzzards, peregrine falcons, badgers and foxes regularly delight the guests with their unscheduled appearances. The stream in front of the hotel marks the border with neighbouring Wales.

All the bedrooms have modern amenities and overlook the attractively terraced hotel gardens. In the cooler months, log fires burning in the two homely lounges help to create a cosy and informal atmosphere in which to relax and forget the pressures of everyday life. The best of British cuisine is served in the hotel's renowned restaurant which has been awarded two rosettes by the AA. Adventurous menus offer dishes using the finest fresh, local ingredients including their own free range eggs and traditional English puddings are a speciality. The hotel is fully licensed and has an extensive wine list.

Although Pen-y-Dyffryn provides the perfect setting for total relaxation, for more active guests there are facilities for hill-walking and riding on the doorstep, six 18-hole golf courses within 15 miles and a trout pool just yards away.
Places of interest nearby: Powys and Chirk Castles, Erddig and Attingham. Historic towns of Shrewsbury and Chester. Excursions to Snowdonia. **Directions: From Oswestry town centre take B4580 Llansilin road for 3m due West. After sharp bend turn left in village.**

THE TOWER

OTTERBURN, NORTHUMBERLAND, NE19 1NS
TEL: 01830 520620 FAX: 01830 521504 E-MAIL: reservations@thetower.co.uk

OWNERS: David and Anne Slocombe
CHEF: Jeremy Collar

S: £49–£79
D: £70–£130
suite: £130

The Tower is a magnificent sight. A thick, stone walled fortress, tall and solid with shoulder high ramparts and arrow-slit windows that look out over beautiful Northumberland and National Park countryside. Standing in 32 acres of formal terraced gardens and lush woodland The Tower has witnessed centuries of history. It was built in 1076 as a defence against marauding Scots by a cousin of William the Conqueror.

Reminders of its turbulent past remain but once guests have strolled through its imposing, arched entranceway topped by a carved heraldic shield they find comfortable and relaxing surroundings with the warmth of a family home. Elegant public rooms have luxurious furnishings and blazing log fires in winter. Seventeen spacious, en suite guest rooms, some with four-poster beds and large open fireplaces, are individually designed and offer superb comfort and views over the grounds. One of the fireplaces is listed and depicts scenes from the Battle of Otterburn in 1388 when Scots forces lost their leader while defeating the English. Dining at The Tower is a delight with chef Jeremy Collar creating imaginative and tasty lunch and dinner menus using the finest local produce.

Places of interest nearby: Hadrian's Wall, Holy Island and Bamburgh Castle are within easy reach. **Directions: From Newcastle take A696 to Otterburn.**

 OWLPEN

OWLPEN MANOR

NR ULEY, GLOUCESTERSHIRE GL11 5BZ
TEL: 01453 860261 FAX: 01453 860819 E-MAIL: Nicky@owlpen.demon.co.uk

OWNERS: Nicholas and Karin Mander
CHEF: Karin Mander

From:
£50-£150
(minimum stay conditions may apply)

Set in its own remote and picturesque wooded valley in the heart of the South Cotswolds, Owlpen Manor is one of the country's most romantic Tudor manor houses. It is steeped in peace and timeless English beauty with the surrounding estate leading the wildlife lover through miles of private woodland paths. Scattered along the valley are distinctive historic cottages, sleeping from two to eight and managed in the style of a country house hotel. There are snug medieval barns and byres, a watermill first restored in 1464, the Court House of the 1620s, weavers' and keepers' cottages and even a modern farmhouse.

All are equipped with every home-from-home comfort, from antiques and chintzes to prints and plants. They are individually furnished in traditional English style and stand in their own secluded gardens. Some have open fireplaces or four-poster beds. An atmospheric restaurant in the medieval cyder house serves seasonal produce from the estate. For sporting visitors fly-fishing and shooting can be arranged. Riding, gliding and golf are nearby.

Places of interest nearby: Owlpen Manor, Uley Tumulus, Westonbirt Arboretum, Berkeley Castle and the Wildfowl Trust at Slimbridge. **Directions: From the M4, exit at junction 18, or M5 junctions 13 or 14, and head for the B4066 to Uley. Owlpen is signposted from the Old Crown opposite the church, or follow the brown signs.**

FALLOWFIELDS

KINGSTON BAGPUIZE WITH SOUTHMOOR, OXON OX13 5BH
TEL: 01865 820416 FAX: 01865 821275 E-MAIL: stay@fallowfields.com

OWNERS: Peta and Anthony Lloyd

  S: £89–£105
D: £110–£150

Fallowfields, once the home of Begum Aga Khan, dates back more than 300 years. It has been updated and extended over past decades and today boasts a lovely early Victorian Gothic southern aspect. The house is set in two acres of gardens, surrounded by ten acres of grassland.

The guests' bedrooms, which offer a choice of four poster or coroneted beds, are large and well appointed and offer every modern amenity to ensure maximum comfort and convenience. The house is centrally heated throughout and during the winter months, there are welcoming log fires in the elegant main reception rooms.

The cuisine is mainly British, imaginative in style and presentation and there is a good choice of menus available. The walled kitchen garden provides most of the vegetables and salads for the table and locally grown and organic produce is otherwise used wherever possible. **Places of interest nearby:** Fallowfields is close to Stratford, the Cotswolds, Stonehenge, Bath and Bristol to the west, Oxford, Henley on Thames, the Chilterns and Windsor to the east. Heathrow airport is under an hour away. **Directions: Take the Kingston Bagpuize exit on the A420 Oxford to Swindon. Fallowfields is at the west end of Southmoor, just after the Longworth sign.**

CROSS HOUSE HOTEL

CHURCH STREET, PADSTOW, CORNWALL PL28 8BG
TEL: 01841 532391 FAX: 01841 533633 E-MAIL: info@crosshouse.co.uk

OWNERS: Cross House Hotel Limited
MANAGER: Nichola Gidlow

| 9 rms | 9 ens | SMALL HOTEL |

S: £60
D: £80–£120

Tucked away in the quiet and serene area of Padstow, the Cross House Hotel is a delightful Georgian Grade II listed house. Luxury and comfort are important criteria and the décor is distinctly elegant with beautiful fabrics and tasteful paintings. The bedrooms, four of which are in their house adjacent to the hotel, are individually furnished and offer every modern amenity as well as extra touches such as air-conditioning and videos. With large fluffy towels, soft bathrobes and fine toiletries, the en suite facilities are both stylish and well-equipped.

Guests often frequent the lounge during the afternoon and enjoy reading or playing a board game in front of the cosy, glowing fire. With its comfortable furnishings and elegant chandeliers, the bar is the ideal place to recline during the evening and enjoy an apéritif. There is a choice of either Full English or Continental breakfast and the fresh pastries are delicious. Many fine restaurants are recommended nearby.

Beautiful walks along the Cornish coast, sea-fishing, cycling and trying the various water sports offered at the Estuary are some of the many pastimes available nearby. Golf enthusiasts will be delighted with the challenging courses.

Places of interest nearby: Prideaux House and Deer Park, the Camel Estuary and the picturesque town of Wadebridge are all within easy reach. **Directions: On approaching Padstow from A30, take 3rd turn on the right, following signs to the parish church. The hotel is 50 yards on the left.**

TEMPLE SOWERBY HOUSE HOTEL

TEMPLE SOWERBY, PENRITH, CUMBRIA CA10 1RZ
TEL: 017683 61578 FAX: 017683 61958 FREE PHONE: 0800 146157 E-MAIL: stay@temple–sowerby.com

OWNERS: Geoffrey and Cécile Temple

S: £65–£75
D: £96–£116

Temple Sowerby House looks over at Cross Fell, the highest peak in the Pennines, noted for its spectacular ridge walk. This old Cumbrian farmhouse is set in two acres of gardens and guests are assured of peace and quiet. Geoffrey and Cécile Temple offer a warm, hospitable and friendly family service upon which the hotel prides itself.

Awarded an AA Rosette, the restaurant has two dining rooms – the panelled room with its cosy atmosphere and the Garden Room. Delicious, home-cooked dishes might include a starter of a pithiviers of creamed wild mushrooms served with crisp salad leaves in a truffle and olive oil dressing, followed by tuna fillet served on a purée of spiced rhubarb with poppy seed vinegar, rounded off with iced chocolate parfait served with a white chocolate sauce. The individually furnished bedrooms all have private bathrooms. Four of the rooms are situated in the Coach House, just yards from the main house. During the winter, apéritifs are taken by the fireside, while in the summer, guests can sip drinks on the terrace and enjoy views across the fells. Private fishing, with tuition if required, takes place on the River Eden, two miles away. Fishing breaks available.

Places of interest nearby: Lakes Ullswater and Derwentwater, the Borders, Scottish Lowlands, Hadrian's Wall and Yorkshire Dales are within easy reach by car. **Directions: Temple Sowerby lies on A66, seven miles from exit 40 of M6, between Penrith and Appleby. (Special breaks available).**

THE SUMMER HOUSE

CORNWALL TERRACE, PENZANCE, CORNWALL TR18 4HL
TEL: 01736 363744 FAX: 01736 360959 E-MAIL: summerhouse@dial.pipex.com

OWNERS: Ciro and Linda Zaino

5 rms 5 ens

S: £40–£65
D: £65–£75

The Summer House is a delightful fusion blend of Regency architecture and bright Mediterranean colours. This Grade II listed former dower house is comfortably tucked away amid the tumbledown streets of Penzance, yet only yards from the sea. Beautifully converted into a small hotel, decorated in sunny yellows and nautical blues, The Summer House appeals to every sense.

The hotel's five bedrooms offer total comfort and the odd touches of originality that contribute so much to the informal atmosphere. Food plays a central part in the life of The Summer House: Ciro Zaino, co-owner with his wife Linda, spent years managing some of London's leading restaurants. To the menu at The Summer House he brings his love of simplicity, combined with the use of the fresh ingredients for which Cornwall is renowned. An inspired menu is served in the attractive restaurant, which opens out onto a walled garden.

The Summer House is an ideal base from which to explore the treasures of Penzance and the surrounding Cornish coast.

Places of interest nearby: St Michael's Mount. Lands End. The Minack Theatre. The St Ives Tate Gallery. The Scilly Isles. **Direction: On approaching Penzance, drive along the harbour and follow the Promenade. Immediately after the Queens Hotel turn right. The Summer House is about 30 yards on the left.**

LANGRISH HOUSE

LANGRISH, NR PETERSFIELD, HAMPSHIRE GU32 1RN
TEL: 01730 266941 FAX: 01730 260543

OWNERS: Nigel and Robina Talbot-Ponsonby
CHEF: Brett Sutton

S: £59–£65
D: £72–£98

Standing in 12 acres of beautiful mature grounds including a picturesque lake, Langrish House combines the welcoming ambience of a traditional country house with the facilities expected from a modern hotel. Extended by the present owners' forbears in 1842, it opened as a hotel in 1979 and remains very much a family home. Today, new life is being breathed into the house by Nigel and Robina Talbot-Ponsonby whose family portraits and heirlooms once again adorn the rooms.

Each of the bedrooms overlooks the grounds, giving guests ample opportunity to savour Langrish's peace and tranquillity. All are fully equipped with en suite bathrooms, direct dial telephones, colour televisions and many thoughtful touches.

The recently refurbished Cellar Restaurant and Dungeon Bar are now complemented by the addition of the Garden Room Restaurant, which affords glorious views of the lawns. Fresh regional produce features in the fine cuisine. Langrish House is an ideal venue for wedding receptions and business conferences and offers dining facilities for up to 120 people.
Places of interest nearby: This is an excellent base for touring the Hampshire countryside and the New Forest. Gilbert White's Selbourne, Jane Austen's Chawton, Goodwood and Cowdray Park are also close by. **Directions: Follow A272 from the M3/A31 at Winchester (16 miles) or from A3 at Petersfield (3 miles). Langrish House is signposted from the village on the road to East Meon.**

THE OLD RAILWAY STATION

COULTERSHAW BRIDGE, PETWORTH, WEST SUSSEX GU28 OJF
TEL: 01798 342346 FAX: 01798 342346 E-MAIL: mlr@old-station.co.uk

OWNER: Mary-Louise Rapley

S: £45–£65
D: £64–£94

This is a splendid and stylish conversion of an old railway station, built in 1894 and Grade II listed. Just a short drive from the medieval town of Petworth, with its winding narrow streets and half-timbered Tudor houses, The Old Railway Station is elegant, comfortable and offers all modern facilities. It is an ideal retreat in which to relax from the busy modern world and has earned widespread praise from its guests.

The platform area and track make a delightful garden and the recent addition of two Pullman cars – refitted to provide four bedrooms – complete a beautiful and enchanting picture. Built in the same era as the Titanic, the Petworth Pullmans, Alicante and Mimosa were the most stately of coaches and offered rail passengers unrestrained luxury and comfort.

Today they are delightfully converted individual suites which, like the two station building bedrooms, have full en suite facilities, plush furnishings, every home-from-home comfort and their own private entrances from the platform. Breakfast is served either on the platform, or in the impressive former waiting room with its vaulted ceiling and original ticket office windows, or in your carriage, Orient Express style. Dinner is not available but excellent meals are served in the local pubs.

Places of interest nearby: Petworth House, Goodwood House, Arundel Castle, Chichester and the market town of Midhurst.
Directions: On A285 just south of Petworth, reached from Gatwick via A264 and A29 to Billinghurst and then A272.

THE COTTAGE HOTEL

PORLOCK WEIR, PORLOCK, SOMERSET TA24 8PB
TEL: 01643 863300 FAX: 01643 863311 E-MAIL: cottage@netcomuk.co.uk

OWNERS: Christopher and Ann Baker

5 rms | 5 ens | SMALL HOTEL

S: £55–£95
D: £65–£110

Guests will be enchanted by the lovely location of The Cottage Hotel, overlooking a tiny harbour where Exmoor meets the rugged coastline and sea. It is wonderful walking country abounding in history and scenic delights. With origins dating back to the 18th century, the hotel is surrounded by colourful, terraced gardens where visitors can relax in summer shade and breathe in sweet floral scents.

Owners Christopher and Ann Baker offer a very friendly welcome and excellent value for money. The bedrooms are a delight, comfortable, beautifully decorated and well-equipped with all modern necessities.

Drinks can be taken in the attractively draped lounge with its deep, soft sofas and chairs with beautiful views over the harbour. Light suppers are available by prior arrangement.

Places of interest nearby: Dunster's Norman castle, the smallest church in England at Culbone, Lynmouth's picturesque harbour, Minehead, the scenic, wild delights and attractive stone cottage villages of Exmoor.

Directions: From the M5, exit at junctions 23 or 24 and join the A39 towards Minehead, Porlock and Porlock Weir.

 NEW PORLOCK WEIR

PORLOCK VALE HOUSE

PORLOCK WEIR, SOMERSET TA24 8NY
TEL: 01643 862338 FAX: 01643 863338 E-MAIL: info@porlockvale.co.uk

OWNERS: Helen and Kim Youd
CHEFS: Nick Robinson and Christine Collins

    S: £39–£59
D: £60–£95

This former hunting lodge positioned in a truly spectacular setting pinioned by the sea and lush forest, offers a welcome friendly, informal and comforting atmosphere to visitors tired of the formality of traditional hotel accommodation.

Porlock Vale's extensive gardens are a sight to behold, visitors always cherish fond memories of the lazy summer afternoons spent there in quiet repose. Winter season also sticks in the mind, with the coast and the Bristol channel viewed from the tranquillity of the lounge with its crackling log fire. Visitors dine in a beautiful dining room, where top-notch local fare is served within mouth-watering menus. The delightful bedrooms are all individually styled, commanding views of the ocean, the tastefully laid out gardens or the wooded combe that flanks the hotel.

Places of interest nearby: At the heart of the Exmoor National Park, the Porlock Vale House is the ideal base for a walking tour around this region of dramatic beauty. The area is literally awash with quaint traditional villages dotted along the awe-inspiring coast. Famous landmarks, such as the Dunkery Beacon and the Doone Valley, are also close at hand. **Directions: Join the A39 and follow the signs to Minehead. When in Porlock Village, pick up the signs for Porlock Weir.**

152

www.johansens.com

TYE ROCK COUNTRY HOUSE HOTEL AND APARTMENTS

LOE BAR ROAD, PORTHLEVEN, NR HELSTON, SOUTH CORNWALL TR13 9EW
TEL/FAX: 01326 572695 RESIDENTS NO: 01326 563087 E-MAIL: tyerockhotel@compuserve.com

OWNERS: Richard and Pat Palmer

S: £65–£75
D: £84–£100
(Room only)

Tye Rock stands high, mighty and solid on rugged cliff tops overlooking Mounts Bay with magnificent views extending from The Lizard to Land's End. Surrounded by 3½ acres of terraced gardens and the wild expanse of National Trust land, this former 19th century manor house offers a relaxing and welcoming atmosphere.

It has a stylish air of quiet seclusion yet is only a short walk from the pretty fishing harbour of Portleven and within two miles of the market town of Helston, famed for its annual Furry Dance through the streets on Flora Day, May 8.

Richard and Pat Palmer have created a delightful, friendly country house hotel with dramatically fashioned rooms encompassing various themes. All seven, comfortable en suite bedrooms have sea views and are individually decorated to high standards. There are also eight self catering apartments in the grounds which offer guests the independence of their own front door.

Delicious, traditional English cuisine is served in the elegant Victorian restaurant which opens onto a terrace from which guests can enjoy the views while sipping pre- and after-dinner drinks. Winter breaks and activity weekends are also available. **Places of interest nearby:** St Michael's Mount, Goonhilly Earth Satellite Station, Mullion Cove, Land's End and many Cornish gardens. **Directions: From Helston take the Portleven road, then follow signs for Loe Bar. Take first left, first right and left at the T-junction.**

THE BEAUFORT HOTEL

71 FESTING ROAD, SOUTHSEA, PORTSMOUTH, HAMPSHIRE PO4 ONQ
TEL: 01705 823707 FAX: 01705 870270 FREEPHONE: 0800 919237 E-MAIL: enquiries@beauforthotel.co.uk

OWNERS Anthony and Penelope Freemantle
CHEF: Michael Freyne

| 18 rms | 18 ens | SMALL HOTEL | | | S: from £55 D: from £86 |

Conveniently located in the heart of Southsea, just one minute's walk from the sea, lies The Beaufort Hotel. A relaxed and friendly atmosphere pervades this comfortable and spotless hotel, creating an ideal setting for relaxation. Owners Penny and Tony Freemantle and their staff pride themselves on providing guests with a personal service that is second to none.

The 18 bedrooms have all been designed to give them individual character, from the magnificent Oxford Room, decorated in royal blue and gold, to the bright and sunny Cambridge Room which is tastefully decorated in Burgundy and overlooks the Canoe lake. All the attractive bathrooms feature porcelain and gold fittings and include a selection of luxurious toiletries.

A comfortable cocktail bar is the ideal place to enjoy a pre-dinner drink before moving on to the charming restaurant. The Beaufort is proud to hold the highest percentage rating by the AA of any hotel in Portsmouth. **Places of interest nearby:** The Mary Rose, H.M.S Warrior, H.M.S Victory and the Royal Naval Museum provide a fascinating insight into life on board Britain's most famous warships. The Isle of Wight and Le Havre and Cherbourg in France are all within easy cruising distance. **Directions: Festing Road is off St Helen's Parade at the eastern end of the seafront.**

PICKERING PARK COUNTRY HOUSE

GARSTANG ROAD, CATTERALL, GARSTANG, LANCASHIRE PR3 0HD
TEL: 01995 600999 FAX: 01995 602100

OWNERS: Jim and Irene Farrimond
CHEF: Keith Dalton

S: £55–£60
D: £76–£140

Dating from the mid 18th century, Pickering Park stands in two acres of beautiful parkland midway between Preston and Lancaster on the doorstep of The Forest of Bowland, gateway to the Lake District. It was transformed from family house to hotel in 1978, extended in 1989 and present owners Jim and Irene Farrimond began to restore the hotel to its former eminence with a friendly Lancashire welcome from their arrival in 1997.

The surrounding countryside is designated an area of outstanding natural beauty and close to the hotel is the pretty little town of Garstang whose main street market dates back to King Edward II. Although ancient in origin, Pickering Park offers every modern comfort. All bedrooms are en suite, tastefully decorated and furnished and provide every amenity. Some have four-poster beds. There are two dining rooms where chef Keith Dalton produces imaginative and tasty lunch and dinner cuisine. His expansive menus are complemented by excellent wines from an "Open" cellar of 250 bins which guests can visit and choose from.

Places of interest nearby: The Lake District, Trough of Bowland, Lancaster and Blackpool. **Directions: From the south, exit M6 at junction 32 and take the A6 towards Garstang. Turn right onto the B6430 and the hotel is on the right. From the north, exit M6 at junction 33 and take the A6 south. Turn left at Catteral and at the T-junction turn right. The hotel is on the left.**

CHEQUERS HOTEL

CHURCH PLACE, PULBOROUGH, WEST SUSSEX RH20 1AD
TEL: 01798 872486 FAX: 01798 872715

OWNERS: Martin and Pandora Pellett
CHEF: Paul Lewis

S: £49.50–£59.50
D: £85–£99

A warm welcome awaits visitors to this historic hotel built in 1548 and Grade II listed. Situated on a sandstone ridge, Chequers has enviable views across the beautiful Arun Valley to the South Downs beyond.

New owners Martin and Pandora Pellett have brought fresh ideas and set new high standards for this delightful small hotel. All 11 bedrooms have private facilities, 10 of which are en suite. There are 4 bedrooms on the ground floor and three family rooms. Public rooms are comfortably furnished, with a log fire in the lounge on winter evenings.

In warmer weather, guests may linger over an apéritif on the patio or in the secluded garden, before dining in the restaurant, where the cosmopolitan menu changes daily. The hotel is set in the heart of the local conservation area and its adjacent nine acre meadow is an ideal spot for walking your dog.

Places of interest nearby: Chequers Hotel is conveniently placed for the Roman city of Chichester, Goodwood, Arundel Castle, Petworth and the Sussex coast. Packed lunches can be provided. 2 RAC Merit Awards and 2 AA Rosettes. **Directions: At the top of the hill, at the northern end of the village, the hotel is opposite the church.**

MOORTOWN LODGE

244 CHRISTCHURCH ROAD, RINGWOOD, HAMPSHIRE BH24 3AS
TEL: 01425 471404 FAX: 01425 476052 E-MAIL: hotel@burrows–jones.freeserve.co.uk

OWNERS: Bob and Jilly Burrows-Jones
CHEF: Jilly Burrows-Jones

5 rms	5 ens	SMALL HOTEL

  S: from £45
D: from £65

The busy market town of Ringwood stands on the edge of the vast and beautiful New Forest with its abundance of woodland, wildlife and enchanting walks. Moortown Lodge is a perfect base from which to explore this rolling and historic countryside. Dating back to the 1760s this charming, family-run hotel stands just outside the town on the main road to Christchurch and is renowned for its warm and welcoming ambiance. Owners Bob and Jilly Burrows-Jones are justly proud to have been one of the first recipients of an AA Courtesy and Care Award for hospitality.

All the hotel's rooms are well-proportioned and enlivened with furnishing, fabrics and colourings to create a restful atmosphere. There are five en suite double and twin-bedded rooms, including one with a luxury four-poster. All have every amenity and facility to make visitors feel at home.

The intimate restaurant is the ideal place to enjoy some of the finest food in the area. Jilly's menus are varied and she uses local produce whenever possible. Her high standard of cuisine has won two AA Rosettes and has been acclaimed as excellent yet delightfully uncomplicated.

Places of interest nearby: Broadlands, the old home of Lord Mountbatten, Beaulieu, Breamore House and the New Forest. Bournemouth, Poole, Southampton and Salisbury are within easy reach. **Directions: Enter Ringwood from the A31 and follow the signs for the B3347. Moortown Lodge is approximately 1½ miles south of the town.**

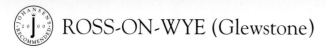

GLEWSTONE COURT

NR ROSS-ON-WYE, HEREFORDSHIRE HR9 6AW
TEL: 01989 770367 FAX: 01989 770282 E-MAIL: glewstone@aol.com

OWNERS: Bill and Christine Reeve-Tucker

  SMALL HOTEL

  S: £45–£75
D: £70–£105

Glewstone Court is set in three acres of orchards, lawns and flower-beds. Although secluded, it is only three miles from Ross-on-Wye. Furnishings and décor reflect the hospitable personality of the owners and the variety of prints, antiques and bric-à-brac always excites curiosity.

Most country pursuits can be arranged, including canoeing, hot-air ballooning, fishing and riding. This is marvellous country for walking – or just lazing around, too!

Christine's food is always innovative and both the restaurant and extensive bar menus feature local recipes using only the freshest of ingredients. Dishes are both traditional and unusual and are always prepared and served with care and attention to detail. Now in their thirteenth year, accolades awarded are a Rosette for good food from the AA and the Which? Hotel Guide Hotel of the Year for Hereford and Worcester. The restaurant and the drawing room bar feature log fires and like the rest of the hotel, are furnished for comfort.

The bedrooms are large and comfortable too. Each has en suite facilities, a hospitality tray, direct dial phone and colour television. Closed Christmas Day and Boxing Day. **Places of interest nearby:** Ross-on-Wye, Hay-on-Wye, the Welsh Marches, Hereford Cathedral and the Brecon Beacons. **Directions: From M50 junction 4 follow A40 signposted Monmouth. One mile past Wilton roundabout turn right to Glewstone; the Court is ¹/₂ mile on left.**

WHITE VINE HOUSE

HIGH STREET, RYE, EAST SUSSEX TN31 7JF
TEL: 01797 224748 FAX: 01797 223599 E-MAIL: irene@whitevinehouse.freeserve.co.uk

MANAGER: Irene Cheetham

S: from £35
D: £60–£100

Despite its Georgian exterior this fine timber framed house is much older. Originally built around a courtyard that now forms the reception hallway, the hotel stands over Medieval cellars on the site of the ancient Whyte Vyne Inn. At the hub of the daytime bustle of this fascinating little market town, the house retains a unique character and restful atmosphere.

In the morning guests can savour the pleasant surroundings while enjoying breakfast from an impressive choice. Lunch is served daily with an interesting selection of dishes from light options to the more traditional, complemented by a range of good value wines. Small meetings and private dining are offered and the beautifully oak panelled Elizabethan Room is a comfortable residents lounge. Staff will happily recommend good restaurants from the many within strolling distance of the hotel door and make dinner reservations on behalf of guests to match individual preferences. Complimentary aperitifs are available every evening.

Places of interest nearby: Rye is a town of great historical interest and boasts many art galleries, potteries, antique dealers and book sellers. **Directions: Take the A21 to Flimwell, then the A268 to Rye. Telephone first for parking advice.**

THE COUNTRYMAN AT TRINK HOTEL

OLD COACH ROAD, ST IVES, CORNWALL TR26 3JQ
TEL: 01736 797571 FAX: 01736 797571

OWNERS: Howard and Cathy Massey

S: £38
D: £60–£70

Five minutes drive from the quaint town of St Ives is the Countryman Hotel at Trink. St Ives has become a mecca for artists and one of the latest attractions is the new Tate Gallery with its collection of modern paintings and contemporary exhibits. Cornwall has a wealth of interesting things to see not least its dramatic coastline ideal for lovers of nature and walkers.

The Countryman dates from the 17th century. Today the small hotel has been renovated to meet the needs of the modern visitor, all rooms have en suite shower and toilet, colour television and tea making facilities.

The atmosphere of the hotel is friendly and inviting, the emphasis being on cheerful service and good value for money. This is a totally no smoking hotel. In the restaurant, Howard Massey, the chef-patron, likes cooking to order from his varied and interesting menu containing Cornish fish supported by a sensibly priced wine-list. St Ives has always had a tradition for generous hospitality. A former mayor, the legendary John Knill, bequeathed £10 for an annual banquet. Prices may have altered a little but the high quality of the local cooking has not changed.

Places of interest nearby: Tate Gallery, Lands End. Barbara Hepworth's house, St Michael's Mount. Golf, riding and the sea. **Directions: A30, A3074 to St Ives, then B3311 for about two miles.**

THE HUNDRED HOUSE HOTEL

RUAN HIGHLANES, NR TRURO, CORNWALL TR2 5JR
TEL: 01872 501336 FAX: 01872 501151

OWNERS: Mike and Kitty Eccles

  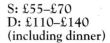

S: £55–£70
D: £110–£140
(including dinner)

Situated on Cornwall's beautiful Roseland Peninsula is The Hundred House Hotel, an 18th century Cornish country house set in three acres of gardens. It commands panoramic views over the countryside and is close to the sea and the lovely Fal estuary.

Once inside the wide hall with its handsome Edwardian staircase, there is the feeling of an elegant English home. Mike and Kitty Eccles have created a delightful hotel where guests can relax in the pretty sitting room, furnished with antiques and browse among the books of local interest. On cooler days they can enjoy a Cornish cream tea by a log fire and in the summer a game of croquet on the lawn. Each bedroom is individually decorated and has full en suite bath or shower room.

Guests regularly return to enjoy the delicious imaginative dinners and the hearty Cornish breakfast prepared by Kitty Eccles who has been awarded a Red Rosette by the AA. She uses fresh seasonal ingredients and specialities include baked avocado, fillet of lemon sole with a salmon mousse and a honey and lavender ice cream.

Places of interest nearby: Picturesque fishing villages, superb cliff walks and sandy beaches. Cornwall Gardens Festival, mid March to 31 May. Boat trips on Fal Estuary. Lanhydrock House (NT). Cathedral city of Truro 12 miles away. **Directions: A390 from St Austell, left on B3278 to Tregony, then A3078 to St Mawes. Hotel is then 4 miles on.**

BROOM HALL

RICHMOND ROAD, SAHAM TONEY, THETFORD, NORFOLK IP25 7EX
TEL: 01953 882125 FAX: 01953 882125

OWNERS: Nigel and Angela Rowling
MANAGER: Simon Rowling

8 rms | 8 ens | SMALL HOTEL

S: £52
D: £75–£98

Situated in 15 acres of mature gardens and parkland Broom Hall is a charming Victorian country house offering peace and tranquillity. Airy and spacious bedrooms each individually furnished and most offering lovely views provide guests with both comfort and a range of modern amenities.

A feature of the public rooms are the ornate ceilings and in the lounge a large open fire can be enjoyed in the winter months. An indoor heated swimming pool and full size snooker table are available for guests' use.

Fresh vegetables, from Broom Hall's own garden when in season, and many old fashioned desserts ensure that dinner in the dining room overlooking the garden is an enjoyable occasion. Small conferences can be arranged and the entire house can be 'taken over' for your family reunion or celebration. Seasonable breaks are available.

Places of interest nearby: Norwich, Cambridge, Ely and Bury St Edmunds are within easy reach. Sandringham and many National Trust properties, Thetford Forest, Norfolk Broads and coastline offering nature reserves and bird sanctuaries are also close by. **Directions: Half mile north of Watton on B1077 towards Swaffham.**

PRESTON HOUSE HOTEL

SAUNTON, BRAUNTON, NORTH DEVON EX33 1LG
TEL: 01271 890472 FAX: 01271 890555

OWNER: Jan Poole
CHEF: Kevin Little

S: £65–£85
D: £75–£105

Miles of flat, golden sands and white-capped Atlantic rollers greet guests seeking peace, quiet and relaxation at Preston House, standing high on the glorious coastline of North Devon.Terraced, lawned gardens sweep down to the sea and an atmosphere of undisturbed continuity and tranquillity surrounds and influences the hotel which dates back to the Victorian era. The views are spectacular.

Eleven of the twelve en suite bedrooms face seawards. All are individually decorated, tastefully furnished and contain all modern amenities from colour television and direct dial telephone to tea and coffee facilities. Some have a four-poster bed, balcony and the added luxury of a Jacuzzi.

A spacious and comfortable lounge provides the perfect relaxed environment. Breakfast can be leisurely enjoyed in the hotel's conservatory which overlooks the garden, sands and ocean and chef Kevin Little serves delicious and imaginative cuisine in the elegant restaurant or overlooking the magnificent view in the conservatory.

Places of interest nearby: Lynton, Lynmouth, Exmoor and many National Trust properties. **Directions: From the M5, exit at junction 27 and take the A361 towards Barnstaple. Continue on to Braunton and when there turn left at the traffic lights towards Croyde. The hotel is on the left after approximately two miles.**

SEAVINGTON ST MARY (Nr Ilminster)

THE PHEASANT HOTEL

SEAVINGTON ST MARY, NR ILMINSTER, SOMERSET TA19 0HQ
TEL: 01460 240502 FAX: 01460 242388

OWNERS: Mark and Tania Harris
CHEF: Danny Kilpatrick

S: from £75
D: from £95
Suite: from £105

Visitors to The Pheasant are immediately captivated by the distinctive charm and character of this sumptuously furnished old-world style hotel and restaurant. Set in the heart of glorious Somerset countryside and surrounded by landscaped lawns and delightful gardens, it has an intimacy and warmth of welcome that make it the perfect 'escape' for both pleasure and business. The luxurious suites and charming bedrooms are individually styled and very tastefully appointed.

Sympathetic décor and furnishings complement the traditional character of both the cosy bar with its vast inglenooks and the beautiful oak-beamed restaurant where Head Chef, Danny Kilpatrick, using the very best of fresh local produce, presides over an imaginative menu with a range of exciting dishes to suit all tastes.

Places of interest nearby: Being situated near the Somerset border close to both Dorset and Devon, there are many attractions to suit all age groups, including Montacute House, the abbey town of Sherborne, the Fleet Air Museum at Yeovilton and Cricket St Thomas, where the BBC television series *To The Manor Born* was filmed. **Directions: Leave the A303 at South Petherton roundabout by Ilminster bypass. Take the left spur, (Seavington St Michael), followed by Seavington exit at the next roundabout. Left by the Volunteer Public House and The Pheasant is 200 yards further on the right.**

THE EASTBURY HOTEL

LONG STREET, SHERBORNE, DORSET DT9 3BY
TEL: 01935 813131 FAX: 01935 817296

OWNERS: Tom and Alison Pickford

15 rms | 15 ens | SMALL HOTEL

S: £49.50–£72.50
D: £79–£89

The Eastbury Hotel is a traditional town house which was built in 1740 during the reign of George II. During its recent refurbishment great care was taken to preserve its 18th century character. In fine weather guests can enjoy the seclusion of the hotel's private walled garden, which encompasses an acre of shrubs and formal plants and a noteworthy listed walnut tree.

Bedrooms are individually named after well-known English garden flowers and each is equipped with a full range of modern comforts and conveniences. The Eastbury is ideal for parents visiting sons or daughters who board at the Sherborne schools.

Traditional English cooking is a feature of the Eastbury restaurant and the dishes are complemented by an extensive list of the world's fine wines.

Places of interest nearby: Sherborne is rich in history and has a magnificent 15th century Perpendicular Abbey Church and two castles, in one of which Sir Walter Raleigh founded the national smoking habit. At Compton is a silk farm and a collection of butterflies. Beyond Yeovil is Montacute House (NT) and at Yeovilton is the Fleet Air Arm Museum. **Directions: Long Street is in the town centre, south of and parallel to the A30. Parking is at the rear of the hotel.**

THE SHAVEN CROWN HOTEL

HIGH STREET, SHIPTON-UNDER-WYCHWOOD, OXFORDSHIRE OX7 6BA
TEL: 01993 830330 FAX: 01993 832136

OWNERS: Mr and Mrs Robert Burpitt

 S: £53
D: £75–£100

Built of honey-coloured stone around an attractive central courtyard, The Shaven Crown Hotel dates back to the 14th century, when it served as a monks' hospice. The proprietors have preserved the inn's many historic features, such as the medieval hall with its ancient timbered roof. This is now the residents' lounge. Each of the bedrooms has en suite facilities and has been sympathetically furnished in a style befitting its own unique character. Rooms of various style and sizes are available, including a huge family room and ground-floor accommodation. Dining in the intimate, candlelit room is an enjoyable experience, with meals served at the tables beautifully laid with fine accessories. The best ingredients are combined to create original dishes with a cosmopolitan flair. The table d'hôte menu offers a wide and eclectic choice with a daily vegetarian dish among the specialities. An imaginative selection of dishes is offered every lunchtime and evening in the Monks Bar.

Places of interest nearby: The Shaven Crown is ideal for day trips to the Cotswolds, Oxford, Stratford-upon-Avon and Bath. There are three golf courses and tennis courts close by. Trout fishing and antique-hunting are popular activities in the area. **Directions: Take the A40 Oxford–Cheltenham road. At Burford follow the A361 towards Chipping Norton. The inn is situated directly opposite the village green in Shipton-under-Wychwood.**

UPPER BROMPTON FARM

CROSS HOUSES, SHREWSBURY, SHROPSHIRE SY5 6LE
TEL: 01743 761629 FAX: 01743 761679 E-MAIL: upper–brompton.farm@dial.pipex.com

OWNERS: Christine and George Yates-Roberts

S: £50–£60
D: £65–£80

This is a lovely, compact Georgian farmhouse retreat situated in the heart of rural Shropshire. Close to the River Severn, it is a working mixed farm of 315 acres which guests are welcome to stroll around. Owners Christine and George Yates-Roberts are generous with their welcome and hospitality, offering a relaxed and comfortable atmosphere with superior accommodation and delicious home cooking.

The farm's bedrooms are attractive and offer views over the pleasant garden and Shropshire hills. Each is en suite and decorated and furnished to a comfortable and high standard with many welcoming touches. Two of the spacious rooms have four-poster beds. The others, one dating from 1650, have a cottage-style décor and

atmosphere. Guests can relax before an open fire in the large lounge and full English breakfasts are served in the fine dining room. Dinner by arrangement but for those who enjoy eating out a recommended list of restaurants and pubs can be provided. Recently awarded the Heart of England Tourist Board's Best Bed and Breakfast 1999.

Places of interest nearby: Shrewsbury, The National Trust property of Altringham Park, Ironbridge Gorge, the Viriconium at Wroxeter, the Severn Valley Railway at Bridgnorth and superb walks on the Longmynd and Wenlock Edge. **Directions: 4 miles south of Shrewsbury on the Much Wenlock Road. Turn left at Cross Houses, signed Atcham, 1 mile. Continue down lane to Brompton.**

SIMONSBATH HOUSE HOTEL

SIMONSBATH, EXMOOR, SOMERSET TA24 7SH
TEL: 01643 831259 FAX: 01643 831557 E-MAIL: simonsbath@aol.com

OWNERS: Terry and Marilyn Richardson

S: £50–£55
D: £80–£90

Simonsbath House was built by James Boevey, Warden of the Forest of Exmoor, in 1654, on rising ground facing due south across the beautiful valley of the River Barle. You are welcomed with log fires in the oak-panelled lounge and with mineral water in the bedrooms. A relaxing atmosphere pervades throughout the house, which is still essentially a home, with welcoming owners and caring staff to pamper you with old-fashioned hospitality.

The bedroom windows overlook beech forests of everchanging hue, a crystal river bubbling through the valley and fold after fold of heather-clad hills. Locally there are many riding stables where guests can ride off to Exmoor's highest point – Dunkery Beacon – or set out on foot. The surrounding forests are ideal for strollers; hikers will enjoy the challenge of the high moorlands. There is a daily changing 5 course dinner using whenever possible fresh local produce. Vegetarian meals by arrangement. Kennels are available in the hotel grounds for guests wishing to bring their dogs. **Places of interest nearby:** The cathedral cities of Exeter and Wells; Glastonbury, Bath and Devon's beautiful coast. **Directions: Simonsbath is on the B3223, situated within the village, nine miles south of Lynton.**

BUTLEY PRIORY

NR WOODBRIDGE, SUFFOLK IP12 3NR
TEL: 01394 450046 FAX: 01394 450482

OWNERS: Mrs F Cavendish

S: £35.50–£47.50
D: £75
Suite: £95

Historically interesting and architecturally fascinating Butley Priory, once an Augustan monastery is set in an area of outstanding natural beauty. The high vaulted ceilings, stone carvings, open fireplaces, antique furniture and fresh flowers make this country house ideal for a romantic weekend, a retreat from a hectic lifestyle or a suitable venue for corporate lunches and business meetings.

Bedrooms have stylish modern luxuries coupled with glowing log fires and sumptuous goose-down duvets. Guests can enjoy a buffet-style breakfast and relax with an informal supper, prepared by arrangement only, in the large airy dining room which opens onto the garden.

Pastimes include exploring the acres of natural gardens with 12th century monks ponds. These are now stocked with rainbow trout and anglers are invited to try their luck. The surrounding forests are the perfect setting for walks or horse-riding and nature enthusiasts can enjoy the deer and wildlife, in particular the rare seabird and avocet population. Sailing is offered at nearby Orford and Woodbridge.

Places of interest nearby: Snape Maltings and Concert Hall, Framlington Castle, Minsmere Nature Reserve and Sutton Hoo. **Directions: From A12 to Woodbridge turn onto B1084 towards Orford which takes you to the village of Butley. Detailed directions will be supplied.**

HORSLEY HALL

EASTGATE, NR STANHOPE, BISHOP AUCKLAND, CO. DURHAM DL13 2LJ
TEL: 01388 517239 FAX: 01388 517608 E-MAIL: hotel@horsleyhall.co.uk

OWNERS: Derek Glass and Liz Curry

S: £47–£52.50
D: £62.50–£67.50
Family: £99

Horsley Hall is an elegant, three-story manor house nestling in the heart of Weardale, a designated area of outstanding natural beauty. Situated on the road south of the River Wear between Stanhope and Eastgate the hotel enjoys magnificent views across the Dale and easy access to local attractions.

The Hall dates back to the 17th century and was once the home of the Hildyard family, whose existence in the Dale can be traced back nearly 500 years. The owners offer a warm, friendly North East welcome, attentive personal service and are justly proud of their hotel's reputation for homely comfort and good food.

Liz is the chef and produces delicious cuisine and a varied choice of menus using the freshest of local produce. There are fine furnishings and fabrics, stylish décor and open fires throughout the Hall. The en suite bedrooms are extremely comfortable and have all the facilities to make a stay relaxing and enjoyable. They are all non smoking. The Hall is licensed for weddings and the Baronial Hall accommodates up to 80 guests for these, other private functions or business meetings.

Places of interest nearby: Bowes Museum, High Force waterfall, Killhope Wheel and Lead Mining Centre, Derwent Reservoir, Beamish Open Air Museum, Durham Cathedral and Castle. **Directions: From the A68 take the A689 west to Stanhope. Then take the B6278 towards Brotherlee and Hasswicks. Horsley Hall (signposted) is on the right after approximately two miles.**

STANWELL HALL

TOWN LANE, STANWELL, NR STAINES, MIDDLESEX TW19 7PW
TEL: 01784 252292 FAX: 01784 245250

MANAGER: Jean Dunstone
CHEF: Manual Zamora

18 rms | 18 ens | SMALL HOTEL

  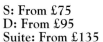

S: From £75
D: From £95
Suite: From £135

Stanwell Hall is an attractive, red brick Victorian hotel with excellent road and rail connections and conveniently situated for Heathrow Airport, London and several of the country's prime tourist attractions. Originally built by a country solicitor, Stanwell Hall was purchased and transformed into a comfortable hotel in 1951 by the Parke family, who still run it today. It is one of the few remaining large houses of its era left around the old Stanwell village.

Recently refurbished bedrooms provide facilities in line with the needs of today's travellers. Extremely good Modern English cuisine, complemented by a comprehensive wine list, is served in the elegant St Anne's restaurant.

The restaurant can accommodate up to 48 guests for a seated wedding reception and up to 60 guests in conjunction with the lounge bar for an informal reception. Light meals are also served at lunchtime and evenings. The Garden Room is ideally suited for a dinner party, private lunch or a small meeting. The hotel is licenced to hold civil wedding ceremonies.

Places of interest nearby: Windsor and its castle, Legoland, Eton, Henley, Hampton Court, Kew Gardens and Thorpe Park. Racing at Ascot, Kempton Park and Sandown.
Directions: Exit M25 at junction 14 and head for Heathrow Terminal 4 and Cargo Terminal. Turn right at roundabout (signed Staines) and at the next traffic lights turn left to Stanwell. Turn into Town Lane at the mini-roundabout.

KINGSTON HOUSE

STAVERTON, TOTNES, DEVON TQ9 6AR
TEL: 01803 762 235 FAX: 01803 762 444 E-MAIL: info@kingston–estate.demon.co.uk

OWNERS: Michael and Elizabeth Corfield

S: £77.50–£87.50
D: £115
Suite: £125–£135

The Kingston Estate nestles amongst the rolling hills and valleys of the South Hams region of Devon, bounded by Dartmoor and the sea, with the focal point, Kingston House, commanding sweeping views of the moor.

The Mansion, together with the superb self-catering cottages, have been sympathetically restored by the Corfield family to their former glory and now offer some of the highest standard accommodation to be found in the South West. The House boasts three period suites, (reached by way of the finest example of a marquetry staircase in England), which are hung with authentic wall papers and fabrics and include a 1735 Angel tester bed and an 1830 four-poster.

Dinner guests dine by candlelight in the elegant dining room at tables set with sparkling crystal, shining silver and starched linen. In winter, log fires crackle in the hearths, whilst in the summer pre-dinner drinks may be taken on the terrace overlooking the formal 18th century gardens. For every visitor to Kingston, hospitality and comfort are assured in this magnificent historic setting.

Places of interest nearby: Dartington Hall, Dartmouth, Totnes, Dartmoor & Devon's famous coastline.
Directions: Take A38 from Exeter or Plymouth, at Buckfastleigh take A384 Totnes road for two miles. Turn left to Staverton. At Sea Trout Inn, take left fork to Kingston and follow signs.

REDCOATS FARMHOUSE HOTEL AND RESTAURANT

REDCOATS GREEN, NEAR HITCHIN, HERTS SG4 7JR
TEL: 01438 729500 FAX: 01438 723322 E-MAIL: info@redcoats.co.uk

OWNERS: The Butterfield Family
CHEF: John Ruffell

S: £70–£85
D: £80–£95

This 15th century farmhouse has been in the Butterfield family's possession for generations and in 1971 Peter and his sister converted it into a hotel. They preserved its traditional character of original beams, exposed brickwork and inglenook fireplaces and furnished it in a comfortable and inviting fashion.

It is set in tranquil gardens – one of the larger rooms has its own garden – in the middle of rolling countryside, not far from A1(M). There are 14 rooms, 12 with en suite bathrooms, diverse in character: those in the main house retaining period charm and those in the stable block more modern.

Meals are served in four dining rooms: the Oak Room and the Old Kitchen, log fire cosiness; the Victorian Room, elegant and formal and the Conservatory, garden room atmosphere. Redcoats has a good reputation for its cuisine, which uses much local produce and a wine list which is as wide ranging geographically as it is in prices.

Places of interest nearby: Redcoats is close to several historic houses including Knebworth House, Hatfield House, Luton Hoo and Woburn. The Roman city of St Albans, the traditional market town of Hitchin and Cambridge University are all within a 30 minute drive. **Directions: Leave the A1(M) at junction 8 for Little Wymondley. At mini-roundabout turn left. At T-Junction go right, hotel is on left.**

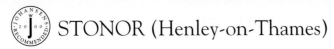

STONOR (Henley-on-Thames)

THE STONOR ARMS HOTEL

STONOR, NR HENLEY-ON-THAMES, OXFORDSHIRE RG9 6HE
TEL: 01491 638866 FAX: 01491 638863 E-MAIL: stonorarms.hotel@virgin.net

OWNERS: Stonor Hotels Ltd
MANAGER: Sophia Williams

S: £99
D: £125

This small hotel is not too far from London and perfectly located for those visiting the Henley Royal Regatta or Racing at Ascot. It is in the pretty village of Stonor, set in the idyllic Chiltern Hills. Originating from an 18th century Coaching Inn the interior has been beautifully decorated combining grace and comfort.

The bedrooms are enchanting, very spacious and each individually furnished with English and French antiques and colourful yet harmonious fabrics offering all the comforts expected by today's discerning traveller.

The hotel has won a high reputation for its first-class food. The restaurant consists of an elegant dining room and conservatories overlooking the traditional walled garden. The cooking is modern English and snacks are also served either alfresco or in the Blades bar, with its flagstoned floor and walls bedecked with rowing memorabilia.

Places of interest nearby: The Royal Borough of Windsor and Oxford Stonor Deer Park are both easily accessible. Sporting activities nearby include boating, golf or following one of the famous walks, The Oxfordshire Way, The Ridgeway or The Thames. **Directions: Leave the M40 at junction 6, following B4009 to Watlington, then turn left onto B480 through Stonor.**

THE TOLLGATE INN

CHURCH STREET, KINGHAM, OXFORDSHIRE OX7 6YA
TEL: 01608 658389 FAX: 01608 659467

OWNER: Penny Simpson
CHEF: Ben Parry

9 rms | 9 ens | SMALL HOTEL

S: £35
D: £50

This beautiful Cotswold stone, Grade II listed building began life as a 17th century farmhouse. Situated in the centre of the peaceful village of Kingham, it is an ideal retreat from the hustle and bustle of the modern world.

The house has been completely refurbished and the result is a superb property offering comfortable accommodation and excellent facilities. The owner and her team have strived hard to create a home-from-home atmosphere. Leading off the flagstoned hall are two lounges with log fires, original beams and cosy armchairs – perfect for reading and relaxing.

The bedrooms are individually decorated and several feature original leaded light windows and window seats. A number open directly onto the walled garden where afternoon tea and evening drinks are served. All the bedrooms are non smoking as is the restaurant. Smoking is allowed in the Bar.

Chef Ben Parry has devised an inspired menu and uses organic produce wherever possible. A typical dinner may begin with hot crab and saffron tart, followed by rib-eye steak in Five Spice glaze with garlic cheese mash and finishing with an iced chocolate terrine.

Places of interest nearby: Burford, Bourton-on-the-Water and many other typical Cotswold towns and villages are all close by. Blenheim Palace, Stratford-upon-Avon and Oxford are also within easy reach. **Directions: The hotel is in the centre of Kingham, which lies between the B4450 and A436 to the east of Stow.**

THE UNICORN HOTEL

SHEEP STREET, STOW-ON-THE-WOLD, GLOUCESTERSHIRE GL54 1HQ
TEL: 01451 830257 FAX: 01451 831090 E-MAIL: bookings@cotswold–inns–hotels.co.uk

OWNERS: Cotswold Inns & Hotels

20 rms	20 ens	SMALL HOTEL

S: £60–£70
D: £105–£120

Low oak-beamed ceilings and large stone fireplaces pay tribute to The Unicorn's lengthy past. Over the last 300 years, the hotel has changed its standards of accommodation, incorporating the latest modern facilities, yet many vestiges of the former centuries remain.

The recently refurbished interior is decorated in a stylish manner featuring Jacobean furniture and antique artefacts whilst log fires abound. Enhanced by floral quilts and comfortable armchairs, the 20 en suite bedrooms are simple yet charming. Fine paintings adorn the walls of the public rooms and the cosy bar offers hand-carved wooden chairs and rich carpets. Modern British cooking is served in the elegant surroundings of the Georgian restaurant from an imaginative à la carte menu. The hotel is well-frequented on Sundays by guests wishing to indulge in the delicious lunchtime roast. Local leisure facilities include horse-riding and the golf course. Shooting and fishing are popular outdoor pursuits.

Places of interest nearby: Many historic buildings and castles are within easy reach including the magnificent Blenheim Palace and Warwick Castle. Nature enthusiasts will be delighted with the splendid gardens at Sudeley Castle. **Directions: The nearest motorway is the M40 junction 10. Then take the A44 or the A436 in the direction of Stow-on-the-Wold.**

GLEBE FARM HOUSE

LOXLEY, WARWICKSHIRE CV35 9JW
TEL/FAX: 01789 842501 E-MAIL: scorpiolimited@msn.com

OWNER: Kate McGovern

S: £69.50
D: £85–£95
Suite: £110

The pleasure of staying at this delightful country house is like that of visiting a private home. Just three miles from historic Stratford-upon-Avon and eight miles from Warwick, Glebe Farm is surrounded by a superb expanse of secluded lawned garden which opens on to 30 acres of beautiful farmland where one can ramble and enjoy the sounds and sights of local wildlife.

Owner Kate McGovern is an accomplished cook and her dinners, served in the attractive surroundings of a conservatory overlooking the gardens, will tempt every palate. Whenever possible fresh organic produce from the kitchen garden are used. Kate is a talented water colour artist and many of her paintings adorn the walls throughout the house which is furnished and decorated with immaculate taste.

There are three pretty en suite bedrooms with four-poster beds and television and tea and coffee facilities. From all bedrooms and the lounge there are splendid views of the countryside. Local sporting activities include golf, shooting and riding.

Places of interest nearby: The hotel is an ideal base for visiting Shakespeare's Stratford-upon-Avon, Warwick's imposing castle, Ragley Hall, Birmingham N.E.C., the Heritage Motor Museum and the Cotswolds. **Directions: From the M40, exit at junction 15. Join the A429 and follow the signs to Wellsbourne and then Loxley. Glebe Farm is on the right as you leave Loxley.**

THE NURSE'S COTTAGE

STATION ROAD, SWAY, LYMINGTON, HAMPSHIRE SO41 6BA
TEL/FAX: 01590 683402 E-MAIL: nurses.cottage@lineone.net

OWNER: Tony Barnfield

3 rms | 3 ens

S: £52.50–£62.50
D: £90

This remarkable little house is centrally situated in a quiet, thriving village on the southern edge of the magnificent New Forest, which is rich in history and famed for its free-roaming ponies and deer. Dating from the early 1900s, The Nurse's Cottage was for nearly 70 years home to Sway's successive District Nurses, from whom the bedrooms are named.

The delightful cottage exudes character and charm with chef patron Tony Barnfield placing great emphasis on attention to detail and value for money. His enterprising dinner menus are served with imagination and flair in an intimate dining room overlooking the attractive garden. A balanced choice of delicious dishes is offered, including house specialities such as avocado, orange and prawn salad and fillet of Scottish salmon in Cointreau and cream. The wine list contains over 60 selections, many in half bottles.

All three en suite ground floor bedrooms are immaculately and tastefully furnished. Thoughtful extras include refrigerator, complimentary fruit juices, biscuits and Beaulieu chocolates. No smoking throughout. Closed Nov 15– Dec 15.
Places of interest nearby: A number of stately homes, including Broadlands and Wilton House, the National Motor Museum at Beaulieu, Rothschild's Exbury Gardens, the yachting town of Lymington and historic Stonehenge.
Directions: From M27, junction 1 take the A337 to Brockenhurst and then the B3055 signed to New Milton. Station Road is on the right in Sway.

WILLINGTON HALL HOTEL

WILLINGTON, NR TARPORLEY, CHESHIRE CW6 0NB
TEL: 01829 752321 FAX: 01829 752596

OWNERS: Stuart and Diana Begbie

S: £58–£68
D: £90–£100

Built by Cheshire landowner Charles Tomkinson, Willington Hall was converted into a hotel by one of his descendants and in 1999 was bought by Stuart and Diana Begbie. Set in 17 acres of woods and parkland, the hotel affords wonderful views across the Cheshire countryside towards the Welsh mountains. There are both formally landscaped and 'wild' gardens, which create a beautiful backdrop for the handsome architectural proportions of the house. The hotel is a comfortable and friendly retreat for those seeking peace and seclusion. Under the personal supervision of Diana and Stuart, Willington Hall has acquired a good reputation with local people for its extensive bar meals and à la carte restaurant, along with friendly and attentive service. The menus offer traditional English cooking, with dishes such as roast duckling with black cherry sauce.

Places of interest nearby: It is an ideal location for visiting the Roman city of Chester, Tatton Park, Beeston Castle and Oulton Park racetrack. North Wales is easily accessible from Willington Hall. The hotel is closed on Christmas Day. **Directions: Take the A51 from Tarporley to Chester and turn right at the Bull's Head public house at Clotton. Willington Hall Hotel is one mile ahead on the left.**

TEWKESBURY (Kemerton)

UPPER COURT

KEMERTON, NR TEWKESBURY, GLOUCESTERSHIRE GL20 7HY
TEL: 01386 725351 FAX: 01386 725472 E-MAIL: uppercourt@compuserve.com

OWNERS: Bill and Diana Herford

| 3 rms | 3 ens | |

S: £65
D: £80–£120

Upper Court is an outstanding Georgian manor with flower filled Coaching yard with holiday cottages. An ideal place for private house parties and business meetings. Guests are warmly welcomed whether staying in the manor or in one of the cottages. The four-poster or twin bedrooms all en suite, furnished in traditional English Country house style with lovely chintzes, needlework and linens.

The main feature of The National Garden Scheme garden is the lake, a 2 acre haven for a variety of wildfowl and for those who seek peace. The idyllic grounds also have a Doomsday watermill and a dovecote.

Kemerton is a splendid location on Bredon Hill with views of 5 counties, and a stroll down the lane is the excellent Crown Inn. Weekend use of the holiday cottages costs £170, please enquire for availability.

Places of interest nearby: Stratford, Sudeley and Warwick Castles, Hidcote, Snowshill Manor, Oxford, Bath, Cheltenham and Broadway. **Directions: From Cheltenham north on A435/B4079. One mile after A46 crossroads sign to Kemerton on the right. Turn off main road at War Memorial. House behind church. From M5 junction 9, go east on A46 to the B4079 crossroads, then left and one mile as above.**

THURLESTONE SANDS (Nr Salcombe)

HERON HOUSE HOTEL

THURLESTONE SANDS, NR SALCOMBE, SOUTH DEVON TQ7 3JY
TEL: 01548 561308 FAX: 01548 560180

OWNER: Mrs Pearl Rowland
MANAGER: June Rundle
CHEF: David Newland

S: £60–£90
D: £100–£170

Visitors to South Devon couldn't ask for a more peaceful location than that of this very welcoming hotel. Heron House stands adjacent to a Blue Flag sandy beach on the coast path next to a lovely bird reserve with wetlands to attract waders. Surrounded by unspoilt countryside it is an area of outstanding beauty with spectacular views across Bigbury Bay to Burgh Island, Plymouth Sound and the Cornish coast.

All 17 bedrooms are en suite, furnished to a high standard and have either sea or country views. A large, newly furnished lounge with an attractive bar provides comfort and relaxation after a day on the sands, swimming in the heated pool, rambling or touring the countryside. A second quiet lounge overlooks the pool. Pearl Rowland has owned the hotel since 1983 and ensures guests receive the best personal attention.

Head chef David Newland also ensures that evening meals are something special with his menus living up to the Rosette Award given by the AA for the past three years. Riding, fishing, sailing and Thurlestone golf course are all close by.

Places of interest nearby: South Hams, Dartmoor National Park and many National Trust properties. Plymouth, Totnes and Buckfastleigh. **Directions: From the Exeter to Plymouth A38 take A381 to Totnes and Kingsbridge. Take the road to Salcombe (ignore signs to Thurlestone), after approx. 2 miles turn right to South Milton. In village centre turn left to Thurlestone Rock/South Milton Sands. After approx. 1 mile continue along unmade beach road for 300yds to hotel.**

 TINTAGEL (Trenale)

TREBREA LODGE

TRENALE, TINTAGEL, CORNWALL PL34 0HR
TEL: 01840 770410 FAX: 01840 770092

OWNERS: John Charlick and Sean Devlin

    SMALL HOTEL

    S: £60–£65
D: £84–£94

Winner of the Johansens 1994 Country House Award, Trebrea Lodge overlooks the beauty and grandeur of the North Cornish coast and is set in 4½ acres of wooded hillside. This Grade II listed house was built on land granted to the Bray family by the Black Prince in the 14th century and has been lived in and improved by successive generations of the Brays for almost 600 years.

All the bedrooms are individually decorated with traditional and antique furniture and they offer uninterrupted views across open fields to the Atlantic Ocean. The elegant first-floor drawing room also boasts spectacular views, while there is a comfortable smoking room downstairs with an open log fire.

A full English breakfast and four-course dinner are served in the oak-panelled dining room and the menu changes daily. The cook uses the finest local ingredients, including sea trout and wild salmon from the River Tamar and they have been awarded an AA Rosette.

Places of interest nearby: Tintagel Island and Boscastle. Bodmin Moor, Lanhydrock House and gardens, Pencarrow House and extensive coastal walks.
Directions: From Launceston take Wadebridge–Camelford road. At A39 follow Tintagel sign – turn left for Trenale ½ mile before reaching Tintagel.

HOOKE HALL

HIGH STREET, UCKFIELD, EAST SUSSEX TN22 1EN
TEL: 01825 761578 FAX: 01825 768025 E-MAIL: a.percy@virgin.net

OWNERS: Alister and Juliet Percy

| 10 rms | 10 ens | SMALL HOTEL |

S: from £55
D: from £75

Uckfield lies on the borders of Ashdown Forest, near the South Downs and resorts of Brighton and Eastbourne and 40 minutes from Gatwick Airport. Hooke Hall is an elegant Queen Anne town house, the home of its owners, Juliet and Alister Percy, who have carried out extensive renovations.

The comfortable bedrooms are individually decorated to a high standard with private facilities. In the panelled study guests can relax by the open fire and enjoy sampling the excellent range of malt whiskies on offer from the well-stocked 'Honesty Bar'. Breakfast is served in a delightful room with french windows opening onto the terrace and the garden beyond. There are several restaurants within easy walking distance of the hotel and further choices only minutes away by car.

Places of interest nearby: Within easy reach are Leeds, Hever and Bodiam Castles, Penshurst Place and Battle Abbey. The gardens of Sissinghurst, Nymans, Great Dixter, Sheffield Park, Wakehurst Place and Leonardslee are no distance nor is Batemans, Rudyard Kipling's home. Glyndebourne Opera is only 15 minutes by car. There are several English vineyards nearby to be visited. Closed for Christmas. **Directions: From M25 take the exit for East Grinstead and continue South on the A22 to Uckfield. Hooke Hall is at the northern end of the High Street.**

TREHELLAS HOUSE & MEMORIES OF MALAYA RESTAURANT

WASHAWAY, BODMIN, CORNWALL PL30 3AD
TEL: 01208 72700 FAX: 01208 73336

OWNERS: Robin and Lee Boyle
CHEF: Lee Boyle

12 rms | 12 ens

S: £37
D: £50
Suite: £80

This early 18th century former posting inn, steeped in history, is surrounded by two acres of grounds. The bedrooms are charming, varying in size, with five in the main house and others in the former coach house and barn. Following a recent refurbishment, the rooms are enhanced by the comfortable furnishings including patchwork quilts, iron bedsteads and en suite facilities.

The Memories of Malaya restaurant, with its beautifully preserved slate floor and elegant décor, serves a unique style of cuisine known as Nonya. Originating from the Pacific Rim, the dishes are authentically reproduced and flavoured with aromatic herbs and spices. Cornish breakfasts are served with locally produced organic bacon, sausages and free-range eggs.

Guests may wish to stroll in the pleasant gardens or enjoy the heated swimming pool. There are ample parking facilities.

Places of interest nearby: Pencarrow House and Lanhydrock House and Gardens are both within easy reach. The village of Rock is a popular base for sailing and fishing whilst cyclists and ramblers will enjoy the trails to Padstow and the Bodmin Moor. **Directions: Washaway is located on the A389 half-way between the towns of Bodmin and Wadebridge. Approaching from Bodmin, Trehellas House is situated to the right, set back from the main road and accessed by a slip road.**

KEMPS COUNTRY HOUSE HOTEL AND RESTAURANT

EAST STOKE, WAREHAM, DORSET BH20 6AL
TEL: 01929 462563 FAX: 01929 405287

OWNERS: Jill and Paul Warren

S: £55–£75
D: £80–£130

This small and welcoming country house hotel, surrounded by unspoilt Dorset countryside, overlooks the Frome Valley and offers lovely views of the Purbeck Hills. The house was originally a Victorian Rectory and its tasteful extension was undertaken with great care to preserve Victorian atmosphere.

There are five bedrooms in the main house and another six with ground floor access facing the gardens and the Purbecks. Some have whirlpool baths and one features a traditional four-poster bed. Another four en suite bedrooms are located in the Old Coach House conversion.

The bar features the ornate wallpaper and heavy hangings of the Victorian period. The comfortable dining room extends into the conservatory, from which there are picturesque views of the hills. Kemps restaurant, which has been awarded an AA Rosette, enjoys an excellent local reputation for first-rate cuisine. The table d'hôte menu changes daily and there is also an à la carte menu. Food is prepared to order, everything possible is home-made.
Places of interest nearby: Lulworth and Corfe Castles, Athelhampton House and gardens. **Directions: In its own grounds on the A352 between Wareham and Wool.**

THE ARDENCOTE MANOR HOTEL AND COUNTRY CLUB

LYE GREEN ROAD, CLAVERDON, WARWICKSHIRE CV35 8LS
TEL: 01926 843111 FAX 01926 842646 E-MAIL: hotel@ardencote.com

MANAGER: Paul Williams
CHEF: Simon Douglas

   SMALL HOTEL

S: £87.50
D: £135

Situated deep in the Warwickshire countryside yet just minutes from the motorway network, this charming, historic gentleman's residence is a tranquil retreat with an extensive range of sports and leisure facilities. There is an indoor swimming pool with Jacuzzi, solarium and steam rooms, two fully equipped gymnasia, two all-weather tennis courts, four glass-backed squash courts, 3 acre trout lake and 9-hole pitch & putt course. Alternatively, guests can pamper themselves with one of the range of head-to-toe beauty treatments in the hotel's Health and Beauty Suite.

The en suite bedrooms are spacious and tastefully furnished. A creatively designed table d'hôte menu is served in the intimate Oak Room Restaurant with its elegant country house atmosphere. The large, stylish Palms Conservatory which opens onto the gardens provides an ideal venue for weddings and the Hotel's own programme of entertainment events, such as Murder Mystery Evenings and Jazz Brunches.

A traditional log cabin Sports Lodge overlooking a large, trout filled lake and incorporating a separate and informal bar restaurant, nestles gracefully within the 40 acres of immaculate landscaped grounds, gardens and waterways.

Places of interest nearby: Birmingham City attractions and Warwick's imposing castle. Stratford-upon-Avon is within easy reach. **Directions: From M40 follow signs to Henley-in-Arden, taking the A4189 to Claverdon/Warwick.**

BERYL

WELLS, SOMERSET BA5 3JP
TEL: 01749 678738 FAX: 01749 670508

OWNERS: Eddie and Holly Nowell

S: £50–£70
D: £70–£95

This nineteenth century Gothic mansion is tastefully furnished with antiques. It also offers hospitality of the highest order.

The host is a famous antique dealer, with a long established shop in Wells, his gardening talents are reflected in the 13 acres of parkland which he has restored with great skill.

His wife is a charming and talented hostess, evident in the attention paid to detail and an excellent cook. Dinner is served by arrangement in the elegant dining room, with a set menu and house wines, pre-dinner and after-dinner drinks are available. It is possible to have small conferences or private celebrations. The en suite bedrooms have interesting views, with all the requisites for modern comfort.

Places of interest nearby: Wells Cathedral (1 mile), The Roman Baths at Bath, Glastonbury Abbey, Longleat House, Stourhead, Farleigh Castle, theatres in Bath and Bristol and many more fascinating places. For more active guests, there is marvellous golf, fishing, riding, excellent walking and a nearby leisure centre. **Directions: Leave Wells on Radstock Road B3139. Follow the signs to 'The Horringtons' and the 'H' sign for hospital. Opposite the B.P. garage turn left into Hawkers Lane, Beryl is signed at the top with a leafy 500 yard drive to the main gate.**

COXLEY VINEYARD

COXLEY, WELLS, SOMERSET BA5 1RQ
TEL: 01749 670285 FAX: 01749 679708

OWNERS: William Jones and Anita England
CHEF: Simon Jackson

10 rms | 10 ens | SMALL HOTEL

S: £70
D: from £80

Built around a suntrap courtyard in the heart of four acres of grapevines, this small, charming hotel has a Mediterranean ambience. Pastel décor, terracotta tiled flooring, pine furniture and ceilings enhance the continental family atmosphere created by owners Bill Jones and Anita England.

Coxley Vineyard is a hotel providing excellent service and hospitality, where guests can completely relax and enjoy the delights of their surroundings. The ten bedrooms are luxuriously en suite and have every home comfort and facility. Two, including the Bridal/Master room, have large four-posters. Children are very welcome and cots and baby monitoring services are available if required.

A superbly prepared selection of lunch and dinner table d'hôte and à la carte dishes are served in the large, newly refurbished restaurant. Chef Simon Jackson uses the best local produce and his cuisine can be complemented by wine from an extensive list. This includes the hotel's own vintage which is renowned for its distinctive fruity flavour. On warm summer evenings guests can dine in the attractive courtyard.

The hotel has a 40ft heated swimming pool in the grounds, has its own fishing ponds on the moors and can arrange fishing and shooting excursions.

Places of interest nearby: Wells Cathedral, Glastonbury Abbey, Longleat House, Stourhead, the Cheddar Gorge and caves, Wookey Hole, Stonehenge and Bristol. **Directions: Two miles from Wells on A39 road to Glastonbury.**

GLENCOT HOUSE

GLENCOT LANE, WOOKEY HOLE, NR WELLS, SOMERSET BA5 1BH
TEL: 01749 677160 FAX: 01749 670210 E-MAIL: Glencot@ukonline.co.uk

OWNER: Jenny Attia

13 rms | 13 ens | SMALL HOTEL

S: from £62
D: £85–£110

Idyllically situated in 18 acres of sheltered gardens and parkland with river frontage, Glencot House is an imposing Grade II listed Victorian mansion built in grand Jacobean style. It has been sensitively renovated to its former glory to provide comfortable country house accommodation and a homely atmosphere.

This elegantly furnished hotel has countless beautiful features: carved ceilings, walnut panelling, mullioned windows, massive fireplaces, antiques and sumptuous chandeliers. The bedrooms are decorated and furnished with period pieces. All have full en suite facilities and splendid views. Many have four-poster or half tester beds.

Guests can enjoy pleasant walks in the garden, trout fishing in the river, snooker, table tennis, a sauna or a dip in the jet-stream pool. The small, intimate bar has a balcony overlooking the grounds and diverse and delicious fare is served in the restaurant, enriched by beautiful glassware, silver and china.

Places of interest nearby: The caves at Wookey Hole, the cathedral town of Wells, the houses and gardens of Longleat, Stourhead and Montacute, Glastonbury, Bath, the Mendip Hills and the Cheddar Gorge. **Directions: From the M4, exit at junction 18. Take the A46 to Bath and then follow the signs to Wells and Wookey Hole. From the M5, exit at junction 22. Join the A38 and then the A371 towards Wells and Wookey Hole.**

SOULTON HALL

NR WEM, SHROPSHIRE SY4 5RS
TEL: 01939 232786 FAX: 01939 234097 E-MAIL: soultonhall@go2.co.uk

OWNERS: John and Ann Ashton
CHEF: Ann Ashton

S: £38–£49
D: £76–£99

Historic and imposing Soulton Hall stands in 550 acres of beautiful Shropshire parkland two miles east of the ancient market town of Wem. Dating from the 15th and 17 centuries, this Tudor brick built manor, with a magnificent pillared courtyard and beautiful walled garden, retains much of the grandeur and character of those bygone days, enhanced with all modern facilities.

Ann and John Ashton, descendants of the Protestant Lord Mayor of London who bought Soulton in 1556, have created a hotel of warmth whilst retaining many of the unique features in the four spacious bedrooms in the house. The two more modern bedrooms in the coach house are equally comfortably and provide total privacy.

Ann Ashton presides in the kitchen where her skills in traditional English cooking are enhanced by imagination and flair. Specialities might include hand-raised game pie or butter baked salmon served with saffron oil. There is a congenial bar and ample parking space.

Places of interest nearby: Hawkstone country park, Hodnet Hall and gardens, Grinshill, Nescliffe Hill, Ironbridge and Shrewsbury. Chester, Stoke and Worcester are within easy reach. **Directions: M54 to end, then A5 to junction with A49. North on A49, then join B5065 west to Wem.**

BEECHLEAS

17 POOLE ROAD, WIMBORNE MINSTER, DORSET BH21 1QA
TEL: 01202 841684 FAX: 01202 849344

OWNER: Josephine McQuillan

S: £69–£89
D: £89–£99

Beechleas is a delightful Georgian Grade II listed town house hotel. It has been carefully restored and offers guests comfortable accommodation in beautifully furnished quality en suite bedrooms.

The hotel's own charming restaurant, which overlooks a pretty walled garden, is bright and airy in the summer and warmed by cosy log fires in the winter. The carefully prepared menu is changed daily and offers dishes using natural produce wherever possible along with the finest fresh ingredients available from the local market.

Sailing trips are available from Poole Harbour, where guests may choose to go fishing. They can play golf on one of the many local courses. It takes just five minutes to walk into the centre of Wimborne, a historic market town with an interesting twin tower church built on the site of its old Saxon Abbey during the 12th and 13th centuries.

The hotel, which is closed from 24 December to mid January, has been awarded two Red Stars by the AA and two Rosettes for its restaurant along with a Blue Ribbon from the RAC.

Places of interest nearby: There are many National Trust properties within easy reach, including Kingston Lacy House, Badbury Rings and Corfe Castle. Bournemouth and Poole are a 20 minute drive away. **Directions: From London take M3, M27, A31 and then B3073 to Wimborne.**

HOLBROOK HOUSE HOTEL

WINCANTON, SOMERSET BA9 8BS
TEL: 01963 32377 FAX: 01963 32681 E-MAIL: enquiries@holbrookhouse.co.uk

OWNER: John and Pat McGinley
HOUSE MANAGER: Nigel Preston
EXECUTIVE CHEF: Nathan Preece

S: from £65
D: from £130
Suite: £195

The history of Holbrook dates back to Saxon times, with the earliest records of a property on the site having been drawn up during the reign of Edward III. The house, which is easily accessed from Bath, Bristol and London, has undergone a major refurbishment and lies in a most peaceful country location with glorious views across the Blackmore Vale.

The 14 bedrooms are spacious and are superbly equipped. Each room affords pleasant views of the attractive surrounds. The recently refurbished public rooms are most inviting and include the comfortable lounge and convivial bar. Holder of two AA Rosettes, The Holbrook Restaurant serves fresh meat from traditionally reared animals with venison and game selected from shoots on estates and fresh fish delivered daily.

Sports on offer include swimming, tennis, squash and croquet whilst the newly opened Health Spa will delight those wishing to be pampered. With state-of-the-art equipment, the beauty rooms offer an array of treatments. Seating 200 people, the new function and conference suite provides the latest business facilities and is perfect for wedding receptions, private banqueting and corporate meetings.

Places of interest nearby: The Fleet Air Arm Museum and the great houses and gardens of Montacute, Longleat and Stourhead. **Directions: Leave A303 at Wincanton slip Road and join A371 towards Castle Cary at the first roundabout. Over three more roundabouts and the hotel driveway is on the right immediately after the third.**

FAYRER GARDEN HOUSE HOTEL

LYTH VALLEY ROAD, BOWNESS-ON-WINDERMERE, CUMBRIA LA23 3JP
TEL: 015394 88195 FAX: 015394 45986 E-MAIL: lakescene@fayrergarden.com

OWNERS: Iain and Jackie Garside

  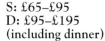

S: £65–£95
D: £95–£195
(including dinner)

Overlooking Lake Windermere in spacious gardens and grounds this lovely Victorian House is a very comfortable hotel where guests enjoy the spectacular views over the water, a real welcome and marvellous value for money.

The delightful lounges and bar and the superb air-conditioned restaurant all enjoy Lake views. There is an excellent table d'hôte menu in the award-winning restaurant changing daily using local produce where possible, fish, game and poultry and also a small à la carte choice. The wine list is excellent and very reasonably priced.

Many of the attractive bedrooms face the Lake, some having four- poster beds and whirlpool baths en suite.

There are also ground floor rooms suitable for the elderly or infirm.

The nearby Parklands Leisure Complex has an indoor pool, sauna, steam room, badminton, snooker and squash complimentary to hotel residents. Special breaks available.
Places of interest nearby: The Windermere Steamboat Museum, Boating from Bowness Pier and golf at Windermere Golf Club and The Beatrix Potter Attraction are all close by. **Directions: Junction 36 off the M6, A590 past Kendal. Take B5284 at the next roundabout, turn left at the end and the hotel is 350 yards on the right.**

WINDERMERE

QUARRY GARTH COUNTRY HOUSE HOTEL AND RESTAURANT

WINDERMERE, CUMBRIA LA23 1L7
TEL: 015394 88282 FAX: 015394 46584

OWNER: Ken MacLean
MANAGER: Scott Anderson

  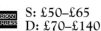

S: £50–£65
D: £70–£140

This mellow Edwardian house enjoys an idyllic setting in eight acres of peaceful woodland gardens near Lake Windermere. Ken MacLean and his staff invite guests to come and sample Quarry Garth's high standards of comfort and hospitality.

The individually designed bedrooms are all en suite some with four-poster or king-size beds. The elegant lounge with its deep soft sofas, open log fire and cocktail bar is the ideal location for relaxation and pre-dinner drinks. The award-winning restaurant 'Le Louvre', which overlooks the tumbling beck and landscaped gardens, serves the finest Anglo-French cuisine prepared using fresh game, fish and locally-produced vegetables. Soft lighting and candles evoke the unique ambience of a country house hotel.

Secluded some 50 yards from the main hotel stands the Quarry Lodge, containing three en suite bedrooms on the ground floor (two with spa baths) and a large lounge dining room on the first floor.

A woodland trail within the grounds offers a relaxing 15 minute walk among rich wildlife. A sauna and spa bathroom is available for use by guests.

Places of interest nearby: The beautiful lakes, the homes of Wordsworth and Beatrix Potter and many historic home and gardens. **Directions: From exit 36 of M6, take A590 for 3 miles then A591 to Windermere. Continue on A591 for 2 miles and the entrance is on the right.**

THE OLD VICARAGE COUNTRY HOUSE HOTEL

CHURCH ROAD, WITHERSLACK, NR GRANGE-OVER- SANDS, CUMBRIA LA11 6RS
TEL: 015395 52381 FAX: 015395 52373 E-MAIL: hotel@old–vic.demon.co.uk

OWNERS: Roger and Jill Brown, Stan and Irene Reeve
CHEF: James Brown MCGB

S: £65–£85
D: £98–£158

Near to the lakes...far from the crowds, this lovely old, family-run historic house offers the tranquil timeless atmosphere that reflects the calm and beauty of the surrounding Lake District National Park.

The delightful, mature garden is stocked with many interesting plants and part of it is left natural for wild flowers, unusual orchids, butterflies, dragonflies and birds. An all-weather tennis court in a delightful setting is for guests' use. Guests also have free use of the nearby Cascades Leisure Club.

In the old house, each of the comfortable bedrooms has its own particular character yet with all the modern facilities. The Orchard House, close by, is set beside an ancient damson orchard and has particularly well-equipped, spacious rooms each with its own woodland terrace. With top culinary awards, the well-planned menus include interesting, good quality locally-produced specialities. Diets can, of course, easily be catered for.

Places of interest nearby: Windermere, Wordsworth Heritage and Sizergh Castle (a member of The National Trust) are all within easy reach. Nature enthusiasts will be delighted to visit the famous topiary gardens at Levens Hall. **Directions: From M6 junction 36, follow A590 to Barrow. After 6 miles turn right into Witherslack, then first left after the telephone box.**

WOODBRIDGE

WOOD HALL COUNTRY HOUSE HOTEL

SHOTTISHAM, WOODBRIDGE, SUFFOLK IP12 3EG
TEL: 01394 411283 FAX: 01394 410007

OWNERS: Harvey and Carole Storch
MANAGERS: Rob and Pat Allan

S: £75
D: £75–£95
Suite: £105

Three miles from Woodbridge, on the Deben estuary, this Elizabethan manor house has been transformed into a secluded and luxurious hotel. A walled garden and lake are just part of the magnificent grounds surrounding Wood Hall – which is approached by a long tree lined drive.

The historic background is evident, the reception rooms having fine panelled walls, ornate ceilings and big, open fireplaces, extremely welcoming on dull afternoons.

The bedrooms are romantic, each with its own colour scheme reflected in lovely fabrics. Antiques vie with modern comforts and the bathrooms are wonderfully equipped.

Guests enjoy cocktails at the bar and a choice of three restaurants with appetising menus that include exotic and traditional dishes, grills and local fish. The wine list is excellent and reasonably priced. Additionally there is a magnificent banqueting suite, ideal for conferences and seminars, with appropriate equipment available.

Places of interest nearby: Residents have complimentary membership of the Wood Hall Country Club, which has squash, tennis, croquet and a heated outdoor pool. Local attractions include ten golf courses, good sailing off the Suffolk Coast at Woodbridge, fishing and shooting, bird sanctuaries, Aldeburgh Music Festival. **Directions: A12 towards Lowestoft, then A1152 through Melton, next roundabout B1083 towards Bawdsey, after 3 miles hotel is on right.**

THE PARSONAGE COUNTRY HOUSE HOTEL

ESCRICK, YORK, NORTH YORKSHIRE YO19 6LF
TEL: 01904 728111 FAX: 01904 728151 E-MAIL: reservations@parsonagehotel.co.uk

OWNERS: Paul and Karan Ridley
MANAGER: Frank McCarten

S: £95–£99
D: £110–£155

Surrounded by wide expanses of lawn, formal gardens and wild woodland, The Parsonage Country House Hotel provides an oasis of comfort and tranquillity. In the nearby breathtakingly beautiful hills and valleys are hidden ancient hamlets and villages still immersed in the old way of life.

The Parsonage has been passed down through various noble families and baronies from Count Alan of Brittany in the early 11th century, to the de Lascelles, the Knyvetts, Thompsons, Lawleys and finally the Forbes Adams retaining all of its charm and many original features.

Each bedroom has been furnished with comfort and luxury in mind and features a full range of modern facilities. Two of the larger rooms contain magnificent four poster beds, ground floor rooms available. 4 individual air conditioned banqueting and conference rooms available to accommodate 150. Large car park. Large conservatory overlooking garden which serves light lunch or afternoon tea.

A highly appetising selection of dishes is created by the chef, who uses only the freshest, high quality local ingredients. A varied and carefully selected wine list is available to complement any meal.

Places of interest nearby: The Parsonage is a perfect base from which to visit York and Harrogate, the estates of Castle Howard, the three Cistercian Abbeys, the Yorkshire coastline or the Yorkshire Dales. **Directions: Escrick is on the A19 a few miles south of York.**

HOPE HOUSE

HIGH STREET, YOXFORD, SAXMUNDHAM, SUFFOLK IP17 3HP
TEL/FAX: 01728 668281 E-MAIL: HopeHouseYoxfordUK@compuserve.com

OWNERS: Michael Block and Roger Mildren

S: £40–£80
D: £75–£95

A Queen Anne style house with recorded 14th century origins situated in a village described as "The Garden of Suffolk" because of its lush setting between stretches of parkland. Built in 1665, Hope House has undergone extensive renovation and been refurbished to the highest standards while respecting all original features.

It is furnished with antiques and modern, comfortable pieces where appropriate. The principal public rooms have handmade carpets and matching upholstery. Rich drapes, paintings and prints enhance the house's natural welcoming atmosphere. The delightfully comfortable and attractive bedrooms contain ingenious bathrooms which the owners have cleverly managed to incorporate without interfering with the rooms' historic styles and proportions.

Easily accessible and with a host of sporting activities available nearby, elegant Hope House and its romantic walled garden is ideally suitable to exclusive use for private parties and business meetings.

Places of interest nearby: Yoxford is ideally situated for touring the Suffolk coast and visiting Southwold, RSPB Minsmere, Aldeburgh, Framlingham Castle, Leiston Abbey and Helmingham Hall. **Directions: Yoxford is just off the A12 between Woodbridge and Lowestoft.**

Johansens Recommended Country Houses & Small Hotels

Wales

Breathtaking scenery, a rich variety of natural, cultural and modern leisure attractions, and the very best accommodation awaits the Johansens visitor in Wales.

Harlech Castle

What's new in Wales?

• Llangollen International Musical Eisteddfod – the 54th International Musical Eisteddfod held at the Royal International Pavilion, Llangollen, between 4th and 9th July 2000. Participants from around 50 countries are drawn together by their love of music, song and dance. A unique cultural festival to be enjoyed by all.
Tel: 01978 860236

• Royal Welsh Show – exhibition of livestock, cattle, horses, machinery, handicrafts, tradestands, sheepdog trials, tug of war plus much more. Held at the Royal Welsh Showground between 24th and 27th July 2000.
Tel: 01982 553683

• Ladies Home International Matches – Golf – annual competition between ladies golf teams from England, Ireland, Scotland & Wales. Held between 13th and 15th September 2000 at the Royal St David's Golf Club.
Tel: 01334 475811

• Welsh International Film Festival – premier welsh film event celebrating the industry in an international context. Held at various venues in Cardiff between 10th and 19th November 2000.
Tel: 01970 617995

For more information please contact:-

Wales Tourist Board
Dept GN
PO Box 1
Cardiff CF1 2XN
Tel: 01222 475226

North Wales Tourism
Tel: 01492 531731

Mid Wales Tourism
Tel: 0800 273747

Tourism South & West Wales
Tel: 01792 781212

PLAS PENHELIG COUNTRY HOUSE HOTEL AND RESTAURANT

ABERDOVEY, GWYNEDD LL35 ONA
TEL: 01654 767676 FAX: 01654 767783 E-MAIL: plaspen.@netcomuk.co.uk

OWNERS: The Richardson Family

S: £64 (including dinner)
D: £108–£128 (including dinner)

A wooded driveway leads the way to Plas Penhelig, a splendid Edwardian country house set in 7 acres of secluded grounds and offering wonderful views across the tranquil Dovey estuary. Guests are given the warmest welcome from the resident owner and his dedicated staff who work hard to create a homely atmosphere.

The hotel lounges, complete with card tables, reading lamps and glowing log fires, provide a restful setting in which to enjoy morning coffee or afternoon tea. Then, when the pure Welsh air has taken effect, a good night's sleep is ensured in the comfortable bedrooms.

Crisp table linen, gleaming cutlery and elegant floral decorations set the scene for an excellent meal in the hotel's restaurant. Freshly supplied local meat, game and fish create a superb range of dishes. Lighter meals and snacks can be enjoyed in the cocktail bar or on the terrace.

While a walk in the award-winning landscaped gardens will prove hard to resist, a putting green and croquet lawn are available for the more energetic. Closed mid-December to mid-March.

Places of interest nearby: The lovely sandy beaches of Cardigan Bay, Snowdonia National Park, craft centres and the Centre for Alternative Technology are all within easy reach. **Directions: On the A493 Machynlleth to Tywyn road in Aberdovey.**

GLANGRWYNEY COURT

GLANGRWYNEY, NR CRICKHOWELL, POWYS NP8 1ES
TEL: 01873 811288 FAX: 01873 810317

OWNERS: Warwick and Christina Jackson

S: £35–£40
D: £65–£75

This graceful Georgian mansion is set in four acres of secluded mature gardens on the Monmouthshire–Powys borders. There is a walled garden and in summer visitors can sit in perfect peace enjoying the views of the rolling hills. The house is furnished with antiques, fine porcelain and paintings. The delightful drawing room and dining room are exclusive to guests. The music room has a grand piano and other instruments. Guests are ensured of a warm welcome.

Hospitality offered includes a traditional breakfast and, by prior discussion, a delicious four-course dinner based on the seasonal fresh produce available.

All the bedrooms have been individually decorated and furnished and the Romantic West Room is especially popular with honeymooners. Four rooms are en suite – The Master room has a steam shower and luxuriously deep bath. The twin room has its own private Jacuzzi. Credit cards are not accepted at Glangrwyney Court.

Places of interest nearby: In summer, guests play croquet, tennis and boules or relax in the garden. If agreed beforehand, dogs are welcome. Golf, pony trekking, and fishing are nearby, also the Brecon Beacons National Park for walkers. Hereford Cathedral and the market towns of Abergavenny and Crickhowell are close by, as are the spectacular Talybont and Gwryne Fawr Reservoirs. **Directions: The Court is signed from Crickhowell on the A40 between Brecon and Abergavenny.**

ABERGAVENNY (Govilon)

LLANWENARTH HOUSE

GOVILON, ABERGAVENNY, MONMOUTHSHIRE NP7 9SF
TEL: 01873 830289 FAX: 01873 832199

OWNERS: Bruce and Amanda Weatherill

S: £56–£64
D: £76–£82

Llanwenarth House overlooks the Vale of Usk and stands in its own beautiful grounds within the Brecon Beacons National Park. It was built from local rose-grey limestone in the 16th century by the Morgan family, ancestors of Sir Henry Morgan, privateer and Lieutenant Governor of Jamaica. The house has been carefully restored over the years, ensuring that it has retained all of its character, while not compromising on the highest levels of comfort.

Guests are personally looked after by the family, who offer comfortable accommodation in period furnished rooms. Many of the elegant spacious bedrooms offer lovely views of the grounds and surrounding countryside. Fine cuisine is prepared by Amanda, a Cordon Bleu cook who makes full use of local game, fish, home-produced meat, poultry and organically grown fruit and vegetables from their own kitchen garden. Dinner is served by candlelight in the beautiful Georgian dining room. Credit cards not accepted.

Sporting activities include trout and salmon fishing on the River Usk, pony-trekking, climbing and golf, the nearest course being 3 miles away.

Places of interest nearby: Chepstow and Raglan Castles and Tintern Abbey. **Directions: From the roundabout 1 mile east of Abergavenny follow A465 towards Merthyr Tydfil for 3 miles to the next roundabout. Take first exit to Govilon, the ½ mile driveway is 150 yards on the right.**

TRE–YSGAWEN HALL

CAPEL COCH, LLANGEFNI, ISLE OF ANGLESEY LL77 7UR
TEL: 01248 750750 FAX: 01248 750035 E-MAIL: enquiries@sue–rowlands–centre.org.uk

OWNERS: Mr and Mrs T Rowlands
CHEF: Paul Halewood

 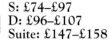

S: £74–£97
D: £96–£107
Suite: £147–£158

This handsomely restored late 19th century stone mansion stands majestically in the heart of beautiful Anglesey countryside with impressive views towards Snowdonia. A hotel since 1990 it is surrounded by landscaped grounds and woodland and offers discerning guests who pass through its tall, pillared entrance door the quality of style, comfort and attentive service expected of a de luxe country establishment.

The interior grandeur encompasses fine wood panelling, twinkling chandeliers and large windows framed with rich, flowing drapes. A magnificent oak staircase leads from the impressive hall to splendidly proportioned bedrooms.

Each of the 19 bedrooms is individually and distinctively designed and all have first-class bathrooms and every comfort.

There is a half suite with a four poster bed and Jacuzzi and two ground floor bedrooms are suitable for the less mobile guest.

Chef Paul Halewood caters for all tastes with a superb choice of table d'hôte and à la carte dishes in the Capel Coch or Britannia dining rooms. A less formal menu is available in the large and light conservatory accommodating 100 diners. Rooms are available for private dining and special menus can be devised to match a wedding, banquet or conference.

Places of interest nearby: Beaumaris and Caernarfon Castles, Portmeiron and the Ffestiniog Railway. **Directions: From A5 to Holyhead, turn right onto A5114 Llangefni. From Langefni follows signs to Amlwch on B5111. Capel Coch and Tre-Ysgawen Hall are signposted two miles along.**

BETWS-Y-COED

TAN-Y-FOEL

CAPEL GARMON, NR BETWS-Y-COED, CONWY LL26 0RE
TEL: 01690 710507 FAX: 01690 710681 E-MAIL: tanyfoel@wiss.co.uk

OWNERS: Peter, Janet and Kelly Pitman
CHEF: Janet Pitman

S: £70–£90
D: £90–£150

This exquisite house, recently described as "a jewel box of colour", has won many accolades as an outstanding small country hotel, that blends finest country elegance with innovative interior design. Set in breathtaking surroundings, it commands magnificent views of the verdant Conwy Valley and the rugged peaks of Snowdonia.

Once inside Tan-y-Foel a "no smoking" policy prevails. There are seven extremely comfortable bedrooms, each with their own strikingly individual style, warm colours and rich decorations. Thoughtful small touches add to their charm and the bathrooms are delightfully appointed.

Celebrated for her impeccable cuisine, Janet sources the best local produce – fresh fish, Welsh Black beef, organically-grown vegetables – for her creatively composed nightly menus which have been recognised with 3 AA Rosettes. The distinguished wine list offers over 90 carefully chosen vintages.

The personal welcome which perfectly complements the nature of the Pitmans' fine house has further resulted in RAC Blue Ribbon and AA 2 Red Star accolades. The popularity of their two-night Special Offer Breaks thus comes as no surprise. **Places of interest nearby:** Great Little Trains of Wales, Bodnant Gardens, Conwy Castle and Snowdonia. **Directions: From Chester, A55 to Llandudno, the A470 towards Betws-y-Coed. 2m outside Llanrwst fork left towards Capel Garmon-Nebo. Tan-y-Foel is just over a mile up the hill on the left.**

OLD GWERNYFED COUNTRY MANOR

FELINDRE, THREE COCKS, BRECON, POWYS LD3 0SU
TEL: 01497 847376 FAX: 01497 847376

OWNERS: Roger and Dawn Beetham

8 rms   8 ens

S: £49
D: £84–£105

Old Gwernyfed is a historian's delight – its passage through the ages has been carefully documented and its antiquated features well preserved. Set in 13 acres in the foothills of the Black Mountains, it was built circa 1600 as a manor house of great importance in its day.

Over the years, Roger and Dawn Beetham have lavished much attention on the building to restore it to its former glory. They have made no attempt to disguise the age of the building, preferring to enhance its original features.

One of the lounges, which is oak panelled from floor to ceiling, is overlooked by the splendid balustraded minstrels gallery. Most of the bedrooms enjoy fine views and there is a choice of four-poster, half-tester and canopied beds.

The dining room is dominated by its cavernous 12 foot fireplace, only rediscovered in recent years. A small table d'hôte menu is changed daily and all dishes are cooked freshly using produce from the garden or local suppliers.

For wedding parties, guests have exclusive use of the house and grounds. There are excellent value three day breaks. Closed mid-December to mid-March. The Manor does not accept credit cards.

Places of interest nearby: Hay-on-Wye and the market town of Brecon. Activities include canoeing, sailing and gliding.

Directions: From Brecon turn off A438 after the Three Cocks Hotel. Take every turning to right for 1³/₄ miles. Go through Felindre, Old Gwernyfed is 200 yards on right.

 CAERNARFON

TY'N RHOS COUNTRY HOTEL

SEION LLANDDEINIOLEN, CAERNARFON, GWYNEDD LL55 3AE
TEL: 01248 670489 FAX: 01248 670079 E-MAIL: enquires@tynrhos.co.uk

OWNERS: Lynda and Nigel Kettle
CHEF: Carys Davies and Lynda Kettle

  S: £49–£70
 D: £70–£96

Award-winning Ty'n Rhos is not the typical country house hotel. The creation of Lynda and Nigel Kettle, it is a 72 acre farm still, but has undergone a magnificent transformation resulting in an immaculate small hotel based on the original farmhouse and former outbuildings.

The ten en suite bedrooms are beautifully appointed with all the comforts of a stylish hotel. Uncompromising standards are offered in the elegant lounge and the West-facing conservatory that enjoys serene views over Caernarfon and the Menai Straits.

Ty'n Rhos's special appeal is based on a unique fusion of personal service and the highest professional standards: perhaps the most important single element is its restaurant food. This former Taste of Wales Restaurant of the Year sources the finest, fresh local ingredients for its seasonal menus: local fishermen and merchants supply daily caught fish and shellfish from Caernarfon Bay and the waters around Anglesey. The Welsh breakfasts are notable for farm-cured bacon, freshly baked rolls and home-made preserves and yogurt. To it's hard-earned reputation for food, service and value for money, Ty'n Rhos adds its enviable location between Snowdonia and the sea.

Places of interest nearby: The hotel is within easy touring distance of all of North Wales. **Directions: Situated in the hamlet of Seion off the B4366 and B4547. Reached from the East by A5 or A55.**

THE OLD RECTORY

LLANRWST ROAD, LLANSANFFRAID GLAN CONWY, COLWYN BAY, CONWY LL28 5LF
TEL: 01492 580611 FAX: 01492 584555 E-MAIL: OldRect@aol.com

OWNERS: Michael and Wendy Vaughan

6 rms **6 ens**

MasterCard VISA S: £99–£129
D: £99–£149

Enjoy dramatic Snowdonian vistas, breathtaking sunsets and views of floodlit Conwy Castle from this idyllic country house set in large gardens overlooking Conwy Bird Reserve. Awarded 2 AA Red Stars for 'outstanding levels of comfort, service and hospitality and 3 Rosettes for food.'

Wendy, a 'Master Chef of Great Britain' features in all of Britain's premier good food guides. Her gourmet three-course dinners combine a lightness of touch and delicacy of flavour with artistic presentation. Welsh mountain lamb, locally reared Welsh black beef and locally landed fish are on her menu. An award-winning wine list complements her fine cuisine. Most diets are catered for.

Antiques and Victorian watercolours decorate the interiors.

The luxury en suite bedrooms have draped beds, bathrobes, ironing centres, fresh fruit and flowers.

Michael is happy to share his knowledge of Welsh history, and culture and to assist in planning touring routes. Three 18-hole golf courses within 10 minutes drive. Relax in the garden and watch the River Conwy ebb and flow and see why this elegant Georgian home is a 'beautiful haven of peace'. An ideal venue for exclusive small conferences.

Places of interest nearby: Bodnant Gardens, Historic Conwy, Victorian Llandudno Spa, Betws-Y-Coed, Snowdonia. Chester, Caernarfon and Angelsey, all within 40 mins. **Directions: On A470, ¹/₂ mile south of A55 junction, 2 miles from Llandudno Junction Station. 3 hrs from London Euston.**

DOLGELLAU (Ganllwyd)

PLAS DOLMELYNLLYN

GANLLWYD, DOLGELLAU, GWYNEDD LL40 2HP
TEL: 01341 440273 FAX: 01341 440640 E-MAIL: info@dolly–hotel.co.uk

OWNERS: Jon Barkwith and Joanna Reddicliffe
CHEF: Joanna Reddicliffe

S: £45–£60
D: £85–£115

The approach to Plas Dolmelynllyn, which is entirely non-smoking, set in the amazing scenery of south Snowdonia, leads through a winding, beech-lined drive that brings guests to the doorway. A house has stood on the site since the 1500s, extended in the 18th and 19th centuries. Bedrooms are individually decorated and comfortably furnished. Joanna Reddicliffe, the daughter of the house, prepares an interesting and varied menu with several choices in each course including vegetarian dishes.

There is a conservatory bar and a large sitting room with full-length windows overlooking the valley. Dogs are allowed in two of the bedrooms only.

The hotel is surrounded by three acres of formal gardens, bounded by a swiftly running stream which flows into a small lake. Guests can take advantage of the hotel's fishing on 10 miles of river and three local lakes.

Places of interest nearby: Adjoining the grounds are 1,200 acres of mountains, meadow and forest, where it is possible to walk all day without seeing a car or crossing a road. Castles, slate caverns, waterfalls and a gold mine can all be visited nearby, but the theme here is relaxation amid wonderful surroundings, comfort, and only the gentlest of activities. **Directions: Plas Dolmelynllyn is off the main A470 Dolgellau– Llandudno road, just north of Dolgellau. Dinner, bed and breakfast, combined rates and short breaks are available.**

STONE HALL

WELSH HOOK, NR FISHGUARD, PEMBROKESHIRE SA62 5NS
TEL: 01348 840212 FAX: 01348 840815

OWNERS: Alan and Martine Watson
CHEF: Jean-Yves Poujade

3 rms | 3 ens |

S: £48–£52
D: £70–£74

Flagstone floors, inglenook fireplaces, decorative ceilings and open stonework are just some of the attractive features of this secluded retreat set in ten acres of gardens and woodlands.

Stone Hall has been the centre of a large estate for nearly 600 years. The earliest known owners traced their lineage to the medieval Prince Gwynfardd Dyfed, whose descendants were at the manor by the year 1400. The building was converted to a country hotel in 1984 and care has been taken to preserve the original features, charm and atmosphere of the different periods of its history.

It is an ideal base from which to enjoy the beautiful, windswept Welsh countryside, coastal walks, rugged cliffside grandeur, the wildlife and superb scenery. There are three extremely comfortable and tastefully furnished and decorated en suite bedrooms with up-to-date facilities, an attractive lounge, dining room, bar and restaurant where the cuisine is unashamedly French. Chef Jean Yves Poujade produces excellent and extensive à la carte and table d'hôte menus to delight the most discerning connoisseur.

Stone Hall is within easy reach of the wild north coast of Pembrokeshire and the long sandy beaches of St Bride's Bay. **Places of interest nearby:** St David's Cathedral, Pembroke Castle, the walled town of Tenby, Pembrokeshire coastal path. **Directions: From M40, follow A40 via Haverfordwest towards Fishguard. After passing through the village of Wolf's Castle turn left for Welsh Hook and Stone Hall.**

MONMOUTH (Whitebrook)

THE CROWN AT WHITEBROOK – RESTAURANT WITH ROOMS

WHITEBROOK, MONMOUTHSHIRE NP5 4TX
TEL: 01600 860254 FAX: 01600 860607 E-MAIL: crown@whitebrook.demon.co.uk

OWNERS: Roger and Sandra Bates

10 rms | 10 ens | SMALL HOTEL

  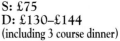

S: £75
D: £130–£144
(including 3 course dinner)

A romantic auberge nestling deep in the Wye Valley, a designated area of outstanding natural beauty, The Crown is ideally situated for those seeking peace and tranquillity, with its two and three night breaks providing particularly good value for money.

Located up the wooded Whitebrook Valley on the fringe of Tintern Forest and only one mile from the River Wye, this is a place where guests can enjoy spectacular scenery. Roger and Sandra Bates offer their guests a genuinely friendly welcome amid the tranquil comforts of the cosy lounge and bar.

Sandra Bates' cooking has earned the Restaurant 3 AA Rosettes and numerous prestigious awards for excellence. Dishes include local Welsh lamb and Wye salmon cooked with a classical French influence, followed by a choice of delicious home-made puddings and a selection of British farm cheeses. Most dietary requirements can be catered for as all food is freshly cooked to order. The extensive wine list is the work of a true enthusiast.

Places of interest nearby: Tintern Abbey, Chepstow Castle and the Brecon Beacons National Park are all within easy reach. **Directions: Whitebrook is situated between the A466 and the B4293 approximately five miles south of Monmouth.**

PLAS BODEGROES

NEFYN ROAD, PWLLHELI, GWYNEDD, WALES LL53 5TH
TEL: 01758 612363 FAX: 01758 701247 E-MAIL: gunna@bodegroes.co.uk

OWNERS: Christopher and Gunna Chown
CHEFS: Christopher Chown and Shaun Mitchell

S: £60–£85
D: £120–£170
(including dinner)

Towering beech trees and magnificent purple rhododendrons frame this splendid Georgian hotel situated close to Pwllheli on the historic Lleyn Peninsula. It is an ideal retreat for those wishing to explore an area quite unlike the rest of North Wales. Distant horizons are broken by dramatic mountains falling sheer to the sea. There are rocky coves, wide bays, enticing beaches, whitewashed cottages on top of round-backed hills and charming fishing villages.

Plas Bodegroes is the ideal base from which to begin any exploratory journey and a warm, friendly haven to return to after a day's experiences. Owner Gunna Chown oversees a delightfully relaxing country house where peace, tranquillity and comfort abound. When the pure Welsh air has taken effect a good night's sleep is ensured in the en suite bedrooms which have every facility to help make guests feel at home.

Crisp table linen and gleaming cutlery set the scene for excellent meals in the restaurant. With three AA Rosettes the cuisine is an integral part of the Bodegroes experience; dinner menus prepared by Chefs Christopher Chown and Shaun Mitchell will satisfy the most discerning diner. Excellent venue for Sunday lunch. Closed in Dec, Jan and Feb.

Places of interest nearby: The ancient town of Nefyn, the colourful harbour of Abersoch and the offshore islands of St Tudwall. Criccieth Castle and, on the lowest of the triple peaks of Yr Eifl, the Town of Giants, an Iron Age encampment are also close by. **Directions: On A497, just west of Pwllheli.**

NORTON HOUSE HOTEL AND RESTAURANT

NORTON ROAD, MUMBLES, SWANSEA SA3 5TQ
TEL: 01792 404891 FAX: 01792 403210

OWNERS: Jan and John Power
CHEF: Mark Comisini

15 rms   15 ens

S: £60–£70
D: £87.50

A really warm Welsh welcome and home-from-home hospitality are generously offered by this elegant hotel's resident proprietors Jan and John Power. Nothing is too much trouble and they are justly proud of the attentive and friendly atmosphere that pervades the whole hotel.

Norton House is attractively Georgian in style. It stands in lovely gardens set back from the Mumbles seafront and although not exactly rural it is run as a country house. Décor, furnishings and fabrics throughout are a tasteful delight.

The bedrooms all have up-to-date private amenities with four of the more spacious rooms offering four-poster beds. The majority of rooms are in a newer wing and are slightly smaller. Ground floor rooms have easy access from a private terrace.

The charming restaurant overlooks the terrace and gardens and chef Mark Comisini has earned a high reputation for tasty and imaginative cuisine with the emphasis on local produce and traditional flavours. Dinner menus are written in Welsh with English translations and include tempting dishes such as Penclawdd cockles and local laverbread and rack of Welsh lamb with black peppercorns and minted sauce.

Places of interest nearby: Sandy beaches of the Gower Peninsula, Swansea's maritime quarter and market.
Directions: Exit M4 at Jct42. Take A483 to Swansea, then A4067 alongside Swansea Bay. 1 mile beyond the Mumbles sign, the hotel is signposted on the right.

WATERWYNCH HOUSE HOTEL

WATERWYNCH BAY, TENBY, PEMBROKESHIRE SA70 8JT
TEL: 01834 842464 FAX: 01834 845076

OWNERS: Bette and Geoff Hampton

S: £40–£56
D: £56–£92
Suite: £80–£112

Waterwynch House is a uniquely secluded retreat nestling in a pretty little cove on the beautiful shores of Carmathen Bay. Surrounded by the Pembrokeshire Coastal National Park and 27 acres of its own woodland and gardens, it is a quiet, intimate hotel with an enviable reputation for friendly hospitality and personal service.

Dating from 1820 when it was built as a family home for Tenby based artist Charles Norris, the hotel retains its peaceful charm of the past. It is an ideal base from which to enjoy coastal walks, the wildlife and superb scenery, or just to relax on the private beach.

The 16 tastefully furnished and decorated bedrooms, all of which are non smoking, offer every modern comfort. Some have balconies and sea views, others overlook the gardens. The superior lounge suites feature Jacuzzi baths in their newly refurbished bathrooms.

A nightly table d'hôte menu caters for the most discerning connoisseur in the dining room with its panoramic view over the bay. As well as some unusual speciality dishes there are a good selection of fish courses. The hotel is closed from November to February.

Places of interest nearby: Superb walking along the adjacent Pembrokeshire coastal path, bird-watching, painting, fishing, golf and croquet, bowls and putting. **Directions: Off the A478 Kilgetty to Tenby road. Signposted on the left half a mile after the New Hedges roundabout.**

PARVA FARMHOUSE AND RESTAURANT

TINTERN, CHEPSTOW, MONMOUTHSHIRE NP16 6SQ
TEL: 01291 689411 FAX: 01291 689557

OWNERS: Dereck and Vickie Stubbs
CHEF: Dereck Stubbs

9 rms	9 ens

S: £48
D: £66–£76

Surrounded by the glorious, wooded hillsides of the beautiful lower Wye Valley and just a mile from 12th century Tintern Abbey, one of the finest relics of Britain's monastic age, Parva Farmhouse is a homely haven where visitors can relax and forget the pressures of their daily world. This is an ideal spot for country lovers. The salmon and trout teeming River Wye flows just 50 yards from the hotel's small, flower-filled garden, there is an abundance of wildlife and hundreds of tempting walks.

Built during the 17th century, Parva today provides every comfort. The bedrooms are well-furnished and most have pretty views across the River Wye. The beamed lounge with its log-burning fireplace, "Honesty Bar" and deep Chesterfield sofas and chairs is the perfect place to relax and chat over the day's happenings.

The crowning glory of Parva is the excellent food, home-cooked by chef-patron Dereck Stubbs and served in the Inglenook Restaurant before a 14-foot beamed fireplace. Golf, shooting and riding are close by and there is horse-racing at Chepstow. Two night breaks inclusive of dinner are especially popular and good value for money.

Places of interest nearby: Tintern Abbey, castles at Abergavenny and Chepstow, Offa's Dyke, the Royal Forest of Dean, many old ruins and ancient monuments. **Directions: Leave M48 at Jct2 and join A466 towards Monmouth. The hotel is on the north edge of Tintern Village.**

Johansens Recommended Country Houses & Small Hotels

Scotland

Myths and mountains, lochs and legends – Scotland's scenic splendour acts as a magnet for visitors from all over the globe. Superb as it is, Scotland's charismatic charm is more than just visual.

Dunrobin Castle

What's new in Scotland?

• The Big Idea – aiming to be open in the spring of 2000, a state-of-the-art permanent exhibition will be launched on the west coast of Scotland on the Ardeer peninsula. This is a visitor experience, not a science museum, nor an exploratorium but a gigantic workshop where visitors are encouraged to have their own big ideas.

•Scottish Seabird Centre – expected to open in May 2000 in North Berwick, offers visitors an amazing insight into the some of the largest seabird colonies in Europe.

•Our Dynamic Earth – this new visitor attraction opened in July 1999 directly opposite the site of the new Scottish parliament and close to the Palace of Holyroodhouse and tells the story of our planet. Using dramatic special effects this attraction takes the visitor through the fascinating journey from the Earth's creation through to the future (whatever it may be!) Travel through time and step aboard a spaceship and see the creation of earth and the splendour of the natural world.

For further information, please contact:-

The Scottish Tourist Board
23 Ravelston Terrace
Edinburgh
EH4 3TP

Tel: 0131 332 2433

BALGONIE COUNTRY HOUSE

BRAEMAR PLACE, BALLATER, ROYAL DEESIDE, ABERDEENSHIRE AB35 5NQ
TEL: 013397 55482 FAX: 013397 55482

OWNERS: John and Priscilla Finnie

S: £65
D: £110

In the heart of one of Scotland's most unspoilt areas, on the outskirts of the village of Ballater, lies Balgonie House. Winner of the 1997 Johansens Country House Award for Excellence. This Edwardian-style building is set within four acres of mature gardens and commands wonderful views over the local golf course towards the hills of Glen Muick beyond. Balgonie's nine bedrooms are each named after a fishing pool on the River Dee. They are individually decorated and furnished and most offer lovely outlooks from their windows. Amenities include private bathrooms, colour television and direct-dial telephones. At the heart of the hotel is the dining room, offering superb Scottish menus: including fresh salmon from the Dee, succulent local game, high quality Aberdeen Angus beef and seafood from the coastal fishing ports and vintage wine chosen from an excellent list. Balgonie has won the coveted Taste of Scotland Prestige Award for its cuisine, also 2 AA Red Star and 2 Rosettes.

Places of interest nearby: The village of Ballater, a five minute walk away, is a thriving community. As suppliers to the Queen, many of its shops sport Royal Warrant shields. This is an ideal centre for golf, hillwalking, sightseeing and touring. Balmoral Castle is within easy reach, as are both the Malt Whisky Trail and Castle Trail.
Directions: Upon entering Ballater from Braemar on the A93, Balgonie House is signposted on the right.

LONGACRE MANOR

ERNESPIE ROAD, CASTLE DOUGLAS, DUMFRIES AND GALLOWAY DG7 1LE
TEL: 01556 503576 FAX: 01556 503886 E-MAIL: BALL.Longacre@btinternet.com

OWNERS: Charles and Elma Ball
MANAGER: Charles Ball
CHEF: Elma Ball

4 rms   4 ens

S: £35–£45
D: £60–£80

An impressive drive skirted by woodland gardens overlooking rich green fields leads visitors up to the house with an oak panelled reception hall of this solid, red-roofed country hotel which stands peacefully in the heart of one of the loveliest areas of Southern Scotland. Built by a local businessman in 1920 it is an ideal base from which to tour one of the last unspoilt areas of Britain. All around are towns with rows of 18th century streets, ruined castles, mysterious earthworks and the legacy of prehistory.

Good food and the elegant comfort of deep, soft sofas and chairs, antique furniture, warm fabrics and a subdued décor are the welcoming ingredients provided under the personal supervision of owners Charles and Elma Ball.

The four bedrooms are spacious, well equipped and have delightful views over the gardens. One of the bedrooms has a king-size double four-poster bed, another room has two single four-poster beds. Breakfast is served at one long antique table and dinner can be ordered by arrangement. The hotel has been awarded four stars by the Scottish Tourist Board.

Places of interest nearby: The area has some fine beaches, more than 20 golf courses and excellent salmon and trout fishing. Logan Botanic Gardens and Threave Gardens, the National Trust School of Gardening, the ruined 14th century Threave Castle on an islet in the River Dee. **Directions: Castle Douglas is approximately 17 miles south west of Dumfries approached via the A75 road to Stranraer.**

COMRIE (Perthshire)

THE ROYAL HOTEL

MELVILLE SQUARE, COMRIE, PERTHSHIRE PH6 2DN
TEL: 01764 679200 FAX: 01764 679219 E-MAIL: reception@royalhotel.co.uk

MANAGER: Edward Gibbons

S: £65–£85
D: £130–£170
Suite: £190

Following a careful and extensive restoration, this glorious country house hotel, set in the Highland village of Comrie, offers a fusion of comfort and opulence. Log fires, period furnishings and fine fabrics adorn the public rooms creating a cosy yet elegant ambience.

The 11 bedrooms are the essence of luxury and have been individually appointed by local craftsmen. Those wishing to be pampered will be delighted with the many thoughtful extras such as scented toiletries, soft bathrobes and private safes.

Natural, local produce including Scotch beef, game, salmon, trout and shell fish is used by the talented chef and his team. Guests may dine informally in the Brasserie or by candlelight in the formal, grand Dining Room. Tasty snacks and beverages may be enjoyed in the Public Bar whilst alfresco diners are seated in the attractive walled garden. This is an ideal residence for golf and fishing enthusiasts as there are some fine courses and rivers nearby.

Places of interest nearby: Day trips to Glenturret Distillery, Comrie's Earthquake House, Auchingarrich Wildlife centre and Stuart Crystal Centre are popular with the hotel's guests. There are many places of historic interest nearby and these include Drummond Castle Gardens, Scone Palace and Fortingall, the birthplace of Roman Governor Pontius Pilate. **Directions: The hotel is situated in the centre of Comrie on the A85, Perth to Fort William Road.**

TRIGONY HOUSE HOTEL

CLOSEBURN, THORNHILL, DUMFRIESSHIRE DG3 5EZ
TEL: 01848 331211 FAX: 01848 331303

OWNERS: Robin and Thelma Pollock
CHEF: Janette Brownrigg

S: £40–£50
D: £70–£90

Trigony was once the home of the oldest woman in Scotland, Miss Frances Shakerley, who lived to be 107. A small, pink sandstone Edwardian house, it stands elegantly in over four acres of secluded gardens and woodlands in the lovely Nithsdale valley of Dumfries. It is an ideal base for discovering and exploring the Land of Burns and the outstanding natural beauty of its unspoilt rolling countryside.

Good food and homely comfort are the ingredients provided under the personal supervision of owners Robin and Thelma Pollock from the moment visitors step into the welcoming hall with its large York stone fireplace and magnificent open stairway. The immaculate en suite bedrooms are comfortable and well equipped and the highest standard of food is served in the charming restaurant, which overlooks the garden. Local produce is extensively used. Taste of Scotland Recommended. Golf, pheasant shooting, horse-riding, and salmon fishing can be arranged locally.

Places of interest nearby: Drumlanrig Castle, home of the Duke of Buccleuch, Maxwelton House, home of Annie Laurie (1682-1764), the Leadhills Mining Museum and historic Dumfries where Robert Burns lived from 1791 until his death in 1796. **Directions: Trigony House is situated off the A76, 13 miles north of Dumfries and one mile south of Thornhill.**

 DUNKELD

THE PEND

5 BRAE STREET, DUNKELD, PERTHSHIRE PH8 0BA
TEL: 01350 727586 FAX: 01350 727173 E-MAIL: react@sol.co.uk

OWNERS: Peter and Marina Braney
CHEF: Marina Braney

S: £50–£60
D: £100–£120
(including dinner)

Set in the heart of Perthshire, this charming Georgian house has preserved most of its original features while displaying many modern amenities.

The six bedrooms are decorated in a tasteful manner and are complemented by antique furniture. Two bathrooms are currently available for the guests' use.

The elegant sitting room is enhanced by a beautiful fireplace and soft furnishings. Continental cuisine and traditional Scottish fare are served in the room at breakfast and dinner. Three or four-course dinners of uncompromising standards are offered accompanied by the small but interesting wine list.

The range of activities available nearby is extensive and includes many outdoor pursuits. Guests wishing to indulge in the breathtaking Scottish landscape will enjoy abseiling, mountaineering, rock-climbing or simply rambling. For the less adventurous, there are castles, museums, theatres and shops to visit or peruse. Personal itineraries and quotations are designed to suit the needs of the group or individual.

Places of interest nearby: The town of Dunkeld and its cathedral, Scone Palace and Blair Castle. The reserve, close to Dunkeld, is maintained by the Scottish Wildlife Trust and is home to many animals and birds, particularly the Osprey. **Directions: From A9, turn off into Dunkeld. Brae Street is off the Main Street.**

GARVOCK HOUSE HOTEL

ST JOHN'S DRIVE, TRANSY, DUNFERMLINE, FIFE KY12 7TU
TEL: 01383 621067 FAX: 01383 621168 E-MAIL: sales@garvock.co.uk

OWNERS: Pamela Wright and Rui Fernandes
CHEF: Trevor Johnson

 S: From £65
D: From £85

Surrounded by rolling lawns and lush parkland, Garvock House is a picture of Georgian splendour close to the town centre of historic Dunfermline. It is a majestic, solid, grey-stoned hotel in a city that for six centuries was the capital of Scotland and the birthplace of several monarchs, including two Stuarts, James I in 1394 and Charles I in 1600.

Owners Pamela Wright and Rui Fernandes have taken great care to create a delightfully relaxed and friendly atmosphere for their guests and offer excellent old-fashioned service and personal attention. Tasteful décor and furnishings throughout enhance the comfortable ambience and impressive exterior. Many original features from the house's early days remain and combine sympathetically with today's modern requirements.

Each of the en suite bedrooms, some of which are in a newly built extension, are spacious and provide every comfort. Chef Trevor Johnson has earned a good reputation for the quality of his cuisine, prepared in a classical style with a modern twist and his extensive menus will suit all tastes.

Places of interest nearby: Dunfermline Abbey, Culross Palace, Stirling Castle, St. Andrews, Deep Sea World and all the attractions of Edinburgh, including its castle, National Gallery, Palace of Holyrood House and a host of historic buildings. **Directions: From Edinburgh cross the Forth Bridge and exit M90 at junction 3. Follow A907 into Dunfermline centre. Take the first left after the football stadium and then first right into St John's Drive.**

CULCREUCH CASTLE HOTEL & COUNTRY PARK

FINTRY, LOCH LOMOND, STIRLING & TROSSACHS, STIRLINGSHIRE G63 0LW
TEL: 01360 860555 FAX: 01360 860556

OWNER: Laird Andrew Haslam

S: £46–£95
D: £76–£150

Less than 20 miles from the bustle of Glasgow, Culcreuch Castle stands among the moors, lochs, glens and pinewooded wilds of Stirlingshire, close to Loch Lomond. Built in 1296, this grand ancestral seat of the once-feared Galbraith clan today overlooks 1,600 acres of superb parkland between the Campsie Fells and the Fintry Hills.

The owners, the Haslams, have renovated Culcreuch as a first-class country hotel while preserving its august past in antiques, oil paintings and old, worn steps. All eight bedrooms are en suite, some with four-poster beds. Their names – The Napier Suite, The Keep Room, or The Speirs' Room – help piece together the Castle's history.

Stay a night in the Chinese Bird Room, with its 18th century hand-painted wallpaper. After dark the Phantom Piper sometimes roams and plays. Dinner prepared by award-winning chef George Reid is served by candlelight in the panelled dining room; a four-course meal prepared from fresh, local produce costs £25.00 and there is a cellar of fine wines. Self-catering accommodation is also available.

Places of interest nearby: Fishing, walking in the Endrick Valley, visiting Loch Lomond, the village of Fintry and Stirling, to the east. Glasgow and Edinburgh airports are a 55 minute drive. **Directions: Exit M9 junction 10. A84 east towards Stirling. First right, then first right again and join A811. Go 10 miles west to junction with B822 at Kippen. Turn left, go via Kippen to Fintry.**

NAIRNS

13 WOODSIDE CRESCENT, GLASGOW G3 7UP
TEL: 0141 353 0707 FAX: 0141 331 1684

OWNERS: Nick and Christopher Nairn
CHEF: Neil Forbes

| 4 rms | 4 ens |

MasterCard VISA AMERICAN EXPRESS

S: £100–£120
D: £125–£140

Fronted by tall black railings, a doorway framed with coloured glasswork, a balustrade roof edge and the hotel name neatly printed on ground floor window blinds, Nairns is the epitome of impressive quiet elegance, style and modernity. It is a haven of peace and tranquillity in busy surrounds.

The hotel is owned by the brothers Nick and Christopher Nairn, the former famed for his cooking and television appearances. With hard work, imagination and flair they have created a cool, restful establishment inside a grey-stone façade that will please the most discerning guest.

Beautiful fabrics, polished wood panelling and floors, open fires and a simplistic display of pictures and furnishings combine to provide a tasteful and welcoming atmosphere.

Each of the four bedrooms is fascinatingly different. With lofty ceilings and windows, they are comfortably and decoratively furnished. The Silver Room, for instance, is just that, even to the four-poster-style metal framed bed. Each en suite bathroom is superb and luxurious with free standing baths and showers and the softest of towels.

The intimate, candlelit restaurant is the ideal place to enjoy some of the finest food in the city. Chef Neil Forbes menus are especially imaginative and interesting.

Places of interest nearby: The city centre, cathedral, university and all the delights of Glasgow and the surrounding areas. **Directions: Nairns is just off junction 18 of M8, close to Sauchiehall Street.**

GLEN CANNICH (By Beauly)

MULLARDOCH HOUSE HOTEL

GLEN CANNICH, BY BEAULY, INVERNESS-SHIRE IV4 7LX
TEL/FAX: 01456 415460 E-MAIL: andy@mullhouse1.demon.co.uk

OWNER: A. R. Johnston

  D: £94–£106

Built in 1912, this former hunting lodge has been carefully refurbished, resulting in a charming small hotel offering character and comfortable accommodation.

Set in the heart of the Highlands with views across the Affric mountains, Mullardoch House Hotel is in an ideal location for those who consider scenery to be an important criterion. After a day of exploring the surrounding countryside, guests may relax in the well appointed public rooms and indulge in a preprandial drink by the log fires.

An inspired menu comprising fresh, local produce such as West Coast shellfish and venison is served in the elegant non-smoking dining room. The extensive range of drinks includes a fine selection of wines and forty malt whiskies.

Keen golf-players may perfect their skills at the challenging courses nearby such as Nairn, Royal Dornoch and Tain. Other outdoor pursuits include hill-walking through the lochs, woodlands and the many Munros, stalking, pheasant and grouse shooting, fishing and horse-riding at the Highland Riding Centre close by.

Places of interest nearby: Heritage enthusiasts will be pleased with the hotel's location as Fort William, Cawdor, Urquhart and Eilean Donan Castles and Culloden Battle Field all lie nearby. Popular activities also include day-trips to Loch Ness and the Isle of Skye. **Directions: From the A9 or A82, take the A831 to Cannich. The hotel is signposted after eight miles on the single track road to Loch Mullardoch.**

CORRIEGOUR LODGE HOTEL

LOCH LOCHY, BY SPEAN BRIDGE, INVERNESS-SHIRE PH34 4EB
TEL: 01397 712685 FAX: 01397 712696 E-MAIL: info@corriegour–lodge–hotel.com

OWNERS: Ian and Christian Drew

   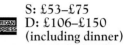

S: £53–£75
D: £106–£150
(including dinner)

Set amid 6 contrasting acres of mature woodland and garden, Corriegour Lodge commands outstanding views over Loch Lochy. Formerly a Victorian hunting lodge, it enjoys one of the finest settings in the 'Great Glen' – an area steeped in history. Enclosed within the grounds is a small lochside beach complete with jetty.

Christian and son Ian place the accent on guests' relaxation and comfort – the service is friendly and nothing is too much trouble. Each bedroom is immaculately decorated, well appointed and most have views of the loch. Gate Lodge self catering accommodation is also available

The Loch View Conservatory Restaurant has splendid views of the boats sailing across Loch Lochy on their way through the Caledonian Canal. A Taste of Scotland establishment, the hotel serves a delicious dinner featuring fine Scottish cuisine and tasty home-baked breads. The excellent wine list is very reasonably priced Corriegour Lodge is STB 4 Stars and represents exceptionally good value for money, especially for a stay of 3 nights or 7 nights. Open at weekends only from November to February, fully open March to October and between Christmas and New Year.

Places of interest nearby: Loch Ness, Ben Nevis and Castle Urquhart. **Directions: 17 miles north of Fort William on the A82, on the south side of Loch Lochy, between Spean Bridge and Invergarry on the way to Skye.**

 HELMSDALE (Sutherland)

NAVIDALE HOUSE HOTEL

HELMSDALE, SUTHERLAND KW8 6JS
TEL: 01431 821258 FAX: 01431 821531

OWNERS: Navidale House Ltd
CHEF: Tommy Bird

 From £60–£75
per person
(including dinner)

Originally built as a hunting lodge for the Dukes of Sutherland in the 1830s, Navidale retains the atmosphere of a country retreat and enjoys spectacular views over the waters of the Moray Firth and Ord of Caithness.

This small, solidly built hotel stands in six acres of woodland and garden which ramble down to the foreshore. The bar, lounge and drawing room have open fires and soft, relaxing chairs and sofas. Ten bedrooms are situated in the main hotel and five are in the adjacent, single storey lodge which has special facilities for disabled guests. All are en suite and have every home-from-home comfort. The majority have glorious sea views. These same stunning views may be enjoyed from the two exceptionally well-equipped and furnished self-catering lodges within the grounds.

Chef Tommy Bird takes full advantage of local produce and freshly caught seafood such as monkfish and oysters, along with Caithness beef, lamb and venison, feature on his extensive menus. For the fishing enthusiast, there are salmon and sea trout in the renowned Helmsdale and Brora rivers and wild brown trout in the Helmsdale Loch system. The hotel has rod and drying rooms and visitors catches can be packed and frozen. Stalking, shooting and golf are also available locally. Closed November, December and January.

Places of interest nearby: Dunrobin Castle, the Clynelish Distillery and Shin Falls. **Directions: Navidale House Hotel is ½ mile north of Helmsdale on main A9 coastal road.**

THE OLD MANSE OF MARNOCH

BRIDGE OF MARNOCH, BY HUNTLY, ABERDEENSHIRE AB54 7RS
TEL: 01466 780873 FAX: 01466 780873

OWNERS: Patrick and Keren Carter
CHEF: Keren Carter

S: £64
D: £98

Dating back to the late 1700s, The Old Manse of Marnoch is set in four acres of mature gardens on the banks of the River Deveron. Designed to create a unique and welcoming atmosphere for guests, this stylish country house is ideal for those seeking peace and quiet in an idyllic setting. The luxurious en suite bedrooms are superbly appointed, tastefully decorated and furnished with antiques. The lounge and dining room echo their striking and individual décor.

Generous Scottish breakfasts and award-winning food are notable features of this delightful establishment. The kitchen garden provides the fresh vegetables and fruit which contribute to the mouth-watering cuisine, with other ingredients supplied locally. Vegetarian and special diets can be catered for without fuss. Along with the better known clarets, Burgundies and Rhône wines, there is a selection of unusual wines to tempt more adventurous palates and to complement the imaginative dishes.

Every country sport is available locally and golfers can choose between parkland or links courses. Spectacular coastal scenery and sandy beaches are within easy reach and the area offers a wealth of lovely walks.

Places of interest nearby: Huntly Castle, Elgin Cathedral and the major cultural centres of Aberdeen and Inverness.
Directions: The Old Manse is on the B9117 less than a mile off the A97 midway between Huntly and Banff.

CULDUTHEL LODGE

14 CULDUTHEL ROAD, INVERNESS, INVERNESS-SHIRE IV2 4AG
TEL/FAX: 01463 240089

OWNERS: David and Marion Bonsor

12 rms	12 ens	SMALL HOTEL

S: £45
D: £85–£105

This beautifully appointed hotel, just a few minutes walk from the town centre, is a Grade II Georgian residence set in its own grounds and offering splendid views of the River Ness and surrounding countryside. Great emphasis is placed on providing good food, comfort and a quiet, friendly atmosphere.

On arrival in their rooms, guests are greeted with fresh fruit, flowers and a small decanter of sherry. Each bedroom is individually decorated and furnished to a high standard of comfort and provides every modern amenity including a CD/cassette player.

Delicious, freshly prepared food is presented by a table d'hôte menu which offers choices at each course, including Scottish fare and local produce. A carefully selected range of wines is available to complement the appetising and nourishing meals.

Places of interest nearby: Inverness is a good base for guests wishing to tour the Highlands and the north and west coasts. The Isle of Skye, Royal Deeside and the splendours of the Spey Valley are within a day's travel. **Directions: Take the B851 out of Inverness. Culduthel Road is a continuation of Castle Street and the Lodge is less than half a mile from the city centre on the right.**

MAPLE COURT

NO. 12 NESS WALK, INVERNESS, INVERNESS-SHIRE IV3 5SQ
TEL: 01463 230 330 FAX: 01463 237700 E-MAIL: maplecourt@macleodhotels.co.uk

OWNERS: Donald Macleod
CHEF: Steven Moffat

   S: £40
D: £60

Nestling by the banks of the Ness River and surrounded by two acres of glorious grounds, Maple Court Hotel is the perfect base from which to explore the Highland capital of Inverness. The former home of Doctor William Simpson, provost of the Ancient Royal Burgh of Inverness, this historical property features an array of modern luxuries and is furnished in a comfortable and tasteful style.

The same standards are evident in the well-appointed bedrooms which feature en suite bathrooms, television and direct dial telephones. Fabrics and furnishings have been hand picked to reflect the surrounding riverside gardens. During the summer months, cool drinks are served alfresco under the shade of the trees whilst in the winter, guests gather by the log fire, sipping one of the many Scottish Malt Whiskeys.

The Chandlery Seafood Restaurant is popular with locals and guests alike. Diners may sit in comfort and watch the river flow by as they sample fine wines and enjoy dishes from the award-winning chef's menu. The kitchen team pride themselves on their preparation and presentation of fresh produce such as West Coast Lobster, Oysters, Langoustine and the best of Highland Game.

Places of interest nearby: Fort George, Culloden Battefield and Inverness, Cawdor and Brodie Castles. **Directions: Bypass Eden Court Theatre and turn into Ness. Walk along the river.**

ARDVOURLIE CASTLE

AIRD A MHULAIDH, ISLE OF HARRIS, WESTERN ISLES HS3 3AB
TEL: 01859 502307 FAX: 01859 502348

OWNER: Derek Martin

S: £80–£110
D: £160–£180
(including dinner)

Despite its name, this was a hunting lodge built in 1863 by the Earl of Dunmore now restored recently to its full glory. Some rooms have gas and oil lamps, and fire-grates from the original period: mahogany-panelled baths with brass fittings add to the luxurious setting. With just four guest rooms, visitors are guaranteed a warm welcome and personal service from brother and sister team Derek and Pamela Martin. Each room has a private bathroom.

The castle stands on the shores of Loch Seaforth: further on are the sandy beaches of the west coast and the rocky wilderness of South Harris. Otters and seals frequent the bay and golden eagles can be seen over the hills.

The menu at Ardvourlie is based upon local produce wherever possible, including salmon, trout, island lamb, Scottish cheeses and Stornaway oatcakes. Vegetarian meals are available by arrangement. The food is Taste of Scotland, Michelin and Good Hotel Guide recommended. Ardvourlie Castle has a residents' licence and a self-service bar.

Places of interest nearby: Hill-walking (it is advisable to bring suitable clothing), beaches of the West Coast, Callanish Stones, Rodel Church. Salmon and trout fishing on Harris. **Directions: The castle stands on the shores of Loch Seaforth 24 miles from Stornoway and 10 miles from Tarbert.**

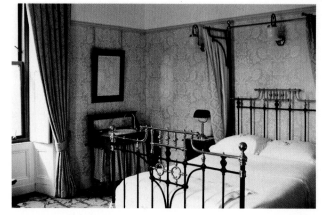

HIGHLAND COTTAGE

BREADALBANE STREET, TOBERMORY, ISLE OF MULL, ARGYLL PA75 6PD
TEL: 01688 302030 FAX: 01688 302727

OWNERS: David and Josephine Currie

 S: £55–£60
D: £80–£100

Situated in Tobermory, the "capital" of the Isle of Mull with frequent access from Oban by modern drive–on car ferry, Highland Cottage stands amidst the quiet elegance of the upper town's Conservation Area – quite literally above the town and yet just a few minute's walk from the hustle and bustle of Main Street and fisherman's pier.

Comfort is an important criterion in this beautifully appointed hotel featuring period décor and stylish ornaments. The bedrooms are furnished with flair and imagination in bright and pleasant shades and are complemented by the fine bathrooms. All bedrooms are fully-equipped, some contain four-poster beds and others are suitable for the disabled.

1999 sees the addition of a sun-lounge extension to the Dining-room and the menu now boasts both AA Rosette and Taste of Scotland awards, as well as an up-dated wine-list.

The Executive Retreat Package comprises luxury accommodation, all meals for each delegate, exclusive use of the cottage and secure meeting facilities.

Places of interest: Outdoor pursuits include fishing, sailing and golf whilst many organised day trips are offered around the scenic region of Mull including Staffa and Iona.

Directions: From the car ferries at Craignure or Fishnish, at roundabout on approach to Tobermory, carry straight on across the narrow bridge and turn immediately right signposted "Tobermory–Breadalbane Street". Follow the road round and Highland Cottage is on the right.

KILLIECHRONAN

KILLIECHRONAN, ISLE OF MULL, ARGYLL PA72 6JU
TEL: 01680 300403 FAX: 01680 300463

OWNERS: The Leroy Family

S: £73–£87
D: £65–£80
(including dinner)

An original Highland lodge, built in 1846, now a superb country house hotel, ideally located at the head of Loch na Keal. The owners already have an established reputation in Scotland with The Manor House Hotel at Oban.

This hotel, is their own family home and contains a magnificent collection of antiques and pictures. Most of the rooms face south, overlooking the sheltered grounds, part of the 5,000 acre estate.

Bringing the chef from the Manor House has ensured those high standards in the restaurant, awarded 1 AA rosette that one associates with the Leroy family and there is a fine wine list to complement the menu.

There are just six bedrooms, all en suite, with telephone and other modern comforts.

The area is renowned for its outstanding beauty. Visit Fingal's Cave, the white beach at Calgary, Duart Castle, the herring village of Tobermory and Torosay set in Italianate gardens. There is fishing, sailing, golf, pony treking and a fairly easy walk to the summit of Ben More. **Directions: Mull is reached by the ferry from Oban (40 minute crossing) or Lochalin. Take A849 to Salen. Left on B8035. House on right 2 miles after.**

BOSVILLE HOTEL & CHANDLERY SEAFOOD RESTAURANT

BOSVILLE TERRACE, PORTREE, ISLE OF SKYE, SCOTLAND IV51 9DG
TEL: 01478 612846 FAX: 01478 613434 E-MAIL: bosville@macleodhotels.co.uk

OWNERS: Donald W MacLeod
CHEF: Steven Moffat

| 15 rms | 15 ens | SMALL HOTEL |

S: £60–£70
D: £76–£96

Named Port an Righ, The King's Port, to commemorate the visit of King James V of Scotland in 1540, there is a strong Celtic feel to Portree whose ubiquitous bilingual signs still indicate a thriving Gaelic language on the island.

A warm welcome and Celtic hospitality mark out the Bosville Hotel, just a step back from the waterfront and overlooking the harbour with Raasay and Ben Tianavaig beyond. There is a convivial feel to the bar and lounge and all the bedrooms have been carefully refurbished to a high standard. Modern luxuries such as telephones and satellite television have recently been added and en suite bathrooms are brightly lit and equally well-appointed.

With no part of Skye more than four miles from the sea, its recurring presence receives marked attention in The Chandlery Seafood Restaurant. Masterminded by chef Steven Moffat the menu features the finest Scottish produce, and the restaurant has been recognised by the AA with one Rosette for food quality. Highland game and venison, Aberdeen Angus beef and West Coast seafood all feature prominently, as do Scottish hand-made cheeses, oatcakes and traditional Cranachan and Clootie Dumplings.

Places of interest nearby: Portree is ideal for exploring the unrestricted countryside with its unspoiled landscapes and abundant wildlife. Fishing and pony trekking can be arranged. **Directions: Take A87 from Kyle of Lochalsh toll bridge to Portree. Bosville Hotel overlooks the harbour.**

ARDSHEAL HOUSE

KENTALLEN OF APPIN, ARGYLL PA38 4BX
TEL: 01631 740227 FAX: 01631 740342 E-MAIL: info@ardsheal.co.uk

OWNERS: Neil and Philippa Sutherland

  S: £39–£45
D: £78–£90

A long private drive winds alongside lovely Loch Linnhe and through ancient woodland to this magnificent 18th century granite and stone manor which stands high on a natural promontory of pink marble with magnificent views over the loch and the mountains of Morvern. The scenery is breathtaking even for the West Highlands.

Set in 800 acres of hills, woods, gardens and shore front, Ardsheal House has a charming country house ambience and a friendly welcome is extended to all visitors by the resident owners.

The reception hall is particularly attractive, with warm polished oak panelling, an imposing open fire and a unique barrel window. Family antiques and bright fabrics are to be found in all the individually furnished bedrooms.

Philippa Sutherland serves memorable, daily changing four-course dinners in the attractive dining room. Vegetables, herbs and fruit from the garden and home-made jellies, jams and preserves form the basis for her innovative set meals.

Places of interest nearby: Islands, castles, lochs and glens, Oban's Cathedral of the Isles and ruined 13th century castle. **Directions: Ardsheal House is on the A828 five miles south of the Ballachulish Bridge between Glencoe and Appin on the way to Oban. From Glasgow and Edinburgh, follow the signs to Crianlarich and take the A82 north to Ballachulish.**

THE KILLIECRANKIE HOTEL

KILLIECRANKIE, BY PITLOCHRY, PERTHSHIRE PH16 5LG
TEL: 01796 473220 FAX: 01796 472451 E-MAIL: killiecrankie.hotel@btinternet.com

OWNERS: Colin and Carole Anderson

S: £66–£88
D: £132–£176
(including dinner)

The Killiecrankie Hotel is peacefully situated in four acres of landscaped gardens overlooking the Pass of Killiecrankie and River Garry. It was here, in 1689, that the Jacobites clashed with William of Orange's men in a battle to gain supremacy over the crowns of England and Scotland – an event which illustrates the area's rich heritage.

Guests will find a friendly welcome and a relaxed, informal style. There are ten charming bedrooms, including two on the ground floor. All are very comfortably furnished and decorated to a high standard. There is a cosy residents' sitting room with a patio in the garden in fine weather.

With two AA Rosettes, the Dining Room has a very good reputation. Fresh ingredients indigenous to Scotland are used and presented with flair and imagination. Menus offer a good, balanced choice: start perhaps with Terrine of Chicken, Wild Mushrooms and Leeks with Apricot Chutney or Goats Cheese Custard with Beetroot Sauce before going to a main course of Fillet of Cod with Saffron Mash and Chive Butter Sauce or Guinea Fowl stuffed with Apple and Walnut Mousseline served with Lyonnaise Potatoes and Meaux Mustard Sauce.

In the bar, a superb range of bar meals is served at lunch and supper time. Closed January. 3 night breaks at Christmas/New Year – also in Spring and Autumn.

Places of interest nearby: Blair Castle, Pitlochry Festival Theatre – golfing, fishing, shooting and hill-walking.
Directions: Turn off the main A9 at sign for Killiecrankie.

THE KINLOCHBERVIE HOTEL

KINLOCHBERVIE, BY LAIRG, SUTHERLAND IV27 4RP
TEL: 01971 521275 FAX: 01971 521438 E-MAIL: klbhotel@aol.com

OWNERS: Stewart and Val McHattie
MANAGER: Linda McHattie
CHEF: Hugh Simpson

    SMALL HOTEL

  D: £90–£110

The Kinlochbervie Hotel stands amongst the awesome beauty of the Atlantic coastline just below Cape Wrath, once the turning point for marauding Viking longships. It overlooks the little fishing port and lochs and offers magnificent views over the open sea whose depths and roaring waves attract divers and surfers from miles around.

The Kinlochbervie incorporates all that visitors would expect from a quality three-star hotel. The lounges and bars are comfortably relaxing, the bedrooms warm and cosy and the restaurant imparts exactly the right atmosphere in which to savour the Scottish delights of the Kinlochbervie's kitchens and cellars. In addition to local lamb and venison, delicious fish figures prominently on the menus, as the daily arrival of deep-sea trawlers to the local market ensures a plentiful supply of shellfish, monkfish, turbot and sole. Excellent wines complement the fine cooking. Ornithologists and naturalists will revel in the abundance of wildlife, golfers will find a challenge on the the most northerly course in Britain, just a short drive away. Fly and sea fishing can be arranged.

Places of interest nearby: Europe's highest waterfall at Kylesku, Handa Island bird sanctuary, Cape Wrath and the sandy stretches of Oldshoremore, Polin and Sheigra. **Directions: Take the A836 and then the A838 north west from Lairg. At Rhiconich, turn left onto the B801 which runs alongside Loch Inchard to Kinlochbervie.**

BALGEDDIE HOUSE HOTEL

BALGEDDIE WAY, LESLIE, NR GLEN ROTHES, FIFE KY6 3ET
TEL: 01592 742511 FAX: 01592 621702 E-MAIL: balgeddie@easynet.co.uk

OWNERS: Bryce and Janice Laing
CHEF: Marc Munro

S: £50–£60
D: £60–£80

Balgeddie has a natural country house character and ambience combining old world charm with modern comforts and facilities. New owners Bryce and Janice Laing provide a very friendly Scottish welcome, do their utmost to make guests feel at home and offer excellent value for money. An attractive-looking hotel with wisteria hung walls, Balgeddie stands proudly in beautiful rural surroundings on the lower slopes of the picturesque Lomond Hills.

All the bedrooms are en suite, decorated in warm tones and offer every home-from-home comfort. Guests can relax over coffee or drinks in an elegant lounge whose window seats offer panoramic views over the gardens. Pre and after dinner drinks are enjoyed in an intimate cocktail bar or The Paddock which stocks a selection of real ales.

Chef Marc Munro has worked at the hotel for 13 years and has a reputation for an imaginative range of dishes which are produced and served in the tastefully furnished restaurant with panache and flair.

Places of interest nearby: Balgonie and Kellie Castles, Balcaskie House and gardens, Falkland Palace, St Andrews, Vane Farm Bird Sanctuary, the Scottish Fisheries Museum and East Neuk fishing villages. **Directions: Exit the M90 at junction 3 and follow the A92 east to Glenrothes. After passing a paper mill turn left at the corner garage into Cadham Road, then Fortmonthills Road. The third street on the left will take you to the hotel.**

POLMAILY HOUSE HOTEL

DRUMNADROCHIT, LOCH NESS, INVERNESS-SHIRE IV3 6XT
TEL: 01456 450343 FAX: 01456 450813 E-MAIL: polmailyhousehotel@btinternet.com

OWNERS: John and Sonia Whittington-Davies

  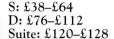

S: £38–£64
D: £76–£112
Suite: £120–£128

Set in extensive grounds, Polmaily House is a family run Edwardian country house offering good accommodation and a plethora of activities for all the family. Whilst welcoming honeymooners and couples to an equally high standard, the property will particularly appeal to families with children as the facilities are excellent. With carefully managed days, spacious rooms and services including children's meals, baby listening and a large selection of videos, younger guests need not intrude on their parents' time.

The 11 en suite rooms comprise bedrooms, family and garden suites and are individually appointed. One ground floor bedroom is suitable for the elderly and disabled guests. Fresh local produce is carefully prepared by the hosts and served in the restaurant. Those wishing to explore the Highlands must visit Polmaily as it is situated at the gateway to Glen Affric. Outdoor sports include golf, trout fishing and tennis. Children will be well entertained with picnics by waterfalls, pony rides or lessons in the owners' riding school, home to 'The Polmaily Arabian Stud' and the aerial slide and tree house. For an exclusive view of the fine surrounds, the hotel's skippered sailing yacht on Loch Ness cannot be surpassed.

Places of interest nearby: Urquhart and Cawdor Castles, Culloden, Fort George and Glen Affric. **Directions: By car from Inverness, follow A82 signed to Fort William, after 16 miles at Drumnadrochit turn onto A831 signed to Glen Affric and hotel is on this road after 2 miles.**

THE DRYFESDALE HOTEL

LOCKERBIE, DUMFRIESSHIRE DG11 2SF
TEL: 01576 202427 FAX: 01576 204187

MANAGER: Angela Dunbobbin
CHEF: Michael Dunbobbin

S: £55–£65
D: £84–£87

The Dryfesdale Hotel, a former manse, is situated in one of the most beautiful settings in the area of Annandale. Built in 1782, it was converted into a country house hotel in the early 1950s.

The Dunbobbin family acquired the hotel in 1995 and have striven to enhance the ambience and standards of old. The lounges and bar are comfortably relaxing whilst the individually decorated bedrooms are warm and cosy.

Recently awarded an AA Rosette for the quality of food and service, the popular restaurant serves traditional cuisine, made with the best of regional produce.

Places of interest nearby: Amongst the many attractions in the surrounding area are Samye Ling Tibetan centre and Temple at Eskdalemuir, Drumlanrigg Castle near Thornhill and the beautiful Galloway coastline passing Shambellie House museum at New Abbey, Gem Rock museum at Cree Town and Threave gardens near Castle Douglas. Dumfries is situated 20 minutes drive to the west of Lockerbie, the home of Robbie Burns monument and museum, historic buildings and shopping centre. A 20 minute drive to the south of Lockerbie takes you to the historic city of Carlisle. Cathedral and the Lanes shopping centre. The beautiful Cumbrian lakes and mountains are also within driving distance from the hotel as are the Scottish cities of Glasgow and Edinburgh.
Directions: The Dryfesdale Hotel is situated on junction 17 of the M74, approximately 27 miles north of Carlisle.

NEW MAYBOLE (Ayrshire)

CULZEAN CASTLE – THE EISENHOWER APARTMENT

MAYBOLE, AYRSHIRE KA19 8LE
TEL: 01655 884455 FAX: 01655 884503 E-MAIL: culzean@nts.org.uk

OWNERS: The National Trust for Scotland
MANAGER: Jonathan Cardale

S: £140–£265
D: £200–£375

Situated at the heart of one of Scotland's most magnificent Country Parks and dramatically perched on a cliff-top with breathtaking sea views, Culzean Castle is the ideal base for a golfing trip in an area that boasts some of Scotland's finest links courses. Originally designed in the late 1700's and recently restored to its former glory, the castle is considered to be one of the finest examples of Robert Adam's architectural genius.

The Castle also contains what is probably Scotland's most prestigious accommodation, the Eisenhower Apartment. Given to General Eisenhower when the Castle was handed over to the National Trust for Scotland in 1945, the top-floor apartment now houses self-contained accommodation in six double bedrooms. The Presidential retreat is also an ideal hideaway for a small business meeting where complete privacy is required. All the bedrooms in the Apartment are spacious and boast antique furniture, while the immaculately prepared food is served in an elegant intimate dining room. The round sitting room has superb sea views across to the Isle of Arran and Mull of Kintyre.

Places of interest nearby: With its walled gardens, woodland, deer park and exotic pagoda, the 560-acre Country Park gives visitors an unrivalled introduction to the rugged beauty of the West Coast of Scotland. **Directions: From Glasgow, take the A77 towards Ayr. Culzean Castle is 12 miles south of Ayr on the A719.**

WELL VIEW HOTEL

BALLPLAY ROAD, MOFFAT, DUMFRIESSHIRE DG10 9JU
TEL: 01683 220184 FAX: 01683 220088

OWNERS: John and Janet Schuckardt

6 rms 6 ens

S: £50–£63
D: £68–£100

This delightful Victorian house on the edge of Moffat has been in excellent hands for the last ten years – the host being elected to the Academy of Wine Service and the hostess a member of the Craft Guild of Chefs, giving master classes on special occasions.

Guests enjoy an apéritif and canapé in the elegant lounge while studying the menu, or, after dinner, relax with home-made sweets accompanying the coffee – and maybe, an excellent malt whisky. Dinner in the charming, non-smoking, dining room, is six courses – including a sorbet – cooked with great flair and beautifully presented. Vegetarian dishes are available by prior request. The Cellar holds many fine wines from all parts of the world.

The bedrooms are all en suite and extremely comfortable, reflecting the high standards of hospitality throughout the hotel.

Places of interest nearby: Moffat is surrounded by mountains: Glasgow is reached over Beattock Summit, Edinburgh over the Devil's Beef Tub. St Mary's Loch and the Border Abbeys are also within driving distance.

Directions: Moffat is three miles from the M74/A74 trunk road between Carlisle and Glasgow. Leave the centre of the town on A708 (Selkirk) and turn left at crossroads into Ballplay Road. The hotel is a short distance on the right.

BOATH HOUSE

AULDEARN, NAIRN, INVERNESS IV12 5TE
TEL: 01667 454896 FAX: 01667 455469 E-MAIL: wendy@boath–house.demon.co.uk

OWNERS: Don and Wendy Matheson
CHEF: Charles Lockley

S: £80–£110
D: £110–£175

This classic Georgian country mansion, set in 20 acres of grounds, has been described as the most beautiful Regency house in Scotland. It was built in 1825 for the Dunbar family, replacing 'the great stone house' mentioned in a court circular from Mary Queen of Scots' time.

Over the years the house passed through various hands and fell into disrepair. In the early 1990s, it was bought by the present owners and sympathetically restored to recreate its original splendour. The six en suite bedrooms, which have all been decorated according to individual themes, are spacious and well furnished. The reception rooms match their high standard of comfort.

The award-winning restaurant, which has 2 AA Rosettes offers excellent views over the lake and menus are chosen daily, dependent on fresh local produce available from the kitchen garden and local suppliers. Vegetarian and healthy options menus are also available.

A small but well-equipped gymnasium complements the beauty and hairdressing salon and a leisure area complete with sauna and heated whirlpool.
Places of interest nearby: Cawdor Castle, Elgin Cathedral, Culloden Battlefield and Brodie Castle.
Directions: Well signposted off the A96 Aberdeen to Inverness Road at Auldrean, 2 miles east of Nairn.

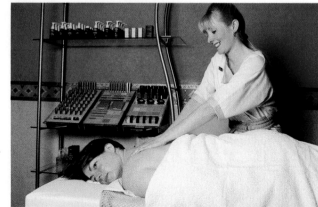

DUNGALLAN HOUSE HOTEL

GALLANACH ROAD, OBAN, ARGYLL PA34 4PD
TEL: 01631 563799 FAX: 01631 566711

OWNERS: George and Janice Stewart

  SMALL HOTEL

  S: £35–£45
D: £70–£90

Peacefully set in five acres of gardens and lawns and with sloping woodland front and rear this impressive old Victorian house offers the warmest of welcomes. Although just a 15 minutes walk away from the bustling main centre of Oban, Dungallan has a restful country atmosphere and enjoys magnificent panoramic views over Oban Bay to the Island of Mull, Lismore and the spectacular Hills of Morvern.

Built in 1870 by the Campbell family, Dungallan House has undergone a major programme of upgrading to provide full facilities for today's visitor and to enhance the elegance of the building. Most bedrooms have a wonderful outlook and are harmoniously decorated reflecting the high standards of hospitality throughout the hotel.

In the spacious dining room guests can savour superb traditional Scottish meals prepared with the best of local produce by Janice Stewart who, with owner and husband George run Dungallan House. A carefully chosen wine list complements the menu. Sporting activities locally include fishing, sailing and golf.

Places of interest nearby: Oban is Scotland's main ferry port for the Western Isles and the many day trips are a splendid way of discovering this beautiful area.
Directions: The Hotel is on the southern outskirts of Oban beyond the ferry terminal and then follow signs for Gallanach.

THE MANOR HOUSE HOTEL

GALLANACH ROAD, OBAN, ARGYLL PA34 4LS
TEL: 01631 562087 FAX: 01631 563053

OWNERS: The Leroy Family

11 rms	11 ens	SMALL HOTEL

S: £66–£110
D: £96–£160
(including dinner)

Late Georgian in style, The Manor House was built in 1780 as the principal residence of the Duke of Argyll's Oban estate. Today it is a hotel where great care has been taken to preserve the elegance of its bygone days. The Manor House occupies a prime position overlooking Oban Bay, the islands and the mountains of Movern and Mull.

In the dining room guests can enjoy a fine blend of Scottish and French cooking, with the emphasis on local seafood and game in season. The table d'hôte menus take pride of place and are changed daily to offer a choice of starters, intermediate fish course or soup, home-made sorbet, choice of main courses, choice of puddings, and to round off, coffee and mints. The restaurant menu is partnered by a cellar of wines and selection of malt whiskies.

The bedrooms have twin or double beds, all with en suite bathrooms, TV and tea-making facilities. The Manor House Hotel is quietly located on the outskirts of Oban, yet within easy walking distance of the town. Special mini-breaks are available for stays of two nights or more. Closed Mondays and Tuesday from mid-November to February. Special Christmas and Hogmanay breaks available.

Places of interest nearby: Oban is Scotland's main ferry port for trips to the Western Isles and the many day tours are a splendid way of discovering this beautiful area.
Directions: The Manor House Hotel is situated on the western outskirts of Oban beyond the ferry boat pier.

KNOCKENDARROCH HOUSE

HIGHER OAKFIELD, PITLOCHRY, PERTHSHIRE PH16 5HT
TEL: 01796 473473 FAX: 01796 474068 E-MAIL: info@knockendarroch.co.uk

OWNERS: Tony and Jane Ross
CHEF: Andrew Steel

S: £65–£79
D: £90–£118
(including 5-course dinner)

This elegant, 19th century Victorian mansion with a grand three-story high peaked tower stands imposingly on a plateau within the picturesque town of Pitlochry offering visitors superb views over the beautiful Tummel Valley. It is surrounded by landscaped gardens and framed by ancient oak trees which give Knockendarroch its name - from the Gaelic, meaning Hill of Oaks.

Owned and run by the friendly Tony and Jane Ross, Knockendarroch House is a totally non-smoking property and has a reputation for its hospitality amid beautiful Highland scenery. Historic sights and castles abound and the battle-famed pass of Killiecrankie lies just a few miles to the north.

Each of the 12 en suite bedrooms is spacious and equipped with every comfort from television to electric blanket. First floor premier rooms have magnificent southerly or westerly views, two of the second-floor standard rooms have balconies. In the elegant restaurant, the finest local produce is the base of the expertly prepared menus and guests can enjoy a complimentary glass of sherry prior to dining. During the Pitlochry Theatre season the restaurant opens from 6pm and the hotel runs a courtesy bus to and from the evening performances.

Places of interest nearby: Pitlochry Festival Theatre, Blair Castle, Scone Palace, Pitlochry Dam. **Directions: A9 out of Perth, take A924 to Pitlochry. Turn right from the Perth Road into East Moulin Road and the hotel is on your left.**

THE LAKE HOTEL

PORT OF MENTEITH, PERTHSHIRE FK8 3RA
TEL: 01877 385258 FAX: 01877 385671

OWNERS: Graeme and Rosaleen McConnachie

S: £62–£98
D: £92–£174
(including dinner)

The Lake Hotel is set in a splendid sheltered position on the banks of the Lake of Menteith in the Trossachs. Its lawn runs down to the edge of the lake, which in winter months often freezes over. When this happens, it is not unusual for locals to bring out their skates for a skim over the ice.

Guests are assured of all the amenities of an STB 4 Crown Highly Commended hotel. A programme of refurbishment has been completed, so the interiors have fresh decoration and furnishings. All bedrooms have en suite facilities and the details that will make your stay comfortable. There is an elegant lounge and a large conservatory from which the vista of lake and mountains is stunning.

The à la carte and table d'hôte menus present a varied choice of imaginatively prepared dishes. The table d'hôte menus are particularly good value: start with chicken & herb terrine with sun dried tomato dressing, followed by sorbet, then after a main course of grilled halibut with spinach, saffron potatoes and an orange & aniseed sauce, enjoy a Drambuie parfait with raspberry coulis before your coffee and home-made petits fours. Special rates are available for mini-breaks of two nights or more.

Places of interest nearby: Inchmahome Priory – haven for both Mary, Queen of Scots and Robert the Bruce – Loch Lomond and Stirling Castle. **Directions: Situated on the A81 road, south of Callander and east of Aberfoyle, on the northern banks of the Lake of Menteith.**

CORROUR HOUSE

INVERDRUIE, AVIEMORE, INVERNESS-SHIRE PH22 1QH
TEL: 01479 810220 FAX: 01479 811500

OWNERS: David and Sheana Catto

S: £60
D: £120
(including dinner)

Corrour House commands a beautiful location within Rothiemurchus Estate and enjoys a spectacular vista of the Cairngorm Mountains. Standing in 4 acres of garden and woodland, where roe deer and red squirrels are regular visitors and birdlife abounds, this former dower house was built in the Victorian era by the Grants of Rothiemurchus and is now a charming country house hotel. Hosts David and Sheana Catto offer their guests – some who return year after year – personal service and true Highland hospitality. Tastefully decorated and furnished throughout, Corrour House combines the elegance of a past age with the modern comforts expected by today's visitor. The 7 bedrooms all have private facilities.

The drawing room has a cosy log fire, ample reading material and a selection of games. There is a Cocktail Lounge with a small bar where guests may enjoy a drink while they peruse the menu and extensive wine list before dinner. In the Dining Room, the daily changing table d'hôte menu uses the best fresh produce from Scotland's larder-locally reared beef, lamb, game and fish with herbs and vegetables from the hotel garden. Away from the madding crowd, Corrour House is the perfect base for a Scottish holiday.

Places of interest nearby: Cairngorm Mountain chairlift; Strathspey Steam Railway; Loch Garten – home to Ospreys; Blair and Ballindalloch Castles; the Whisky Trail. **Directions: Before entering Aviemore from Kingussie, turn right to Coylumbridge (B970), hotel is then 800 yards on right.**

THE ARGYLE HOUSE HOTEL

127 NORTH STREET, ST ANDREWS, FIFE KY16 9AG
TEL: 01334 473387 FAX: 01334 474664 E-MAIL: gorsebriglimited@btinternet.com

OWNERS: Douglas A.M.B. Dick
MANAGER: Rachel Johnson
CHEF: Graham Mitchell

| 10 rms | 10 ens | SMALL HOTEL |

S: £30–£45
D: £50–£90

The Argyle House Hotel, an extremely comfortable modern hotel, belies its position at the centre of a charming historic town. Each of the rooms has been individually designed to the height of luxury, with en suite bathrooms and all other modern conveniences.

After a day spent exploring quaint fishing villages and golden sandy beaches, there is no better place to relax with a dram of malt than the Lizard Lounge, with its diverse mixture of students, guests and locals. The Lounge also offers delectable snacks and bar food. The Argyle also caters for serious gourmets. Exceptional food, made with the freshest of local produce, is swerved in the newly refurbished "Bridges" restaurant and oyster bar. Chef Graham Mitchell specialises in locally-caught game and lobster dishes, which are washed down with some of the most robust wines in the islands.

Places of interest nearby: The Argyle House is at the very centre of medieval St. Andrews. The wind-swept Old Course, the oldest links in the world, is the town's focal point. An historic centre of learning, St. Andrews boasts an imposing cathedral and castle. The beach scene from Chariots of Fire was filmed on the nearby rugged strand. **Directions: approaching St. Andrews on the A91 keep straight at the roundabout onto North Street. The hotel is 300 yards on the left.**

ST BOSWELLS (By Melrose)

CLINT LODGE

ST BOSWELLS, MELROSE, ROXBURGHSHIRE TD6 0DZ
TEL: 01835 822027 FAX: 01835 822656 E-MAIL: Clintlodge@aol.com

PROPRIETORS/CONTACT: Bill and Heather Walker

        S: £25–£40
D: £50–£80

Clint Lodge stands square and solid in the heart of the Borders with magnificent views over the River Tweed to the distant Cheviot hills. Surrounded by a spacious lawned garden it was built in 1869 by Lord Polworth as the family's shooting home and is now owned by the Duke of Sutherland. The Lodge retains many of its original features – large open fireplaces, wooden and tiled floors – and has been carefully refurbished and modernised to provide year round comfort.

The bedrooms are furnished and decorated to a high standard. Three are en suite, two with original deep-fill baths, and one of the double rooms has a private bathroom. There is also an adjacent, self-catering cottage with three bedrooms, lounge, kitchen and bathroom.

Guests can relax during colder months before an open log fire in the Lodge's spacious drawing room and on warmer days enjoy the rural views from an adjoining sun lounge which opens onto a small patio. Heather Walker provides excellent, traditional meals and caters for all diets.

Sporting and leisure pursuits are close by, including salmon and trout fishing, grouse, pheasant and clay pigeon shooting. There are 12 golf courses within a half hour's drive.

Places of interest nearby: Scott's View, Dryburgh Abbey and Melrose Abbey. **Directions: Take B6404 from St Boswells and after two miles turn left onto B6356, signposted Scott's View and Earlston. Clint Lodge is on the right, one mile beyond Clint Mains village.**

 ST FILLANS (Perthshire)

THE FOUR SEASONS HOTEL

ST FILLANS, PERTHSHIRE PH6 2NF
TEL: 01764 685333 FAX: 01764 685444 E-MAIL: info@thefourseasonshotel.co.uk

OWNERS: Andrew Low
CHEF: Jonathan Brown

12 rms	12 ens

 S: £36–£54
D: £72–£88

This rambling, white hotel is delightfully situated on the eastern edge of Loch Earn, which has been described as the jewel in the crown of Perthshire lochs. All around is unspoiled Southern Highland landscape, steep hillsides and towering, rugged mountains whose lower slopes are covered with deep green woodland. It is an area of scenic splendour, about 30 miles west of the historic city of Perth.

The Four Seasons Hotel, under new owner Andrew Low, is excellent in every way and superb value for money. The furnishings and décor throughout the hotel are in simple yet tasteful and open fires and several lounges add to the interior charm. Talented chef Jonathan Brown creates sumptuous, imaginative and traditional cuisine featuring the best local produce.

The bedrooms are beautifully proportioned and cosy. All are on the first floor and each has a private bathroom and home from home comforts. Six fully equipped chalets on the hillside behind the hotel are suitable for families with one or two children or for those visitors seeking extra privacy.

Places of interest nearby: When not enjoying the magnificent views and changing colours from the hotel's south facing terrace, guests can enjoy walking at Ben Vorlich or visiting the picturesque Southern Highlands villages. **Directions: Take the A85 west from Perth.**

QUEEN'S VIEW HOTEL

STRATHTUMMEL, BY PITLOCHRY, PERTHSHIRE PH16 5NR
TEL: 01796 473291 FAX: 01796 473515 E-MAIL: enquiries@queens–view–hotel.co.uk

OWNERS: Richard and Norma Tomlinson
CHEF: Norma Tomlinson

11 rms 11 ens SMALL HOTEL

MasterCard VISA

S: £60–£95
D: £100–£160
(including dinner)

Queen's View Hotel stands high and majestically overlooking the shimmering waters of Loch Tummel, close to the little town of Pitlochry and just a few miles from the ancient city of Perth. All around are the splendours of the Tummel Valley and the good things that Scotland has to offer. Despite its stunning location, the hotel has been a well-kept secret for many years. Owners Richard and Norma Tomlinson have renovated it sympathetically to provide relaxing comfort and modern facilities.

The bedrooms, including a family suite, are furnished to a high standard and have magnificent views over the loch 150 feet below.

There is an attractive and well-furnished lounge, a comfortable bar where you can enjoy a fine malt whisky and out of the ordinary lunchtime food and there is also a very pleasant restaurant with a growing reputation for its innovative and tasty cuisine. Many theatre-goers like to take two courses before the performance returning for a drink or coffee and pudding afterwards. The hotel is closed from mid January to early March.

Places of interest nearby: Pitlochy has its own theatre. Fishing within the grounds. Golf, riding and curling can be arranged. Blair Castle, Bruar Falls, Scone Palace and Balmoral are close. **Directions: A9 to Pitlochry then B8079 north. Turn left onto B8019 for Tummel Bridge and the hotel is three miles miles further on.**

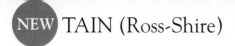 TAIN (Ross-Shire)

GLENMORANGIE HOUSE AT CADBOL

CADBOL, FEARN, BY TAIN, ROSS-SHIRE IV20 1XP
TEL: 01862 871671 FAX: 01862 871625 E-MAIL: relax@glenmorangieplc.co.uk

OWNERS: Glenmorangie Plc
MANAGER: Hugh Boyd

S: £100–£140
D: £200–£280
(including dinner)

The only five-star property in the Scottish highlands, Glenmorangie House is situated on the flat expanse of the Easter Ross Seaboard plain. The clarity of the light and seeming ubiquity of the sea give the impression of being at the heart of the Scottish wilderness. The ambience of the Glenmorangie Highland Home is in marked contrast to the isolation of its seat. With oil paintings, sepia prints and other memorabilia adorning the walls, coupled with the friendly, indulgent staff a feeling of relaxed hospitality and comfort is imparted.

Glenmorangie styles itself as a 'house party' and evening meals are far from abstemious occasions. After pre-dinner drinks, guests are lavished with superb cuisine accompanied by fine wines. Post-prandial malts are served in the homely surroundings of the Buffalo room. The lavishly decorated bedrooms are all well appointed, with views of the walled gardens and the Moray Firth.

Places of interest nearby: The world famous Glenmorangie Distillery, where visitors can learn about the distilling process, is minutes away. The region is known for its golf courses, with the demanding Royal Dornoch Golf Club a short drive away. The area is also renowned for its salmon and trout fishing, as well as hill and heath walking.
Directions: From Inverness, turn right at roundabout signed B1975 Nigg. Turn left at Baltinore signpost, driving through Hilton. The house is signed on the right.

252   www.johansens.com

TALISKER.
A PLACE WHERE THE THUNDER ROLLS OVER YOUR TONGUE.

Of all the islands that defend Scotland's west coast from the Atlantic, Skye is the most dramatic. How fitting then that this is the home of the fiery Talisker. Standing on Skye's western shore, the distillery lies in the shadow of The Cuillins. Jagged mountains that rise out of the sea to skewer the clouds for a thunderous retort. in the shadow of these peaks, next to a fearsome sea, Talisker takes its first breath and draws it all in. Skye's explosive fervour captured forever in its only single malt. That Talisker is not a whisky for the faint-hearted is beyond dispute. Indeed even when one seasoned whisky taster once went as far as calling it "The lava of The Cuillins", no one disagreed.

TALISKER IS THE ISLAND MALT FROM THE CLASSIC MALTS RANGE. TO FIND OUT MORE ABOUT ALL SIX DEFINITIVE EXPRESSIONS OF SCOTLAND'S MAIN MALT-PRODUCING REGIONS, WRITE TO: THE FRIENDS OF THE CLASSIC MALTS, P.O. BOX 87, GLASGOW, SCOTLAND G14 0JF.

As recommended

Johansens Recommended Country Houses & Small Hotels

Ireland

Celtic legends, medieval architecture, racecourses and golf courses, great art collections and a rich history of literature are all to be found amongst the green landscapes of Ireland.

Whiterocks, Co. Antrim, N. Ireland

What's happening in Ireland?

• Wexford Festival Opera – one of Ireland's most internationally renowned festivals and has been held in this small coastal town for almost half a century. Held in Wexford from 14th – 31st October 1999.

• Guinness Cork Jazz '99 Festival – one of Ireland's best known international festivals and has attracted a galaxy of jazz greats over the years. Held in Cork from 22nd – 25th October 1999.

• The Belfast Festival at Queens University – this festival takes place in numerous different venues from the Grand Opera House to the new Waterfront Hall. Held from 29th October – 14th November, this festival includes over four hundred shows of international theatre, dance, classical and pop music, film and arts, jazz and folk.

For more information about Ireland and Northern Ireland please contact:

The Irish Tourist Board
St Andrews Church
Suffolk Street
Dublin 2
Tel: 00 353 1 602 4000

Northern Ireland Tourist Board
St Anne's Court
59 North Street
Belfast BT1 1NB
Tel: 01232 246609

CARAGH LODGE

CARAGH LAKE, CO KERRY
TEL: 00 353 66 9769115 FAX: 00 353 66 9769316 E-MAIL: caraghl@IOL.IE

OWNER: Mary Gaunt

S: IR£75
D: IR£115–IR£145
Suite: IR£200

The breathtaking slopes of Ireland's highest mountain range, McGillycuddy Reeks, rise majestically above this elegant Victorian hotel whose award-winning gardens run gently down to the shore of Caragh Lake. Less than a mile from the spectacular Ring of Kerry, Caragh Lodge offers an unsurpassed blend of luxury, heritage, tranquillity, hospitality and service. It is excellent in every way and an ideal base for the sightseeing, golfing and fishing enthusiast.

All the en suite bedrooms are decorated with period furnishings and antiques, with the converted garden rooms looking over magnificent displays of magnolias, camellias, rhododendrons, azaleas and rare subtropical shrubs. The exquisite dining room overlooks the lake and Mary Gaunt personally prepares menus of the finest Irish food, including freshly caught salmon, succulent Kerry lamb, garden grown vegetables and home-baked breads. Open 21 Apr–15 Oct.

Caragh Lodge's gardens conceal an all-weather tennis court and sauna chalet. Salmon and trout swim in the lake and two boats are available for angling guests. Ghillies or permits for fishing in the two local rivers can be arranged. There are also local golf courses, where tee off times can be organised.

Places of interest nearby: The Ring of Kerry, Dingle Peninsula, Gap of Dunloe, Killarney and Tralee. **Directions: From Killorglin travel on N70 towards Glenbeigh and take second road signposted for Caragh Lake. At lake turn left, Caragh Lodge is on your right.**

CASHEL PALACE HOTEL

MAIN STREET, CASHEL, CO TIPPERARY
TEL: 00 353 62 62707 FAX: 00 353 62 61521 E-MAIL: reception@cashel–palace.ie

OWNERS: Silkestan Ltd
PROPRIETORS: Patrick and Susan Murphy

  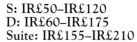

S: IR£50–IR£120
D: IR£60–IR£175
Suite: IR£155–IR£210

This magnificent and luxurious 18th century hotel stands in the shadow of the famous Rock of Cashel. It is at the heart of a heritage town surrounded by a wealth of historical sites. Built in 1730 as a palace for Archbishop Theophilus Bolton it is a jewel of late Queen Anne and early Georgian style. Described as "A place of notable hospitality" in Loveday's Tour of 1732, the Cashel Palace Hotel's beauty is complemented by 22 acres of walled gardens which include a private walk to the Rock of Cashel and two mulberry trees planted in 1702 to commemorate the coronation of Queen Anne.

The hotel has been lovingly restored with great attention given to preserving its character and integrity.

Spacious bedrooms echo the style and elegance of the 18th century and are individually furnished to the highest standards. The tradition of fine food continues in the relaxed ambience of the Bishops Buttery which specialises in lighter modern Irish cuisine with classical influences.

Local leisure activities include pony trekking, horse riding, golf, tennis, trout and salmon fishing.

Places of interest nearby: Cashel is an ideal base from which to tour Munster and the South East and is within easy reach of Cahir Castle, the Devil's Bit Mountain and Holy Cross. **Directions: Cashel is on the junction of the N8 and N74.**

ROSS LAKE HOUSE HOTEL

ROSSCAHILL, OUGHTERARD, CO GALWAY, IRELAND
TEL: 00 353 91 550109 FAX: 00 353 91 550184

OWNERS: Henry and Elaine Reid

S: £74–£85
D: £113–£135
Suite: £160

Homeliness and relaxation are the hallmarks of this elegant 19th century hotel situated in the beautiful County Galway countryside unspoilt by the advance of time. It is an attractive old house whose former glory has been carefully and tastefully revived by owners Henry and Elaine Reid.

Surrounded by rambling woods and magnificent lawned gardens studded with colourful flowers and evergreen shrubs, Ross Lake was formerly an estate house of landed gentry who prized it for its serenity. The owners pride themselves that the hotel is a haven of peace where recreation comes naturally and service and hospitality are of the highest order.

Public rooms are spacious and combine the elegance of an earlier age with modern comforts. The drawing room, which is a favourite of all those who enjoy afternoon tea, is particularly attractive. Comfort and good taste are also reflected in the hotel's 12 bedrooms which are all en suite and offer lovely views over the gardens.

Quality Irish food is excellently prepared and presented in the intimate restaurant with dishes enhanced by fresh produce from the Connemara hills, streams and lakes.

For the active there is tennis in the grounds, golfing at the Oughterard 18-hole parkland course, game and course fishing. **Places of interest nearby:** Aughnanure Castle, Kylemore Abbey, Connemara National Park, the Aran Islands, Cliffs of Moher and the Burren. **Directions: Ross Lake House is off N59, 14 miles north west of Galway.**

ST CLERANS

CRAUGHWELL, CO GALWAY, IRELAND
TEL: 00 353 91 846555 FAX: 00 353 91 846600 E-MAIL: stcleran@iol.ie

OWNERS: Merv Griffin Hotels
CHEF: Hisashi Kumagai

S: IR£170–IR£260
D: IR£170–IR£260
Suite: IR£170–IR£260

Situated in the heart of the rural splendour of County Galway, the magnificent Georgian manor house, St Clerans, is one of the most attractive houses in Ireland. At least that is what the former owner, Hollywood legend John Huston thought. St Clerans was built by the Burke family in 1784 and remained in their possession for nearly two centuries. In the hands of current owner Merv Griffin, the house has been painstakingly restored to former glory and offers visitors the chance to enjoy the magic that so beguiled royalty and Hollywood celebrities in days gone by.

With its elegant period furniture, works of art collected from all over the world, blazing fires and peaceful gardens, St Clerans offers country house living at its very best. Twelve spacious guest rooms, beautifully appointed with every modern luxury, look out over the glorious Galway countryside. One, a circular bedroom, was the former playroom of Angelica Huston.

The magnificent dining room serves food prepared from the fines and freshest local ingredients. Outdoor pursuits abound and guests may enjoy horse-riding, fishing, horse-racing and hunting with the Galway Blazers.

Places of interest nearby: Golf enthusiasts may enjoy the courses at Galway Bay, Lahinch and Ballybunion. **Directions:** On Galway-Dublin road N6, take 2nd left after passing through Craughwell. Follow road for 2 miles until you come to black gates of house on your right (30 mins from Galway City).

ABERDEEN LODGE

53-55 PARK AVENUE, OFF AILESBURY ROAD, DUBLIN 4
TEL: 00 353 1 2838155 FAX: 00 353 1 2837877 E-MAIL: aberdeen@iol.ie

OWNER: Pat Halpin

S: IR£70–IR£99
D: IR£90–IR£135
Suite: IR£110–IR£185

This symbol of classical Edwardian architecture has a prime site in a serene tree-lined avenue in what is often called Dublin's Embassy Belt. Set in its own large formal gardens, Aberdeen Lodge provides high quality accommodation, comfort and service accompanied by all the modern luxuries which visitors to a flourishing capital city would expect today.

Every room is an elegant reminder of Edwardian grace and Pat Halpin and his family's renowned hotel experience is evident in the detail of décor and operation. They pride themselves on being able to ensure that the needs of guests are met quickly and efficiently.

Each of the tastefully furnished bedrooms is en suite and designed in complete harmony with the house. The spacious suites feature a Jacuzzi and period style furniture.

The award-winning intimate Breakfast Room is complemented by a special menu served between 11am and 10pm, accompanied by a good selection of fine wines from around the world. The new sister property, Merrion Hall, enjoys many accolades and is located at nearby Ballsbridge.

Places of interest nearby: The hotel makes an ideal base from which to explore Dublin and enjoy shopping in the famous Grafton Street. As well as many first-class golf courses there is horse racing and two major marinas along the coast. Lansdowne Road rugby ground is a short walk. **Directions: Off Ailesbury Road, Aberdeen Lodge is 7 minutes from the city centre by D.A.R.T. bus.**

FITZWILLIAM PARK

NO 5, FITZWILLIAM SQUARE, DUBLIN 2, IRELAND
TEL: 00 353 1 662 8280 FAX: 00 353 662 8281 E-MAIL: info@fitzpark.ie

OWNER: Mary Madden

S: IR£85
D: IR£105
Suite: IR£125

Fitzwilliam Park is a luxurious and beautifully restored town house situated in one of Dublin's most elegant and best preserved Georgian squares just a short stroll from the heart of the city. Built in 1816 on land leased from the 5th Viscount Fitzwilliam it is one of the largest houses on the square and retains many of its original period features. It has a charm of casual country elegance, offering high quality, exquisitely furnished accommodation, comfort and service accompanied by all the modern luxuries which today's visitors to a capital city would expect. Each room, with its high ceiling, decorative friezes, tall windows, fine drapes, pastel décor, gold framed mirrors and pictures, is a stylish reminder of Georgian grace. All 20 bedrooms are en suite and designed in complete harmony with the house. A full Irish breakfast can be enjoyed in the first floor Grand Salon overlooking the park or served in the comfort of your bedroom. Full business facilities are available for small conferences, including a private boardroom and secretarial services. There is also secure car parking at the rear of the town house.

Places of interest nearby: Fitzwilliam Park is a five minutes' walk from St Stephen's Green and is an ideal base from which to explore Dublin and visit its busy shopping centres, theatres, museums and art galleries. As well as many first-class golf courses there is horse-racing and two marinas along the coast. **Directions: Fitzwilliam Park is situated in the city centre, a short walk from St Stephen's Green.**

HALPINS HOTEL AND VITTLE'S RESTAURANT

ERIN STREET, KILKEE, CO CLARE
TEL: 00 353 65 9056032 FAX: 00 353 65 9056317 E-MAIL: halpins@iol.ie

OWNER: Pat Halpin
MANAGER: Ann Keane
CHEF: Ethel O'Donnell

  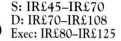

S: IR£45–IR£70
D: IR£70–IR£108
Exec: IR£80–IR£125

The welcome that awaits guests to Halpins Hotel is in the best traditions of Irish hospitality. Built in 1880, this charming hotel with a unique "shop-style" entrance is situated in a terrace at the heart of a popular resort facing a one mile long semi-circular sweep of sand. Surrounded by fine cliff scenery and reputed to be the safest bathing place in Ireland, Kilkee has attracted distinguished visitors from all over Europe for almost two centuries, among them literary figures such as Alfred Tennyson and Charlotte Brontë. The hotel has been Egon Ronay Commended and RAC Highly Acclaimed.

The Halpin family has owned and run the hotel for 15 years and are proud of its reputation for its friendly style and excellent standards. There are 12 prettily decorated en suite bedrooms, all of which are individually furnished.

The bar and lounge are famous for their old world atmosphere, complemented by quality food and fine wines of the world. The hotel restaurant Vittle's is one of the best in town. Chef Ethel O'Donnell produces wonderful modern Irish cuisine to suit all tastes. The new sister property, Merrion Hall, enjoys many accolades and is located at nearby Ballsbridge.
Places of interest nearby: Kilkee Golf Club. The famous cliffs of Moher and Ailwee Caves, Doonbeg castle, Scattery Island's 6th century monastic settlement, Loop Head and the lunar-type landscape of the Burren. **Directions: Kilkee is situated on the N67 road from Galway, just 50 minutes from Shannon airport.**

EARLS COURT HOUSE

WOODLAWN JUNCTION, MUCKROSS ROAD, KILLARNEY, CO KERRY
TEL: 00 353 64 34009 FAX: 00 353 64 34366 E-MAIL: earls@tinet.ie

OWNERS: Ray and Emer Moynihan

S: IR£45–IR£75
D: IR£70–IR£95

Earls Court House stands elevated and shadowed by tall, whispering trees just a five minutes walk from the bustling town centre of Killarney. It is in the heart of beautiful Co Kerry, surrounded by the 25,000 acres of Killarney National Park with its lakes, mountains and magnificent gardens where giant rhododendrons and tropical plants grow in abundance. Owners Ray and Emer Moynihan pride themselves that the hotel is a haven of tranquillity where relaxation comes naturally and service and hospitality is of the highest standards.

Earls Court is a purpose built, spacious hotel in the country house tradition. Fine antiques, prints and fabrics adorn the rooms throughout. Magnificent carved beds complement the charming, en suite bedrooms which are furnished with all modern amenities. Most of the bedrooms have private balconies with views over the open spaces of Muckross Park.

The hotel is an ideal base from which to tour Kerry, to explore Killarney National Park, or play south west Ireland's premier golf courses. Pony trekking, salmon and trout fishing can be arranged. Dinner is not available, but there are many good restaurants close by. The hotel is closed from November 5 to February 28.

Places of interest nearby: Killarney National Park.
Directions: Earls Court House is close to the centre of Killarney, just off the N71 Muckross Road.

KILMEADEN (Co Waterford)

THE OLD RECTORY – KILMEADEN HOUSE

KILMEADEN, CO WATERFORD, IRELAND
TEL: 00 353 51 384254 FAX: 00 353 51 384884

OWNERS: Jerry and Patricia Cronin

 S: IR£80
D: IR£100–IR£120

A truly warm and friendly Irish welcome awaits visitors as they arrive at the lovely Old Rectory situated in seclusion in County Waterford's beautiful landscape, capped from the west by the majestic Comeragh and Monavullagh ranges.

Constructed in the mid 19th century, this solidly built house stands serenely and imposingly in 12 acres of paddock, woodland and gardens just a short drive from Waterford City. The vision of the owners, Jerry Cronin, a local surgeon, and his wife Patricia, is to create simple elegance.

The charm of this country house is in its warm and comfortable atmosphere. Each of the tastefully decorated, non-smoking bedrooms is en suite and designed in complete harmony with the house. They are individually furnished with antiques, high ceilings, wooden sash windows and many personal touches to help guests feel at home. Views from their windows over the delightful garden which contains rare and well known plants are particularly delightful.

Light meals are available in the evening; guests must give 24 hours notice.

Places of interest nearby: Dunmore East - a picturesque fishing village, the Comeragh and Monavullagh mountains and Waterford with its busy harbour. There are five major golf courses within easy reach whilst riding and fishing can be enjoyed locally. **Directions: Approximately 10 miles west of Waterford just off N25 road to Cork.**

CASTLE GROVE COUNTRY HOUSE HOTEL

RAMELTON ROAD, LETTERKENNY, CO DONEGAL
TEL: 00 353 74 51118 FAX: 00 353 74 51384

OWNER: Mary T and Raymond Sweeny

S: IR£45–£50
D: IR£60–IR£100
Suite: IR£130–IR£200

This elegant Georgian House, reached by a mile long avenue through parkland, is in a sheltered position with a spectacular view of Lough Swilly.

True Irish hospitality is offered at this family-owned country residence with its gracious reception rooms and the charming drawing room looking out on the extensive grounds. There is a separate television room.

The dining room is very popular with the people who live in the neighbourhood, so reservations are necessary. The succulent dishes offered on the extensive menu reflecting the marvellous local produce – especially the fish – are served in great style accompanied by wines from a list of the highest calibre. Small corporate lunches are a speciality.

The bedrooms are spacious, all recently refurbished and equipped with modern necessities.

Donegal is famous for its white sand beaches and clean seas. The scenery is superb along the coast roads and in the mountains. Glenveagh National Park is fascinating, with its castle and famous gardens. One can meet Derek Hill at his fine Art Gallery at Churchill. Activities nearby include golf and fishing (lake, river and deep sea). Riding can be arranged on request. **Directions: Castle Grove is three miles from Letterkenny, off the R245.**

RIVERSTOWN (Co Sligo)

COOPERSHILL HOUSE

RIVERSTOWN, CO SLIGO
TEL: 00 353 71 65108 FAX: 00 353 71 65466 E-MAIL: ohara@coopershill.com

OWNERS: Brian and Lindy O'Hara

S: IR£62–IR£70
D: IR£104–IR£120

Winner of Johansens 1995 Country House Award, Coopershill is a fine example of a Georgian family mansion. Home to seven generations of the O'Hara family since 1774, it combines the spaciousness and elegance of an earlier age with modern comforts. Public rooms are furnished in period style with gilt-framed portraits, hunting trophies and antiques. Five of the bedrooms have four-poster or canopy beds and all have private bathrooms.

Dinner is served by candlelight in the elegant dining room, where good cooking is complemented by a wide choice of wines. Open log fires and personal attention from owners Brian and Lindy O'Hara help to create the warm atmosphere and hospitality that typify Coopershill. Out of season the house is open to parties of 10 to 16 people at a special rate. Tariffs are reduced if guests stay for three consecutive nights or more.

The River Arrow winds through the 500-acre estate and boating, trout and coarse fishing are available. Shooting is not permitted, leaving the abundant wildlife undisturbed. There is an excellent hard tennis court and also a croquet lawn. There are marvellous mountain and lakeside walks to enjoy in the area. Closed 1st November to mid-March. **Places of interest nearby:** Sligo and Yeats country. **Directions: Leave N4 Sligo–Dublin road at Drumfin follow signs for Coopershill. One mile on, turn left.**

MARKREE CASTLE

COLLOONEY, COUNTY SLIGO, IRELAND
TEL: 00 353 71 67800 FAX: 00 353 71 67840 E-MAIL: markree@iol.ie

OWNER: Charles Cooper

  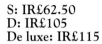

S: IR£62.50
D: IR£105
De luxe: IR£115

Regarded as one of Ireland's major architectural masterpieces, Markree Castle is Sligo's oldest inhabited castle. It has been the home of the Cooper family since 1640, but over the years the house has undergone a number of transformations. Today, the castle retains its family atmosphere and the character of the old building, while providing every modern comfort.

The interior boasts a spectacular oak staircase. This is overlooked by a stained glass window, purportedly tracing the Cooper family tree back to the time of King John of England. There are a variety of notable reception rooms, in addition to the interconnecting dining rooms which feature Louis-Philippe style plasterwork created by Italian craftsmen in 1845. An imaginative menu is provided

The bedrooms vary in character and style, but all offer views over the gardens or surrounding countryside.

Markree is in the heart of "Yeats Country", with magnificent scenery all around. The Rosses Point golf course and the Strandhill course are within a few miles. Trout and salmon fishing can be arranged nearby.

Places of interest nearby: Carrowmore, which has Europe's largest and oldest collection of megalithic remains; Lissadell House; Yeats's grave at Drumcliffe; and the town of Donegal. **Directions: Nine miles from Sligo airport, 125 from Dublin via N4. Collooney is just south of Sligo town.**

THE OLD RECTORY

WICKLOW TOWN, CO WICKLOW, IRELAND
TEL: 00 353 404 67048 FAX: 00 353 404 69181 E-MAIL: mail@oldrectory.ie

OWNERS: Paul and Linda Saunders

S: IR£81
D: IR£108

The Old Rectory is situated in secluded gardens on the edge of the harbour town of Wicklow in County Wicklow, "the Garden of Ireland". A peaceful Victorian house, personally run by Paul and Linda Saunders, it combines charming country house accommodation with an elegant gourmet restaurant. The house is freshly decorated throughout and furnished with style. A small Fitness Suite includes aerobic equipment and a relaxing sauna. Individually designed bedrooms offer en suite bathrooms and lots of little extras to make you feel welcome. This special ambience has made it a winner of the coveted AA "Inspector's Selected" award for Ireland. The restaurant is exceptional and featured on television's "*Gourmet Ireland*" and "*Summer Holiday*" series. Set gourmet and à la carte menus use fresh seafood, local and organic produce enhanced with herbs and edible flowers. Vegetarians welcome. In May/June 10-course "floral dinners" are a highlight of the Wicklow Gardens Festival. The Old Rectory also offers a choice of breakfasts which have won the National Breakfast award for Ireland.

Places of interest nearby: Glendalough, Wicklow Mountains, Wicklow Historic Jail, Powerscourt Gardens, Mount Usher Gardens, Russborough House, "Ballykissangel", 20 golf courses including Druids Glen. **Directions: 30m south of Dublin on N11, then 1m south of Rathnew on R750. Entrance has stone walls.**

Johansens Recommended Country Houses & Small Hotels
Channel Islands

With a wealth of wonderful scenery, magnificent coastlines, historic buildings, natural and man-made attractions plus mouthwatering local produce, the Channel Islands provide a memorable destination that is distinctly different.

St. Aubins Harbour, Jersey

What's happening in Guernsey?

• Millennium Eve Carnival, 31st December 1999 – to start the evening there will be a true Guernsey 'budloe' style boat burning in St Peter Port Harbour, then a torchlit procession, a magical parade of light and music through the streets of St Peter Port. There will also be an Octopussy Big Top with an early evening cabaret, live bands, DJs, sideshows and various artists. The Big Top will be situated on North Beach.

• Gala Millennium Concert – a fantastic musical event featuring the Guernsey Symphony Orchestra, the Guernsey Choral Society, the Guernsey Sinfonia Chorus and the Guernsey Youth Choir all join together for a performance of Beethoven's Symphony No. 9. To be held on 1st July 2000 at Beau Sejour.

For further information, please contact:-

Guernsey Tourist Board
PO Box 23
St Peter Port
Guernsey GY1 3AN
Tel: 01481 723557

What's happening in Jersey?

• Jersey Jazz Festival – taking place at various venues around the Island. Held between 6th and 9th April 2000.

• The Jersey International Food Festival – this event gives visitors the chance to taste the finest local produce and experience the skills of top Jersey Chefs. Held between 13th and 21st May 2000.

• Jersey Battle of Flowers – this parade is held on 10th August 2000 and features floats covered in flowers, musicians, dancers and carnival queens.

For further information, please contact:-

Jersey Tourism
Liberation Square
St Helier
Jersey JE1 1BB
Tel: 01534 500700

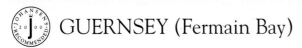

LA FAVORITA HOTEL

FERMAIN BAY, GUERNSEY, CHANNEL ISLANDS GY4 6SD
TEL: 01481 35666 FAX: 01481 35413 E-MAIL: info@favorita.com

OWNERS: Simon and Helen Wood

S: from £41
D: from £76

Once a fine private country house, La Favorita retains all the charm and character of those former days. The hotel is comfortable and fully licensed. Set in its own grounds, a few minutes walk from Guernsey's famous Fermain Bay, it enjoys spectacular views over the sea towards Jersey.

The bedrooms, all non smoking, are comfortable and provide every modern amenity, including colour television, radio and refreshment tray. Guernsey's mild climate means that it has much to offer out of season and the hotel also has a full range of facilities to satisfy the extra needs of spring, autumn and winter guests, including the indoor pool.

La Favorita has an excellent reputation for traditional English cooking and island seafood specialities. The restaurant is strictly no smoking. A coffee shop serves a wide range of lunch dishes and bar suppers for those who enjoy a more informal meal.

St Peter Port is within easy walking distance, whether taking the woodland walk which follows the coastline or the more direct route past Victor Hugo's house.

Places of interest nearby: The coast of Guernsey and all the island's attractions. Boat trips to Jersey, Alderney, Herm and Sark can easily be arranged. **Directions: Fermain Bay is 10 minutes from the airport and five minutes from St Peter Port on the east coast of Guernsey.**

BELLA LUCE HOTEL & RESTAURANT

LA FOSSE, ST MARTIN, GUERNSEY, CHANNEL ISLANDS GY4 6EB
TEL: 01481 38764 FAX: 01481 39561 E-MAIL: info@bellalucehotel.guernsey.net

OWNER: Richard Cann
MANAGER: John Cockcroft

S: From £27
D: From £52

The Bella Luce is one of Guernsey's original Norman manor houses. Set in splendid grounds on the most select side of the island, this perfectly preserved house includes extensions built in the 14th century. Happily the utmost care has been taken to maintain its period character during upgrading, so today's hotel offers excellent accommodation with every modern amenity.

Drinks are served throughout the day in the hotel's lounge bar, which dates back to the 11th century and is the oldest part of the building. Here, under the fine oak beamed ceiling, guests can enjoy a lunch and savour the cheerful and serene old world.

A varied table d'hôte menu, offering a wide range of English and Continental dishes, is provided in the restaurant which enjoys an excellent reputation throughout the island. A comprehensive à la carte menu featuring fresh seafood specialities is also available.

In a sun-trapped corner of the gardens there is a swimming pool surrounded by sun-beds and providing a perfect location for relaxation. Refreshments are served throughout the day and there is a sauna/solarium room nearby.

Places of interest nearby: Within easy reach of the three most beautiful south coast bays of Moulin Huet, Petit Port and Saints. Marine trips operate daily in season to Herm, Sark, Jersey and the nearby coast of France. **Directions: 5 minutes from the airport and St Peter Port.**

THE WHITE HOUSE

HERM ISLAND, GUERNSEY, CHANNEL ISLANDS GY1 3HR
TEL: 01481 722159 FAX: 01481 710066 E-MAIL: hotel@herm–island.com

OWNERS: Adrian and Pennie Heyworth
MANAGER: Sue Hester
CHEF: Chris Walder

**Room rate: from
£57 per person
(including dinner)**

As wards of Herm Island, Adrian and Pennie Heyworth assume responsibility for the well-being of all visitors to their island home which is for all to enjoy at leisure. For an island just 1½ miles long its diversity is remarkable and during a two-hour stroll that takes in its cliff walks, white sandy coves and abundant wildlife no two moments are the same.

The magic starts to work from the moment of arrival at the pretty harbour, for in the absence of cars on Herm a tractor laden with guests' luggage chugs up from the jetty to The White House. Here, relaxation is the key, and guests can enjoy afternoon tea or a drink in its succession of homely lounges, in the bar or on the poolside patio.

In keeping with a cherished tradition there are no televisions, no clocks nor telephones in the hotel's 38 bedrooms, the best of which have balconies and sea views. Appointments are nonetheless faultless and all include spacious up-to-date private bathrooms. Families are made particularly welcome and high tea is a popular event with younger guests.

Seafood plays a prominent part on the menus: the hotel has its own oyster farm. Guernsey lobster, scallops and crab are landed regularly. Self-catering holiday cottages also available.
Places of interest nearby: There is excellent fishing and snorkelling; yachts and cruisers can be chartered; and there are regular trips to Sark, Guernsey, Jersey and France.
Directions: Herm is reached by boat from Guernsey.

HOTEL LA TOUR

RUE DE CROQUET, ST AUBIN, JERSEY JE3 8BR
TEL: 01534 743770 FAX: 01534 747143

OWNERS: Samantha and Victor Gomes
CHEF: Victor Gomes

S: £23–£40.50
D: £23–£40.50
(price per person)

Samantha and Victor Gomes are continually seeking to improve their quiet little High Street hotel with special trimmings and extra personal touches and have now introduced a lovely, compact landscaped garden for guests to relax in on sunny days and balmy evenings. La Tour stands alongside elegant houses built for merchants who traded when St Aubin was Jersey's main port. The hotel has character, style and commanding views over the town's historic harbour and fort.

There is a variety of bedroom styles. Each room is extremely comfortable and has everything a visitor would expect. Some en suite bathrooms feature spa baths. The Tower Suite has a terrace from which guests can sit and enjoy magnificent views of St Aubin's Bay. Chef-patron Victor prides himself on the award-winning meals he provides for discerning diners in the intimate Rook's restaurant. The use of fresh Jersey produce complements a good selection of fine wines.

Activities available nearby are swimming, sea fishing, sailing, water sports, walking and golf at two 18-hole courses. **Places of interest nearby:** St Helier, three miles away, the central fish and vegetable markets, Jersey Museum and all the island's attractions. **Directions: Heading towards St Aubin from the Beaumont roundabout, take the second right turn signed La Haule. Then take the left fork into Rue de Croquet. The hotel is on the right.**

 SARK (Guernsey)

LA SABLONNERIE

LITTLE SARK, SARK, CHANNEL ISLANDS GY9 0SD
TEL: 01481 832061 FAX: 01481 832408

OWNERS: Elizabeth Perée

  SMALL HOTEL

S: £77.50–£84.50
D: £145–£169
(including dinner)

Owner and manager Elizabeth Perrée considers La Sablonnerie an oasis of good living and courtesy rather than a luxury hotel. It is truly that – and more! It is an hotel of rare quality situated in a time warp of simplicity on a tiny, idyllic island where no motor cars are allowed and life ambles along at a peaceful, unhurried pace.

A vintage horse drawn carriage collects guests from Little Sark's harbour to convey them in style to the former 16th century farmhouse and cottages which comprise La Sablonnerie. Tranquil intimacy, cosiness, friendliness and sophistication characterise this hotel with its low ceilings and oak beams.

Opened in 1948 and retaining many of the characteristics of the old farmhouse, La Sablonnerie has been extended and discreetly modernised to provide 22 bedrooms which are charmingly individual in style and offer every amenity. The granite-walled bar, with its open fire, is a comfortable extra lounge where pre-dinner drinks can be enjoyed before sampling the delights of the candlelit restaurant. The hotel has a reputation for superb cuisine. Many of the dishes are prepared from produce grown on its own farm and gardens and enhanced by locally caught lobster and oysters.

Places of interest nearby: Many beauty spots such as Grande Grève, one of Sark's best sandy beaches, and the famous pools of Venus and Adonis. **Directions: By air or sea to Guernsey and then by ferry from St Peter Port.**

MARSH
An MMC Company

Marsh, the world's leading insurance broker,
is proud to be the appointed Preferred Insurance Provider
to Johansens Members Worldwide

ARE YOU A HOTELIER?

There is never a spare moment when you're running a Hotel, Inn, Restaurant or Country House. If you're not with a customer, your mind is on stocktaking. Sound familiar?

At Marsh, we realise you have little time to worry about your insurance policy, instead, you require peace of mind that you are covered.

That is why for over 20 years Marsh have been providing better cover for businesses like yours.

Our unique services are developed specifically for establishments meeting the high standards required for entry in a Johansens guide.

CONTACT US NOW FOR DETAILS
OF THE INSURANCE
POLICY FOR JOHANSENS
01892 553160 (UK)

ARE YOU AN INDEPENDENT TRAVELLER?

Insurance is probably the last thing on your mind. Especially when you are going on holiday or on a business trip. But are you protected when travelling? Is your home protected while you are away?

Marsh offer a wide range of insurances that gives you peace of mind when travelling.

FOR DETAILS ON THESE SERVICES RING (UK):

TRAVEL	**01462 428041**
PENSIONS & FINANCIAL	
SERVICES	**0171 357 3307**
HOUSEHOLD	**01462 428200**
MOTOR	**01462 428100**
HEALTHCARE	**01462 428000**

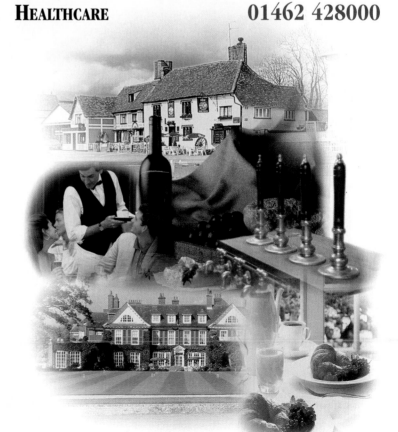

Insurance Policy for Johansens members arranged by:
Marsh UK Ltd.
Mount Pleasant House,
Lonsdale Gardens,
Tunbridge Wells, Kent TN1 1NY

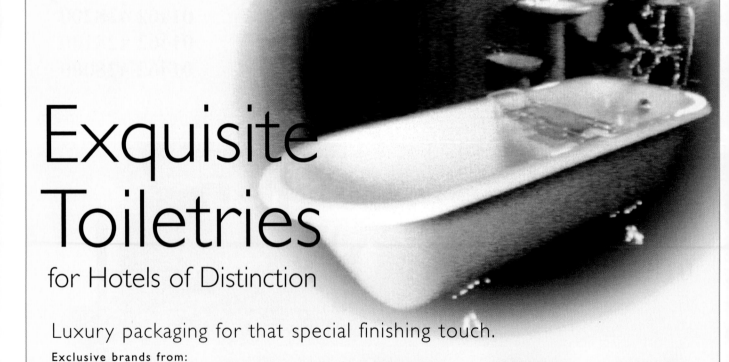

Johansens Recommended Traditional Inns, Hotels & Restaurants in Great Britain

ENGLAND

Aldbury (Ashridge N.T Estate) – The Greyhound Inn, The Greyhound Inn, Stocks Road, Aldbury, Near Tring, Hertfordshire HP23 5RT. Tel: 01442 851228

Aldeburgh – The Dolphin Inn, The Dolphin Inn, Thorpeness, Aldeburgh, Suffolk IP16 4NA. Tel: 01728 454994

Alfriston – Deans Place Hotel, Deans Place Hotel, Seaford Road, Alfriston, East Sussex BN26 5TW. Tel: 01323 870248

Amberley (Near Arundel) – The Boathouse Brasserie, The Boathouse Brasserie, Houghton Bridge, Amberley, Nr Arundel, West Sussex BN18 9LR. Tel: 01798 831059

Ambleside (Great Langdale) – The New Dungeon Ghyll Hotel, The New Dungeon Ghyll Hotel, Great Langdale, Ambleside, Cumbria LA22 9JY. Tel: 015394 37213

Appleby-In-Westmorland – The Royal Oak Inn, The Royal Oak Inn, Bongate, Appleby-In-Westmorland , Cumbria CA16 6UN. Tel: 017683 51463

Ashbourne (Hognaston) – Red Lion Inn, Red Lion Inn, Main Street, Hognaston, Ashbourne, Derbyshire DE6 1PR. Tel: 01335 370396

Ashbourne (Waldley) – Beeches Country Restaurant, Beeches Country Restaurant, Waldley, Doveridge, Nr Ashbourne, Derbyshire DE6 5LR. Tel: 01889 590288

Axminster (Chardstock) – Tytherleigh Cot Hotel, Tytherleigh Cot Hotel, Chardstock, Axminster, Devon EX13 7BN. Tel: 01460 221170

Badby Nr Daventry – The Windmill At Badby, The Windmill At Badby, Main Street, Badby, Nr Daventry, Northamptonshire NN11 6AN. Tel: 01327 702363

Bamburgh – The Victoria Hotel, The Victoria Hotel, Front Street, Bamburgh, Northumberland NE69 7BP. Tel: 01668 214431

Bassenthwaite Lake – The Pheasant, The Pheasant, Bassenthwaite Lake, Nr Cockermouth, Cumbria CA13 9YE. Tel: 017687 76234

Beckington Nr Bath – The Woolpack Inn, The Woolpack Inn, Beckington, Nr Bath, Somerset BA3 6SP. Tel: 01373 831244

Belford – The Blue Bell Hotel, The Blue Bell Hotel, Market Place, Belford, Northumberland NE70 7NE. Tel: 01668 213543

Bibury – The Catherine Wheel, The Catherine Wheel, Bibury, Nr Cirencester, Gloucestershire GL7 5ND. Tel: 01285 740250

Bickleigh (Nr Tiverton) – The Fisherman's Cot, The Fisherman's Cot, Bickleigh, Nr Tiverton, Devon EX16 8RW. Tel: 01884 855237 / 855289

Binfield – Stag & Hounds, Stag & Hounds, Forest Road, Binfield, Berkshire RG12 9HA. Tel: 01344 483553

Blakeney – White Horse Hotel, White Horse Hotel, 4 High Street, Blakeney, Holt, Norfolk NR25 7AL. Tel: 01263 740574

Bourton-On-The-Water – Dial House Hotel, Dial House Hotel, The Chestnuts, High Street, Bourton-On-The-Water , Gloucestershire GL54 2AN. Tel: 01451 822244

Bridport (West Bexington) – The Manor Hotel, The Manor Hotel, West Bexington, Dorchester, Dorset DT2 9DF. Tel: 01308 897616

Bristol – The New Inn, The New Inn, Badminton Road, Mayshill, Nr Frampton Cottrell, Bristol BS36 2NT. Tel: 01454 773161

Bristol (Aust) – The Boars Head, The Boars Head, Main Road, Aust, Bristol BS12 3AX. Tel: 01454 632581

Broadway – The Broadway Hotel, The Broadway Hotel, The Green, Broadway, Worcestershire WR12 7AA. Tel: 01386 852401

Brockenhurst – The Snakecatcher, The Snakecatcher, Lyndhurst, Brockenhurst, Hampshire SO42 7RL. Tel: 01590 622348

Burford – Cotswold Gateway Hotel, Cotswold Gateway Hotel, Cheltenham Road, Burford, Oxfordshire OX18 4HX. Tel: 01993 822695

Burford – The Golden Pheasant Hotel & Restaurant, The Golden Pheasant Hotel & Restaurant, The High Street, Burford, Oxford OX18 4QA. Tel: 01993 823417

Burford – The Lamb Inn, The Lamb Inn, Sheep Street, Burford, Oxfordshire OX18 4LR. Tel: 01993 823155

Burford (The Barringtons) – The Inn For All Seasons, The Inn For All Seasons, The Barringtons, Burford, Oxfordshire OX18 4TN. Tel: 01451 844324

Burnham Market – The Hoste Arms Hotel, The Hoste Arms Hotel, The Green, Burnham Market, Norfolk PE31 8HD. Tel: 01328 738777

Burnley (Fence) – Fence Gate Inn, Fence Gate Inn, Wheatley Lane Road, Fence, Nr Burnley, Lancashire BB12 9EE. Tel: 01282 618101

Burnsall (Skipton) – The Red Lion, The Red Lion, By the bridge at Burnsall, Near Skipton, North Yorkshire BD23 6BU. Tel: 01756 720204

Burton upon Trent – Ye Olde Dog & Partridge, Ye Olde Dog & Partridge, High Street, Tutbury, Burton upon Trent, Staffordshire DE13 9LS. Tel: 01283 813030

Burton Upon Trent (Sudbury) – Boar's Head Hotel, Boar's Head Hotel, Lichfield Road, Sudbury, Derbyshire DE6 5GX. Tel: 01283 820344

Calver (Near Bakewell) – The Chequers Inn, The Chequers Inn, Froggatt Edge, Nr Calver, Derbyshire S30 1ZB. Tel: 01433 630231

Camborne – Tyacks Hotel, Tyacks Hotel, 27 Commercial Street, Camborne, Cornwall TR14 8LD. Tel: 01209 612424

Cambridge (Withersfield) – The White Horse Inn, The White Horse Inn, Hollow Hill, Withersfield, Haverhill, Suffolk CB9 7SH. Tel: 01440 706081

Carlisle (Talkin Tarn) – The Tarn End House Hotel, The Tarn End House Hotel, Talkin Tarn, Brampton, Cumbria CA8 1LS. Tel: 016977 2340

Castle Ashby – The Falcon Hotel, The Falcon Hotel, Castle Ashby, Northampton, Northamptonshire NN7 1LF. Tel: 01604 696200

Chippenham – The Crown Inn, The Crown Inn, Giddea Hall, Yatton Keynell, Chippenham, Wiltshire SN14 7ER. Tel: 01249 782229

Chipping Sodbury – The Codrington Arms, The Codrington Arms, Wapley Road, Codrington, Nr Chipping Sodbury, Bristol BS37 6RY. Tel: 01454 313145

Christchurch (Highcliffe on Sea) – The Lord Bute, The Lord Bute, 181 / 185 Lymington Road, Highcliffe on Sea, Christchurch , Dorset BH23 4JS. Tel: 01425 278884

Cirencester (Coln St-Aldwyns) – The New Inn at Coln, The New Inn at Coln, Coln St-Aldwyns, Nr Cirencester, Gloucestershire GL7 5AN. Tel: 01285 750651

Cirencester (South Cerney) – The Eliot Arms Hotel, The Eliot Arms Hotel, Clarks Hay, South Cerney, Cirencester, Gloucestershire GL7 2UA. Tel: 01285 860215

Clare (Hundon) – The Plough Inn, The Plough Inn, Brockley Green, Sudbury, Nr Hundon, Suffolk CO10 8DT. Tel: 01440 786789

Clavering (Stansted) – The Cricketers, The Cricketers, Clavering, Nr Saffron Walden, Essex CB11 4QT. Tel: 01799 550442

Cleobury Mortimer – Crown At Hopton, Crown At Hopton, Hopton Wafers, Cleobury Mortimer, Shropshire DY14 0NB. Tel: 01299 270372

Cleobury Mortimer – The Redfern Hotel, The Redfern Hotel, Cleobury Mortimer, Shropshire DY14 8AA. Tel: 01299 270 395

Colchester (Coggeshall) – The White Hart Hotel & Restaurant, The White Hart Hotel & Restaurant, Market End, Coggeshall, Essex CO6 1NH. Tel: 01376 561654

Coleford – The New Inn, The New Inn, Coleford, Crediton, Devon EX17 5BZ. Tel: 01363 84242

Dartmouth – The Little Admiral Hotel, The Little Admiral Hotel, Victoria Road, Dartmouth, Devon TQ6 9RT. Tel: 01803 832572

Ditcheat (Nr Wells) – The Manor House Inn, The Manor House Inn, Ditcheat, Somerset BA4 6RB. Tel: 01749 860276

Doncaster – Hamilton's Restaurant & Hotel, Hamilton's Restaurant & Hotel, Carr House Road, Doncaster, South Yorkshire DN4 5HP. Tel: 01302 760770

Dorchester-On-Thames – The George Hotel, The George Hotel, High Street, Dorchester-On-Thames, Oxford OX10 7HH. Tel: 01865 340404

East Witton (Wensleydale) – The Blue Lion, The Blue Lion, East Witton, Nr Leyburn, North Yorkshire DL8 4SN. Tel: 01969 624273

Eccleshall – The George Inn, The George Inn, Eccleshall, Staffordshire ST21 6DF. Tel: 01785 850300

Edenbridge – Ye Old Crown, Ye Old Crown, High Street, Edenbridge, Kent TN8 5AR. Tel: 01732 867896

Egton (Nr Whitby) – The Wheatsheaf Inn, The Wheatsheaf Inn, Egton, Nr Whitby, North Yorkshire YO21 1TZ. Tel: 01947 895271

Eton (Windsor) – The Christopher Hotel, The Christopher Hotel, High Street, Eton, Windsor, Berkshire SL4 6AN. Tel: 01753 811677 / 852359

Evershot – The Acorn Inn Hotel, The Acorn Inn Hotel, Fore Street, Evershot, Nr Dorchester, Dorset DT2 0JW. Tel: 01935 83228

Evesham – The Northwick Hotel, The Northwick Hotel, Waterside, Evesham, Worcestershire WR11 6BT. Tel: 01386 40322

Evesham (Offenham) – Riverside Restaurant And Hotel, Riverside Restaurant And Hotel, The Parks, Offenham Road, Nr Evesham, Worcestershire WR11 5JP. Tel: 01386 446200

Exmoor – The Royal Oak Inn, The Royal Oak Inn, Winsford, Exmoor National Park, Somerset TA24 7JE. Tel: 01643 851455

Falmouth (Constantine) – Trengilly Wartha Country Inn & Restaurant, Trengilly Wartha Country Inn & Restaurant, Nancenoy, Constantine, Falmouth, Cornwall TR11 5RP. Tel: 01326 340332

Fifield (Nr Burford) – The Merrymouth Inn, The Merrymouth Inn, Stow Road, Fifield, Nr Burford, Oxford OX7 6HR. Tel: 01993 831652

Ford, Nr Bath – The White Hart, The White Hart, Ford, Chippenham, Wiltshire SN14 8RP. Tel: 01249 782213

Fordingbridge (New Forest) – The Woodfalls Inn, The Woodfalls Inn, The Ridge, Woodfalls, Fordingbridge, Hampshire SP5 2LN. Tel: 01725 513222

Goring-On-Thames – The Leatherne Bottel Riverside Inn & Restaurant, The Leatherne Bottel Riverside Inn & Restaurant, The Bridleway, Goring-On-Thames, Berkshire RG8 0HS. Tel: 01491 872667

Grimsthorpe (Bourne) – The Black Horse Inn, The Black Horse Inn, Grimsthorpe, Bourne, Lincolnshire PE10 0LY. Tel: 01778 591247

Grindleford – The Maynard Arms, The Maynard Arms, Main Road, Grindleford, Derbyshire S32 2HE. Tel: 01433 630321

Halifax/Huddersfield – The Rock Inn Hotel, The Rock Inn Hotel, Holywell Green, Halifax, West Yorkshire HX4 9BS. Tel: 01422 379721

Handcross (Slaugham) – The Chequers At Slaugham, The Chequers At Slaugham, Slaugham, Nr Handcross, West Sussex RH17 6AQ. Tel: 01444 400239/400996

Harrogate – The George & Newboulds Restaurant, The George & Newboulds Restaurant, Wormald Green, Nr Harrogate, North Yorkshire HG3 3PR. Tel: 01765 677214

Harrogate (Killinghall) – The Low Hall Hotel, The Low Hall Hotel, Ripon Road, Killinghall, Harrogate, North Yorkshire HG3 2AY. Tel: 01423 508598

Harrogate (Knaresborough) – The Dower House, The Dower House, Bond End, Knaresborough, Nr Harrogate, North Yorkshire HG5 9AL. Tel: 01423 863302

Harrogate (Ripley Castle) – The Boar's Head Hotel, The Boar's Head Hotel, Ripley, Harrogate, North Yorkshire HG3 3AY. Tel: 01423 771888

Hartley Wintney (Bramshill) – The Hatchgate, The Hatchgate, Bramshill, Nr Hook, Hampshire RG27 0JX. Tel: 01189 32666

Hathersage – The Plough Inn, The Plough Inn, Leadmill Bridge, Hathersage, Derbyshire S30 1BA. Tel: 01433 650319

Hay-On-Wye – Rhydspence Inn, Rhydspence Inn, Whitney-On-Wye, Nr Hay-On-Wye, Herefordshire HR3 6EU. Tel: 01497 831262

Hayfield (High Peak) – The Waltzing Weasel, The Waltzing Weasel, New Mills Road, Birch Vale, High Peak, Derbyshire SK22 1BT. Tel: 01663 743402

Helmsley – The Feathers Hotel, The Feathers Hotel, Market Place, Helmsley, North Yorkshire YO6 5BH. Tel: 01439 770275

Helmsley (Near York) – The Feversham Arms Hotel, The Feversham Arms Hotel, Helmsley , North Yorkshire YO6 5AG. Tel: 01439 770766

Hindon, Nr Salisbury – The Lamb at Hindon, The Lamb at Hindon, High Street, Hindon, Salisbury, Wiltshire SP3 6DP. Tel: 01747 820573

Hindon (Nr Salisbury) not opposite Lamb – The Grosvenor Arms, The Grosvenor Arms, Hindon, Salisbury, Wiltshire SP3 6DJ. Tel: 01747 820696

Honiton (Wilmington) – Home Farm Hotel, Home Farm Hotel, Wilmington, Nr Honiton, Devon EX14 9JR. Tel: 01404 831278

Huddersfield (Golcar) – The Weavers Shed Restaurant with Rooms, The Weavers Shed Restaurant with Rooms, Knowl Road, Golcar, Huddersfield, West Yorkshire HD7 4AN. Tel: 01484 654284

Ilchester – Northover Manor, Northover Manor, Ilchester, Somerset BA22 8LD. Tel: 01935 840447

Kenilworth – Clarendon House Bar Brasserie Hotel, Clarendon House Bar Brasserie Hotel, High Street, Kenilworth, Warwickshire CV8 1LZ. Tel: 01926 857668

Kingskerswell (Nr Torquay) – The Barn Owl Inn, The Barn Owl Inn, Aller Mills, Kingskerswell, Devon TQ12 5AN. Tel: 01803 872130

Knutsford – Longview Hotel And Restaurant, Longview Hotel And Restaurant, 51/55 Manchester Road, Knutsford, Cheshire WA16 0LX. Tel: 01565 632119

Ledbury – Feathers Hotel, Feathers Hotel, High Street, Ledbury, Herefordshire HR8 1DS. Tel: 01531 635266

Leek (Blackshaw Moor) – The Three Horseshoes Inn & Kirk's Restaurant, The Three Horseshoes Inn & Kirk's Restaurant, Buxton Road, Blackshaw Moor, Nr Leek, Staffordshire ST13 8TW. Tel: 01538 300296

Long Melford – The Countrymen, The Countrymen, The Green, Long Melford, Suffolk CO10 9DN. Tel: 01787 312356

Longleat (Horningsham) – The Bath Arms, The Bath Arms, Horningsham, Warminster, Wiltshire BA12 7LY. Tel: 01985 844308

Lymington – The Angel Inn, The Angel Inn, High Street, New Forest, Hampshire SO41 9AP. Tel: 01590 672050

Lynmouth – The Rising Sun, The Rising Sun, Harbourside, Lynmouth, Devon EX35 6EQ. Tel: 01598 753223

Maidstone (Ringlestone) – Ringlestone Inn, Ringlestone Inn, 'Twixt Harrietsham and Wormshill, Nr Maidstone, Kent ME17 1NX. Tel: 01622 859900

Malmesbury – The Horse And Groom Inn, The Horse And Groom Inn, Charlton, Near Malmesbury, Wiltshire SN16 9DL. Tel: 01666 823904

Mells (Nr Bath) – The Talbot Inn at Mells, The Talbot Inn at Mells, High Street, Mells, Nr Bath, Somerset BA11 3PN. Tel: 01373 812254

Newbury (Gt Shefford) – The Swan Inn, The Swan Inn, Newbury Road, Great Shefford, Newbury, Berkshire RG17 7DS. Tel: 01488 648271

Newby Bridge – The Swan Hotel, The Swan Hotel, Newby Bridge, Nr Ulverston, Cumbria LA12 8NB. Tel: 015395 31681

North Walsham – Elderton Lodge, Elderton Lodge, Gunton Park, Thorpe Market, Nr North Walsham, Norfolk NR11 8TZ. Tel: 01263 833547

Nottingham – Hotel Des Clos, Hotel Des Clos, Old Lenton Lane, Nottingham, Nottinghamshire NG7 2SA. Tel: 01159 866566

Old Hunstanton – The Lodge Hotel & Restaurant, The Lodge Hotel & Restaurant, Old Hunstanton, Norfolk PE36 6HX. Tel: 01485 532896

Oxford (Banbury) – Holcombe Hotel, Holcombe Hotel, High Street, Deddington, Nr Woodstock, Oxfordshire OX15 0SL. Tel: 01869 338274

Oxford (Middleton Stoney) – The Jersey Arms, The Jersey Arms, Middleton Stoney, Oxfordshire OX6 8SE. Tel: 01869 343234

Oxford (Minster Lovell) – The Mill & Old Swan, The Mill & Old Swan, Minster Lovell, Nr Burford, Oxfordshire OX8 5RN. Tel: 01993 774441

Pelynt, Nr Looe – Jubilee Inn, Jubilee Inn, Pelynt, Nr Looe, Cornwall PL13 2JZ. Tel: 01503 220312

Penistone (Ingbirchworth) – The Fountain Inn & Rooms, The Fountain Inn & Rooms, Wellthorne Lane, Ingbirchworth, Nr Penistone, South Yorkshire S36 7GJ. Tel: 01226 763125

Petworth – The Stonemason's Inn, The Stonemason's Inn, North Street, Petworth, West Sussex GU28 9NL. Tel: 01798 342510

Petworth (Coultershaw Bridge) – Badgers, Badgers, Coultershaw Bridge, Petworth, West Sussex GU28 0JF. Tel: 01798 342651

Petworth (Fittleworth) – The Swan Inn, The Swan Inn, Lower Street, Fittleworth, Nr Petworth, West Sussex RH20 1EN. Tel: 01798 865429

Petworth (Sutton) – White Horse Inn, White Horse Inn, Sutton, Nr Pulborough, West Sussex RH20 1PS. Tel: 01798 869 221

Port Gaverne – The Port Gaverne Hotel, The Port Gaverne Hotel, Nr Port Isaac, North Cornwall PL29 3SQ. Tel: 01208 880244

Preston (Goosnargh) – Ye Horn's Inn, Ye Horn's Inn, Horn's Lane, Goosnargh, Nr Preston, Lancashire PR3 2FJ. Tel: 01772 865230

Reading (Streatley) – The Bull at Streatley, The Bull at Streatley, Reading Road, Reading, Berkshire RG8 9TJ. Tel: 01491 875231

Romsey (Greatbridge) – Duke's Head, Duke's Head, Greatbridge, Nr Romsey, Hampshire SO51 0HB. Tel: 01794 514450

Rugby (Easenhall) – The Golden Lion Inn of Easenhall, The Golden Lion Inn of Easenhall, Easenhall, Nr Rugby, Warwickshire CV23 0JA. Tel: 01788 832265

Rye – The George Hotel, The George Hotel, High Street, Rye, East Sussex TN31 7JP. Tel: 01797 222114

Saddleworth (Delph) – The Old Bell Inn Hotel, The Old Bell Inn Hotel, Huddersfield Road, Delph, Saddleworth, Nr Oldham, Greater Manchester OL3 5EG. Tel: 01457 870130

Salisbury (Downton) – The White Horse, The White Horse, Downton, Salisbury, Wiltshire SP5 3LY. Tel: 01725 510408

Sheffield (Dronfield) – Manor House Hotel & Restaurant, Manor House Hotel & Restaurant, High Street, Old Dronfield, Derbyshire S18 1PY. Tel: 01246 413971

Sherborne – The Half Moon Inn, The Half Moon Inn, Half Moon Street, Sherborne, Dorset DT9 3LN. Tel: 01935 812017

Sherborne (Oborne) – The Grange Hotel & Restaurant, The Grange Hotel & Restaurant, Oborne, Nr Sherborne, Dorset DT9 4LA. Tel: 01935 813463

Sherborne (West Camel) – The Walnut Tree, The Walnut Tree, West Camel, Nr Sherborne, Somerset BA22 7QW. Tel: 01935 851292

Shifnal (Telford) – Naughty Nell's, Naughty Nell's, 1 Park Street, Shifnal, Shropshire TF11 9BA. Tel: 01952 411412

Shipton Under Wychwood – The Shaven Crown Hotel, The Shaven Crown Hotel, High Street, Shipton Under Wychwood, Oxfordshire OX7 6BA. Tel: 01993 830330

Snettisham (Nr King's Lynn) – The Rose & Crown, The Rose & Crown, Old Church Road, Snettisham, King's Lynn, Norfolk PE31 7LX. Tel: 01485 541382

Southport (Formby) – Tree Tops Country House Restaurant & Hotel, Tree Tops Country House Restaurant & Hotel, Southport Old Road, Formby, Nr Southport, Lancashire L37 0AB. Tel: 01704 572430

Stafford (Ingestre) – The Dower House, The Dower House, Ingestre Park, Great Haywood, Staffordshire ST18 0RE. Tel: 01889 270707

Stamford – The Crown Hotel, The Crown Hotel, All Saints Place, Stamford, Lincolnshire PE9 2AG. Tel: 01780 763136

Stamford (Nr Grantham) – Black Bull Inn, Black Bull Inn, Lobthorpe, Nr Grantham, Lincolnshire NG33 5LL. Tel: 01476 860086

Stow-on-the-Wold – The Unicorn Hotel, The Unicorn Hotel, Sheep Street, Stow-on-the-Wold, Gloucestershire GL54 1HQ. Tel: 01451 830257

Stow-On-The-Wold (Bledington) – The Kings Head Inn & Restaurant, The Kings Head Inn & Restaurant, The Green, Bledington, Oxfordshire OX7 6XQ. Tel: 01608 658365

Stratford-upon-Avon – The Coach House Hotel & Cellar Restaurant, The Coach House Hotel & Cellar Restaurant, 16/17 Warwick Road, Stratford-upon-Avon, Warwickshire CV37 6YW. Tel: 01789 204109 / 299468

Stroud (Frampton Mansell) – The Crown Inn, The Crown Inn, Frampton Mansell, Stroud, Gloucestershire GL6 8JG. Tel: 01285 760601

Sudbury (Long Melford) – The Bull Hotel, The Bull Hotel, Hall Street, Long Melford, Suffolk CO10 9JG. Tel: 01787 378494

Taunton (Staple Fitzpaine) – Greyhound Inn, Greyhound Inn, Staple Fitzpaine, Nr Taunton, Somerset TA3 5SP. Tel: 01823 480227

Telford (Hadley Park) – Hadley Park House Hotel, Hadley Park House Hotel, Hadley Park, Telford, Shropshire TF1 4UL. Tel: 01952 677269

Telford (Norton) – The Hundred House Hotel, The Hundred House Hotel, Bridgnorth Road, Norton, Nr Shifnal, Telford, Shropshire TF11 9EE. Tel: 01952 730353

Tenterden – The White Lion Hotel, The White Lion Hotel, The High Street, Tenterden, Kent TN30 6BD. Tel: 01580 765077

Thaxted – Recorders House Restaurant (With Rooms), Recorders House Restaurant (With Rooms), 17 Town Street, Thaxted, Essex CM6 2LD. Tel: 01371 830438

Thirsk – Crab & Lobster, Crab & Lobster, Asenby, North Yorkshire YO7 3QL. Tel: 01845 577286

Thornham – The Lifeboat Inn, The Lifeboat Inn, Ship Lane, Thornham, Norfolk PE36 6LT. Tel: 01485 512236

Thorpe Market – Green Farm Restaurant And Hotel, Green Farm Restaurant And Hotel, North Walsham Road, Thorpe Market, Norfolk NR11 8TH. Tel: 01263 833602

Tintagel (Trebarwith Strand) – The Port William, The Port William, Trebarwith Strand, Nr Tintagel, Cornwall PL34 0HB. Tel: 01840 770230

Totnes (Bow Bridge, Ashprington) – The Watermans Arms, The Watermans Arms, Bow Bridge, Ashprington, Nr Totnes, Devon TQ9 7EG. Tel: 01803 732214

Totnes (Staverton) – The Sea Trout Inn, The Sea Trout Inn, Staverton, Nr Totnes, Devon TQ9 6PA. Tel: 01803 762274

Troutbeck (Near Windermere) – The Mortal Man Hotel, The Mortal Man Hotel, Troutbeck, Nr Windermere, Cumbria LA23 1PL. Tel: 015394 33193

Upton-Upon-Severn, Nr Malvern – The White Lion Hotel, The White Lion Hotel, High Street, Upton-Upon-Severn, Nr Malvern, Worcestershire WR8 0HJ. Tel: 01684 592551

Warminster (Upton Scudamore) – The Angel Inn, The Angel Inn, Upton Scudamore, Warminster, Wiltshire BA12 0AG. Tel: 01985 213225

Wells – The Market Place, Wells, Somerset BA5 2RW. Tel: 01749 672616

Weobley – The Salutation Inn, The Salutation Inn, Market Pitch, Weobley, Herefordshire HR4 8SJ. Tel: 01544 318443

West Auckland – The Manor House Hotel & Country Club, The Manor House Hotel & Country Club, The Green, West Auckland, County Durham DL14 9HW. Tel: 01388 834834

West Witton (Wensleydale) – The Wensleydale Heifer Inn, The Wensleydale Heifer Inn, West Witton, Wensleydale, North Yorkshire DL8 4LS. Tel: 01969 622322

Whitewell – The Inn At Whitewell, The Inn At Whitewell, Forest Of Bowland, Clitheroe, Lancashire BB7 3AT. Tel: 01200 448222

Witney (Hailey) – The Bird in Hand, The Bird in Hand, Hailey, Witney, Oxfordshire OX8 5XP. Tel: 01993 868321

Wooler – The Tankerville Arms Hotel, The Tankerville Arms Hotel, Wooler, Northumberland NE71 6AD. Tel: 01668 281581

Worthing (Bramber) – The Old Tollgate Restaurant And Hotel, The Old Tollgate Restaurant And Hotel, The Street, Bramber, Steyning, West Sussex BN44 3WE. Tel: 01903 879494

Wroxham – The Barton Angler Country Inn, The Barton Angler Country Inn, Irstead Road, Neatishead, Nr Wroxham, Norfolk NR12 8XP. Tel: 01692 630740

York (Easingwold) – The George at Easingwold, The George at Easingwold, Market Place, Easingwold, York, North Yorkshire YO6 3AD. Tel: 01347 821698

WALES

Chepstow – The Castle View Hotel, The Castle View Hotel, 16 Bridge Street, Chepstow, Monmouthshire NP6 5EZ. Tel: 01291 620349

Llanarmon Dyffryn Ceiriog – The West Arms Hotel, The West Arms Hotel, Llanarmon D C, Nr Llangollen, Denbighshire LL20 7LD. Tel: 01691 600665

Llandeilo (Rhosmaen) – The Plough Inn, The Plough Inn, Rhosmaen, Llandeilo, Carmarthenshire SA19 6NP. Tel: 01558 823431

Machynlleth – The Wynnstay, The Wynnstay, Maengwyn Street, Machynlleth, Powys SY20 8AE. Tel: 01654 702941

Presteigne – The Radnorshire Arms, The Radnorshire Arms, High Street, Presteigne, Powys. Tel: 01544 267406

SCOTLAND

Glendevon (South Perthshire) – Tormaukin Hotel, Tormaukin Hotel, Glendevon, By Dollar, Perthshire FK14 7JY. Tel: 01259 781252

Inverness (Farr) – Grouse & Trout, Grouse & Trout, Flichity, By Farr, Inverness, IV1 2XE. Tel: 01808 521314

Isle Of Skye (Eilean Iarmain) – Hotel Eilean Iarmain, Hotel Eilean Iarmain, Sleat, Isle Of Skye IV43 8QR. Tel: 01471 833332

Isle Of Skye (Uig) – Uig Hotel, Uig Hotel, Uig, Isle Of Skye, Isle Of Skye IV51 9YE. Tel: 01470 542205

Kylesku (Sutherland) – Kylesku Hotel, Kylesku Hotel, Kylesku, Via Lairg, Sutherland IV27 4HW. Tel: 01971 502231/502200

Loch Earn (Perthshire) – Achray House on Loch Earn, Achray House on Loch Earn, Loch Earn, St Fillan, Perthshire PH6 2NF. Tel: 01764 685231

Moffat – Annandale Arms Hotel, Annandale Arms Hotel, High Street, Moffat, Dumfriesshire DG10 9HF. Tel: 01683 220013

Pitlochry – The Moulin Hotel, The Moulin Hotel, Moulin, By Pitlochry, Perthshire PH16 5EW. Tel: 01796 472196

Plockton (By Kyle of Lochalsh) – The Plockton Hotel & Garden Restaurant, The Plockton Hotel & Garden Restaurant, Harbour Street, Plockton, Wester Ross IV52 8TN. Tel: 01599 544274

Poolewe (Wester Ross) – Pool House Hotel, Pool House Hotel, Poolewe, Achnasheen, Wester Ross IV22 2LD. Tel: 01445 781272

CHANNEL ISLANDS

Guernsey (St Peter Port) – Les Rocquettes Hotel, Les Rocquettes Hotel, Les Gravees, St Peter Port, GY1 1RN. Tel: 01481 722176

JOHANSENS RECOMMENDED HOTEL

JOHANSENS RECOMMENDED INN OR RESTAURANT

JOHANSENS RECOMMENDED COUNTRY HOUSE

To Dublin/ Dun Laoghaire

To Rosslare

To Rosslare

To Cork

ISLES OF SCILLY

To Santander

To Roscoff

To Guernsey

Holyhead
ANGLESEY
BEAUMARIS
CONWY
LLANDUDNO
CAERNARFON
BETWS-Y-COED
CHESTER
BOLTON
SADDLEWORTH
MANCHESTER
ALTRINCHAM
GLOSSOP
HAYFIELD
MANCHESTER
AIRPORT
MANCHESTER
ALDERLEY EDGE
KNUTSFORD
PRESTBURY
MACCLESFIELD
BUXTON
TARPORLEY
LEEK
NANTWICH
Stoke
CRICCIETH
PORTMEIRION
VILLAGE
CORWEN
LLANDEGLA
WREXHAM
OSWESTRY
ECCLESHALL
STAFFORD
PWLLHELI
ABERSOCH
HARLECH
BALA
LLANARMON
DYFFRYN CEIRIOG
WEM
ACTON
TRUSSELL
BARMOUTH
DOLGELLAU
LAKE
VYRNWY
SHREWSBURY
TELFORD
SHIFNAL
ABERDOVEY
MACHYNLLETH
CHURCH
STRETTON
BRIDGNORTH
WOLVERHAMPTON
BIRMINGHAM
ABERYSTWYTH
KIDDERMINSTER
CHADDESLEY
CORBETT
LUDLOW
CLEOBURY
MORTIMER
BROMSGROVE
PRESTEIGNE
ABBERLEY
ALCESTER
LEOMINSTER
EVESHAM
WEOBLEY
MALVERN
WELLS
UPTON-ON-
SEVERN
BROADWAY
LLANGAMMARCH WELLS
HAY-ON-
WYE
HEREFORD
LEDBURY
TEWKESBURY
CHELTENHAM
BRECON
ROSS-ON-
WYE
CRICKHOWELL
MONMOUTH
PAINSWICK
CIRENCESTER
ABERGAVENNY
STONEHOUSE
CLEARWELL
STROUD
MINCHIN-
HAMPTON
TETBURY
ABERDARE
USK
OWLPEN
FISHGUARD
ST DAVID'S
TINTERN
CHEPSTOW
CHIPPING
SODBURY
FORD
MALMESBURY
PEMBROKE
MILFORD
Haven
TENBY
SWANSEA
CASTLE
COMBE
CHIPPENHAM
BRISTOL
BATH
LACOCK
BRADFORD-
ON-AVON
BRIDGEND
CARDIFF
BECKINGTON
LONGLEAT
MELLS
WARMINSTER
WELLS
SHEPTON
MALLET
HINDON
DITCHEAT
COMBE MARTIN
LYNTON
LYNMOUTH
PORLOCK
WEIR
MIDDLECOMBE
CASTLE
CARY
WINCANTON
WOOLACOMBE
SIMONSBATH
EXFORD
EXMOOR
FIFEHEAD
SAUNTON
BARNSTAPLE
DULVERTON
TAUNTON
ILCHESTER
SHERBORNE
STURMINSTER
NEWTON
CLOVELLY
BIDEFORD
SOUTH
MOLTON
ILMINSTER
EVERSHOT
BURRINGTON
MORCHARD
BISHOP
BICKLEIGH
SEAVINGTON
ST MARY
BEAMINSTER
WIMBORNE
MINSTER
COLEFORD
HONITON
TINTAGEL
LEWDOWN
CREDITON
AXMINSTER
BRIDPORT
BOURNEMOUTH
PORT
GAVERNE
LYDFORD
CHAGFORD
EXETER
LYME
REGIS
DORCHESTER
WAREHAM
PADSTOW
LIFTON
DARTMOOR
SIDMOUTH
BOVEY TRACEY
ILSINGTON
WEYMOUTH
WADEBRIDGE
TAVISTOCK
ASHBURTON
KINGSKERSWELL
TORQUAY
ST AGNES
ST KEYNE
PELYNT
STAVERTON
TOTNES
CAMBORNE
GOLANT
BY FOWEY
LOOE
PLYMOUTH
ST IVES
FOWEY
POLPERRO
VERYAN
DARTMOUTH
KINGSBRIDGE
PENZANCE
HELSTON
ST MAWES
THURLESTONE
SANDS
SALCOMBE
PORTHLEVEN
FALMOUTH

0   20   40   60   80   100 Kilometres
0   10   20   30   40   50 Miles

278

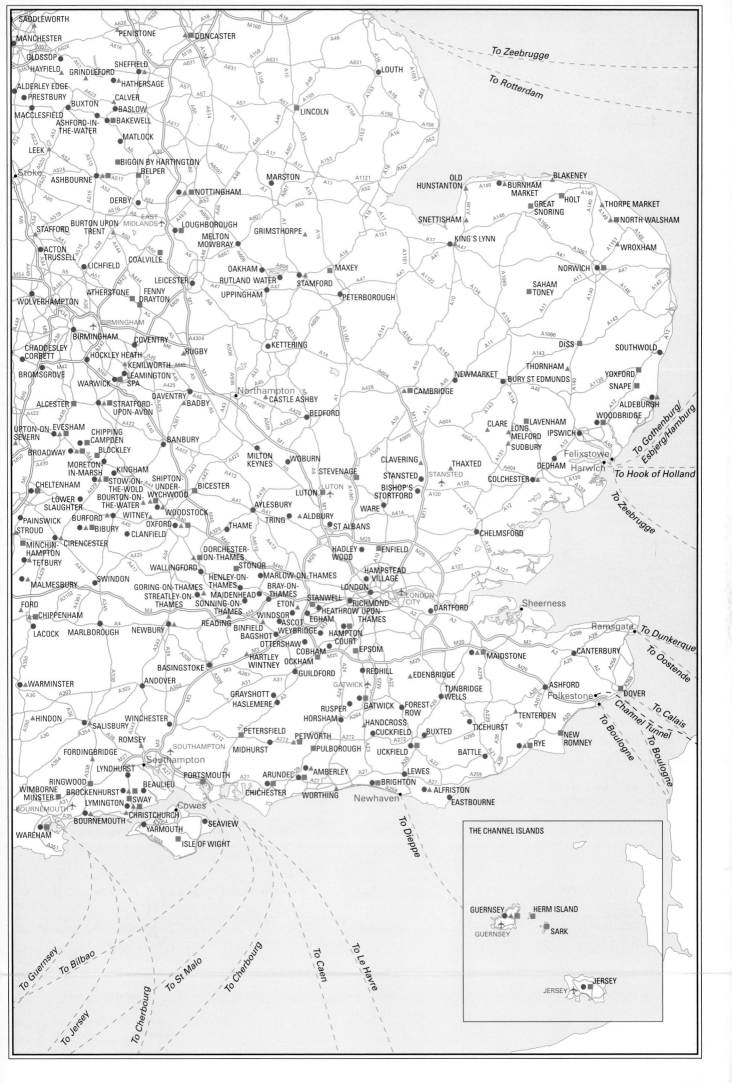

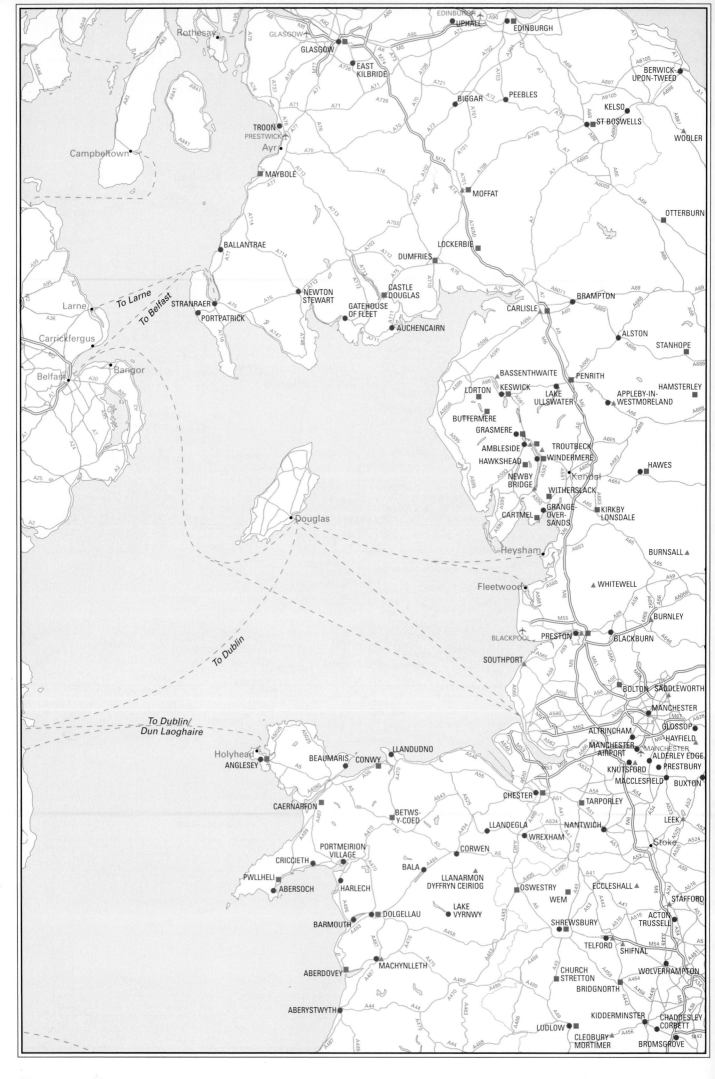

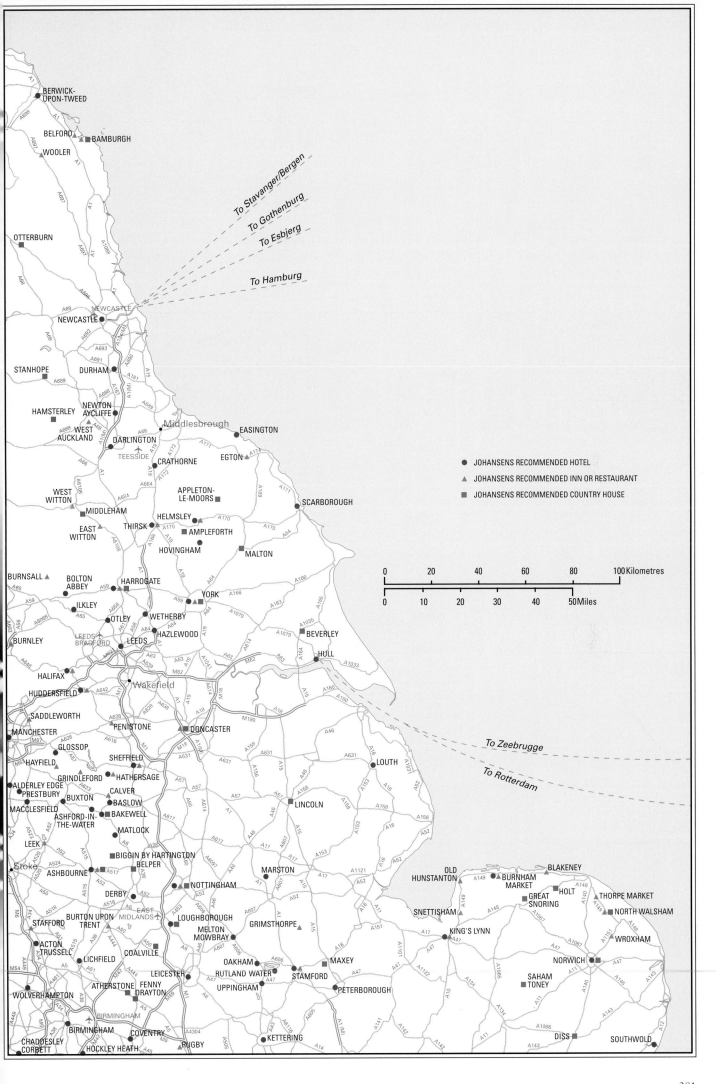

JOHANSENS RECOMMENDED HOTEL

▲ JOHANSENS RECOMMENDED INN OR RESTAURANT

■ JOHANSENS RECOMMENDED COUNTRY HOUSE

0 20 40 60 80 100 Kilometres

0 10 20 30 40 50 Miles

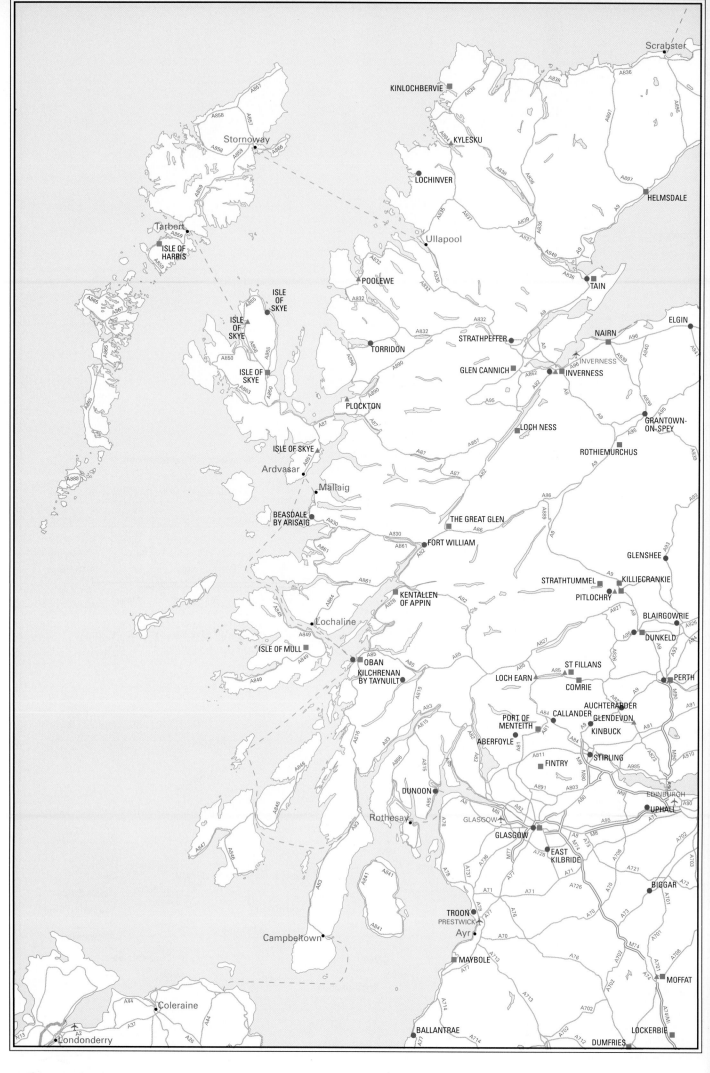

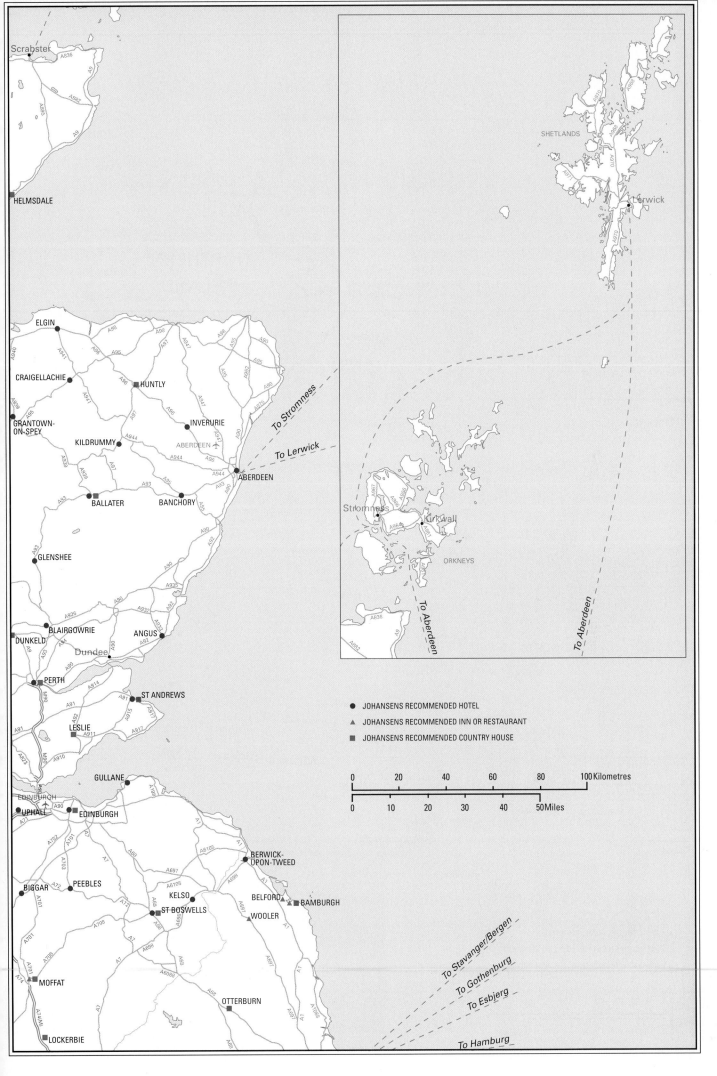

JOHANSENS RECOMMENDED HOTEL
JOHANSENS RECOMMENDED INN OR RESTAURANT
JOHANSENS RECOMMENDED COUNTRY HOUSE

NORTHERN IRELAND

IRELAND

CONNAUGHT

To Stranraer, Cairnryan

To Liverpool, Douglas

To Liverpool, Holyhead

To Holyhead

To Pembroke Dock

To Swansea

Campbeltown

Coleraine
Londonderry
LETTERKENNY
Carrickfergus
Belfast (Aldergrove)
BELFAST
Armagh
Newry
Dundalk
CARRICKMACROSS
Drogheda
ROSSNOWLAGH
SLIGO
RIVERSTOWN
CONNEMARA
CONG
GALWAY
CRAUGHWELL
Gort
NEWMARKET-ON-FERGUS
SHANNON
KILKEE
ADARE
Limerick
DUBLIN
Dun Laoghaire
Bray
RATHNEW
WICKLOW
KILTEGAN
GOREY
Kilkenny
CASHEL
Tralee
Clonmel
KILMEADAN
Waterford
Wexford
ROSSLARE
Fishguard
CARAGH LAKE
KILLARNEY
MALLOW
PARKNASILLA
KENMARE
CORK
CORK
CLONAKILTY

● JOHANSENS RECOMMENDED HOTEL

▲ JOHANSENS RECOMMENDED INN OR RESTAURANT

■ JOHANSENS RECOMMENDED COUNTRY HOUSE

| 0 | 20 | 40 | 60 | 80 | 100 Kilometres |

| 0 | 10 | 20 | 30 | 40 | 50 Miles |

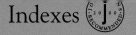
Johansens Recommended Country Houses listed alphabetically by region

To enable you to use your 2000 Johansens Recommended Country Houses and Small Hotels Guide more effectively, the following five pages of indexes contain a wealth of useful information about the establishments featured in the Guide. As well as listing them alphabetically, by region and by county, the indexes also show which Country Houses and Small Hotels offer certain specialised facilities.

The indexes are listed as follows:

- Alphabetically by region
- By county
- With a swimming pool
- With tennis
- With fishing on site
- With riding on site
- With shooting on site

- With golf nearby
- With conference facilities for 30 delegates or more
- Accepting Dogs
- Licensed for Weddings
- Double rooms for £50 or less
- Johansens Preferred Partners

WALES

Country Houses with a swimming pool

Country Houses with tennis

Country Houses with fishing on site

287

Country Houses with shooting on site

Country Houses with riding on site

Country Houses with golf nearby

Country Houses with conference facilities for 30 delegates or more

What does your paper say about you?

Jeremy Hoskins, hotelier, chooses Conqueror* Contour in Oyster, printed in colour.

Starring role. Jeremy Hoskins combed the Conqueror* range to discover the perfect texture for his hotel's letterhead. Ideal for brochures, menus, wine-lists and letterheads, as well as for all corporate and conference stationery, the colours, textures and weights of the Conqueror* range are the best in the business. For a free sample pack or advice on the Conqueror* range and where to find it, call + 44 (0) 1256 728665 or visit www.conqueror.com now. You'll get five stars for presentation.

Star quality. For a free sample pack or advice on the Conqueror* range and where to find it, call + 44 (0) 1256 728665 or visit www.conqueror.com now.

Hildon Ltd., Broughton, Hampshire SO20 8DG, ☎ 01794 - 301 747

ORDER FORM

Call our 24hr credit card hotline FREEPHONE 0800 269 397.

Simply indicate which title(s) you require by putting the quantity in the boxes provided. Choose your preferred method of payment and mail to Johansens, FREEPOST (CB 264), 43 Millharbour, London E14 9BR, England (no stamp needed). Your FREE gifts will automatically be dispatched with your order. Fax orders welcome on 0171 537 3594

CHOOSE FROM 7 SPECIAL GUIDE COLLECTIONS – SAVE UP TO £56

TITLE	*Normal Price*	PRICE	SAVE	QTY	TOTAL
OFFER ONE – The Basic Collection					
3 Johansens Guides A+B+C	*£42.85*	£36.00	£6.85		
OFFER TWO – The Extended Collection					
4 Johansens Guides A+B+C+G	*£58.80*	£46.00	£12.80		
OFFER THREE – The Full Selection					
5 Johansens Guides A+B+C+G+K PLUS Southern Africa Guide **FREE**	*£71.75*	£56.00	£15.75		
OFFER FOUR - The Executive Collection					
Business Meeting Venues Guide & CD-ROM M+R	*£40.00*	£30.00	£10.00		
OFFER FIVE - The Holiday Pack					
3 Johansens Guides D+E+F	*£18.93*	£9.99	£8.94		
OFFER SIX - The Digital Collection					
3 Johansens CD-ROMs N+O+P PLUS Southern Africa CD-ROM Q **FREE**	*£69.85*	£59.85	£10.00		
OFFER SEVEN - The Chairman's Collection					
Business Meeting Venues Guide & CD-ROMs M+R **PLUS** 5 Johansens Boxed Guides A+B+C+G+K, **PLUS** D+E+F, **PLUS** 3 CD-ROMs N+O+P PLUS Southern Africa Guide/CD ROM Q **FREE**, PLUS Mystery Gift **FREE**	*£205.53*	£149.00	£56.53		
Privilege Card PLUS The Millennium Guide		**FREE**			
1 Presentation box for offers 1, 2 and 3		£5.00	£20.00		
			TOTAL 1		

JOHANSENS PRINTED GUIDES 2000

CODE	TITLE	PRICE	QTY	TOTAL
A	Recommended Hotels – Great Britain & Ireland 2000	£19.95		
B	Recommended Country Houses & Small Hotels – Great Britain & Ireland 2000	£11.95		
C	Recommended Traditional Inns, Hotels & Restaurants – Great Britain 2000	£10.95		
NEW D	Recommended Holiday Cottages – Great Britain & Ireland 2000	£4.99		
E	Historic Houses, Castles & Gardens 2000	£4.99		
F	Museums & Galleries 2000	£8.95		
G	Recommended Hotels – Europe & The Mediterranean 2000	£15.95		
NEW H	Recommended Hotels – Europe & The Mediterranean 2000 (*French Language*)	£15.95		
NEW J	Recommended Hotels – Europe & The Mediterranean 2000 (*German Language*)	£15.95		
K	Recommended Hotels & Inns – North America, Bermuda & The Caribbean 2000	£12.95		
NEW L	Recommended Hotels & Game Lodges – Southern Africa, Mauritius & The Seychelles 2000	£9.95		
M	Recommended Business Meeting Venues 2000	£20.00		

JOHANSENS CD ROMs DIGITAL COLLECTION 2000

CODE	TITLE	PRICE	QTY	TOTAL
N	The Guide 2000 – Great Britain & Ireland	£29.95		
O	The Guide 2000 – Europe & The Mediterranean (*English, French, German Language*)	£22.95		
P	The Guide 2000 – North America, Bermuda & The Caribbean	£16.95		
NEW Q	The Guide 2000 – Southern Africa, Mauritius & The Seychelles	£16.95		
R	Business Meeting Venues 2000	£20.00		
S	Privilege Card 2000 (*Free with your order. Additional Cards £20 each*)	£20.00		

Postage & Packing (UK) £4.50 or £2.50 for single order and CD-ROMs
Outside UK add £5 or £3 for single orders and CD-ROMs

TOTAL 2

GRAND TOTAL 1+2+P&P

Name	(Mr/Mrs/Miss)
Address	
	Postcode
Card No.	Exp Date
Signature	

I have chosen my Johansens Guides/CD-ROMs and

☐ I enclose a cheque for £ _____ payable to Johansens

☐ I enclose my order on company letterheading, please invoice (UK only)

☐ Please debit my credit/charge card account (please tick).

☐ MasterCard ☐ Diners ☐ Amex

☐ Visa ☐ Switch (Issue Number) _____

A16

GUEST SURVEY REPORT

**Your own Johansens 'inspection' gives reliability to our guides
and assists in the selection of Award Nominations**

Name of Hotel: _____

Location of Hotel: _____

Page No: _____

Date of visit: _____

Name of guest _____

Address of guest: _____

_____Postcode _____

Please tick one box in each category below:	Excellent	Good	Disappointing	Poor
Bedrooms				
Public Rooms				
Restaurant/Cuisine				
Service				
Welcome/Friendliness				
Value For Money				

Occasionally we may allow other reputable organisations to write with offers which may be of interest.
If you prefer not to hear from them, tick this box ☐

To: Johansens, FREEPOST (CB264), 43 Millharbour, London E14 9BR

ORDER FORM

Call our 24hr credit card hotline FREEPHONE 0800 269 397.

Simply indicate which title(s) you require by putting the quantity in the boxes provided. Choose your preferred method of payment and mail to Johansens, FREEPOST (CB 264), 43 Millharbour, London E14 9BR, England (no stamp needed). Your FREE gifts will automatically be dispatched with your order. Fax orders welcome on 0171 537 3594

CHOOSE FROM 7 SPECIAL GUIDE COLLECTIONS – SAVE UP TO £56

TITLE	Normal Price	PRICE	SAVE	QTY	TOTAL
OFFER ONE – The Basic Collection					
3 Johansens Guides A+B+C	£42.85	£36.00	£6.85		
OFFER TWO – The Extended Collection					
4 Johansens Guides A+B+C+G	£58.80	£46.00	£12.80		
OFFER THREE – The Full Selection					
5 Johansens Guides A+B+C+G+K PLUS Southern Africa Guide **FREE**	£71.75	£56.00	£15.75		
OFFER FOUR - The Executive Collection					
Business Meeting Venues Guide & CD-ROM M+R	£40.00	£30.00	£10.00		
OFFER FIVE - The Holiday Pack					
3 Johansens Guides D+E+F	£18.93	£9.99	£8.94		
OFFER SIX - The Digital Collection					
3 Johansens CD-ROMs N+O+P PLUS Southern Africa CD-ROM Q **FREE**	£69.85	£59.85	£10.00		
OFFER SEVEN - The Chairman's Collection					
Business Meeting Venues Guide & CD-ROMs M+R **PLUS** 5 Johansens Boxed Guides A+B+C+G+K, **PLUS** D+E+F, **PLUS** 3 CD-ROMs N+O+P **PLUS** Southern Africa Guide/CD ROM Q **FREE**, **PLUS** Mystery Gift **FREE**	£205.53	£149.00	£56.53		
Privilege Card PLUS The Millennium Guide		**FREE**			
1 Presentation box for offers 1, 2 and 3		£5.00	£20.00		

TOTAL 1

JOHANSENS PRINTED GUIDES 2000

CODE	TITLE	PRICE	QTY	TOTAL
A	Recommended Hotels – Great Britain & Ireland 2000	£19.95		
B	Recommended Country Houses & Small Hotels – Great Britain & Ireland 2000	£11.95		
C	Recommended Traditional Inns, Hotels & Restaurants – Great Britain 2000	£10.95		
NEW D	Recommended Holiday Cottages – Great Britain & Ireland 2000	£4.99		
E	Historic Houses, Castles & Gardens 2000	£4.99		
F	Museums & Galleries 2000	£8.95		
G	Recommended Hotels – Europe & The Mediterranean 2000	£15.95		
NEW H	Recommended Hotels – Europe & The Mediterranean 2000 (French Language)	£15.95		
NEW J	Recommended Hotels – Europe & The Mediterranean 2000 (German Language)	£15.95		
K	Recommended Hotels & Inns – North America, Bermuda & The Caribbean 2000	£12.95		
NEW L	Recommended Hotels & Game Lodges – Southern Africa, Mauritius & The Seychelles 2000	£9.95		
M	Recommended Business Meeting Venues 2000	£20.00		

JOHANSENS CD ROMs DIGITAL COLLECTION 2000

CODE	TITLE	PRICE	QTY	TOTAL
N	The Guide 2000 – Great Britain & Ireland	£29.95		
O	The Guide 2000 – Europe & The Mediterranean (English, French, German Language)	£22.95		
P	The Guide 2000 – North America, Bermuda & The Caribbean	£16.95		
NEW Q	The Guide 2000 – Southern Africa, Mauritius & The Seychelles	£16.95		
R	Business Meeting Venues 2000	£20.00		
S	Privilege Card 2000 (Free with your order. Additional Cards £20 each)	£20.00		

Postage & Packing (UK) £4.50 or £2.50 for single order and CD-ROMs
Outside UK add £5 or £3 for single orders and CD-ROMs

TOTAL 2

GRAND TOTAL 1+2+P&P

Name	(Mr/Mrs/Miss)
Address	
	Postcode
Card No.	Exp Date
Signature	

I have chosen my Johansens Guides/CD-ROMs and

☐ I enclose a cheque for £ _____ payable to Johansens

☐ I enclose my order on company letterheading, please invoice (UK only)

☐ Please debit my credit/charge card account (please tick).

☐ MasterCard ☐ Diners ☐ Amex

☐ Visa ☐ Switch (Issue Number) _____

A16

GUEST SURVEY REPORT

Your own Johansens 'inspection' gives reliability to our guides and assists in the selection of Award Nominations

Name of Hotel: _____

Location of Hotel: _____

Page No: _____

Date of visit: _____

Name of guest _____

Address of guest: _____

_____Postcode _____

Please tick one box in each category below:	*Excellent*	*Good*	*Disappointing*	*Poor*
Bedrooms				
Public Rooms				
Restaurant/Cuisine				
Service				
Welcome/Friendliness				
Value For Money				

Occasionally we may allow other reputable organisations to write with offers which may be of interest. If you prefer not to hear from them, tick this box ☐

To: Johansens, FREEPOST (CB264), 43 Millharbour, London E14 9BR

ORDER FORM

Call our 24hr credit card hotline FREEPHONE 0800 269 397.

Simply indicate which title(s) you require by putting the quantity in the boxes provided. Choose your preferred method of payment and mail to Johansens, FREEPOST (CB 264), 43 Millharbour, London E14 9BR, England (no stamp needed). Your FREE gifts will automatically be dispatched with your order. Fax orders welcome on 0171 537 3594

CHOOSE FROM 7 SPECIAL GUIDE COLLECTIONS – SAVE UP TO £56

TITLE	Normal Price	PRICE	SAVE	QTY	TOTAL
OFFER ONE – The Basic Collection					
3 Johansens Guides A+B+C	£42.85	£36.00	£6.85		
OFFER TWO – The Extended Collection					
4 Johansens Guides A+B+C+G	£58.80	£46.00	£12.80		
OFFER THREE – The Full Selection					
5 Johansens Guides A+B+C+G+K PLUS Southern Africa Guide **FREE**	£71.75	£56.00	£15.75		
OFFER FOUR - The Executive Collection					
Business Meeting Venues Guide & CD-ROM M+R	£40.00	£30.00	£10.00		
OFFER FIVE - The Holiday Pack					
3 Johansens Guides D+E+F	£18.93	£9.99	£8.94		
OFFER SIX - The Digital Collection					
3 Johansens CD-ROMs N+O+P PLUS Southern Africa CD-ROM Q **FREE**	£69.85	£59.85	£10.00		
OFFER SEVEN - The Chairman's Collection					
Business Meeting Venues Guide & CD-ROMs M+R **PLUS** 5 Johansens Boxed Guides A+B+C+G+K, **PLUS** D+E+F, **PLUS** 3 CD-ROMs N+O+P **PLUS** Southern Africa Guide/CD ROM Q **FREE**, **PLUS** Mystery Gift **FREE**	£205.53	£149.00	£56.53		
Privilege Card PLUS The Millennium Guide		**FREE**			
1 Presentation box for offers 1, 2 and 3		£5.00	£20.00		

TOTAL 1

JOHANSENS PRINTED GUIDES 2000

CODE	TITLE	PRICE	QTY	TOTAL
A	Recommended Hotels – Great Britain & Ireland 2000	£19.95		
B	Recommended Country Houses & Small Hotels – Great Britain & Ireland 2000	£11.95		
C	Recommended Traditional Inns, Hotels & Restaurants – Great Britain 2000	£10.95		
NEW D	Recommended Holiday Cottages – Great Britain & Ireland 2000	£4.99		
E	Historic Houses, Castles & Gardens 2000	£4.99		
F	Museums & Galleries 2000	£8.95		
G	Recommended Hotels – Europe & The Mediterranean 2000	£15.95		
NEW H	Recommended Hotels – Europe & The Mediterranean 2000 (French Language)	£15.95		
NEW J	Recommended Hotels – Europe & The Mediterranean 2000 (German Language)	£15.95		
K	Recommended Hotels & Inns – North America, Bermuda & The Caribbean 2000	£12.95		
NEW L	Recommended Hotels & Game Lodges – Southern Africa, Mauritius & The Seychelles 2000	£9.95		
M	Recommended Business Meeting Venues 2000	£20.00		

JOHANSENS CD ROMs DIGITAL COLLECTION 2000

CODE	TITLE	PRICE	QTY	TOTAL
N	The Guide 2000 – Great Britain & Ireland	£29.95		
O	The Guide 2000 – Europe & The Mediterranean (English, French, German Language)	£22.95		
P	The Guide 2000 – North America, Bermuda & The Caribbean	£16.95		
NEW Q	The Guide 2000 – Southern Africa, Mauritius & The Seychelles	£16.95		
R	Business Meeting Venues 2000	£20.00		
S	Privilege Card 2000 (Free with your order. Additional Cards £20 each)	£20.00		

Postage & Packing (UK) £4.50 or £2.50 for single order and CD-ROMs
Outside UK add £5 or £3 for single orders and CD-ROMs

TOTAL 2

GRAND TOTAL 1+2+P&P

Name (Mr/Mrs/Miss)

Address

Postcode

Card No. **Exp Date**

Signature

I have chosen my Johansens Guides/CD-ROMs and

☐ I enclose a cheque for £ _____ payable to Johansens

☐ I enclose my order on company letterheading, please invoice (UK only)

☐ Please debit my credit/charge card account (please tick).

☐ MasterCard ☐ Diners ☐ Amex

☐ Visa ☐ Switch (Issue Number) _____

A16

GUEST SURVEY REPORT

**Your own Johansens 'inspection' gives reliability to our guides
and assists in the selection of Award Nominations**

Name of Hotel: _____

Location of Hotel: _____

Page No: _____

Date of visit: _____

Name of guest _____

Address of guest: _____

_____Postcode _____

Please tick one box in each category below:	Excellent	Good	Disappointing	Poor
Bedrooms				
Public Rooms				
Restaurant/Cuisine				
Service				
Welcome/Friendliness				
Value For Money				

Occasionally we may allow other reputable organisations to write with offers which may be of interest.
If you prefer not to hear from them, tick this box ☐

To: Johansens, FREEPOST (CB264), 43 Millharbour, London E14 9BR

ORDER FORM

Call our 24hr credit card hotline FREEPHONE 0800 269 397.

Simply indicate which title(s) you require by putting the quantity in the boxes provided. Choose your preferred method of payment and mail to Johansens, FREEPOST (CB 264), 43 Millharbour, London E14 9BR, England (no stamp needed). Your FREE gifts will automatically be dispatched with your order. Fax orders welcome on 0171 537 3594

CHOOSE FROM 7 SPECIAL GUIDE COLLECTIONS – SAVE UP TO £56

TITLE	Normal Price	PRICE	SAVE	QTY	TOTAL
OFFER ONE – The Basic Collection					
3 Johansens Guides A+B+C	£42.85	£36.00	£6.85		
OFFER TWO – The Extended Collection					
4 Johansens Guides A+B+C+G	£58.80	£46.00	£12.80		
OFFER THREE – The Full Selection					
5 Johansens Guides A+B+C+G+K PLUS Southern Africa Guide **FREE**	£71.75	£56.00	£15.75		
OFFER FOUR - The Executive Collection					
Business Meeting Venues Guide & CD-ROM M+R	£40.00	£30.00	£10.00		
OFFER FIVE - The Holiday Pack					
3 Johansens Guides D+E+F	£18.93	£9.99	£8.94		
OFFER SIX - The Digital Collection					
3 Johansens CD-ROMs N+O+P PLUS Southern Africa CD-ROM Q **FREE**	£69.85	£59.85	£10.00		
OFFER SEVEN - The Chairman's Collection					
Business Meeting Venues Guide & CD-ROMs M+R **PLUS** 5 Johansens Boxed Guides A+B+C+G+K, **PLUS** D+E+F, **PLUS** 3 CD-ROMs N+O+P **PLUS** Southern Africa Guide/CD ROM Q **FREE**, **PLUS** Mystery Gift **FREE**	£205.53	£149.00	£56.53		
Privilege Card PLUS The Millennium Guide		FREE			
1 Presentation box for offers 1, 2 and 3		£5.00	£20.00		
			TOTAL 1		

JOHANSENS PRINTED GUIDES 2000

CODE	TITLE	PRICE	QTY	TOTAL
A	Recommended Hotels – Great Britain & Ireland 2000	£19.95		
B	Recommended Country Houses & Small Hotels – Great Britain & Ireland 2000	£11.95		
C	Recommended Traditional Inns, Hotels & Restaurants – Great Britain 2000	£10.95		
NEW D	Recommended Holiday Cottages – Great Britain & Ireland 2000	£4.99		
E	Historic Houses, Castles & Gardens 2000	£4.99		
F	Museums & Galleries 2000	£8.95		
G	Recommended Hotels – Europe & The Mediterranean 2000	£15.95		
NEW H	Recommended Hotels – Europe & The Mediterranean 2000 (French Language)	£15.95		
NEW J	Recommended Hotels – Europe & The Mediterranean 2000 (German Language)	£15.95		
K	Recommended Hotels & Inns – North America, Bermuda & The Caribbean 2000	£12.95		
NEW L	Recommended Hotels & Game Lodges – Southern Africa, Mauritius & The Seychelles 2000	£9.95		
M	Recommended Business Meeting Venues 2000	£20.00		

JOHANSENS CD ROMs DIGITAL COLLECTION 2000

CODE	TITLE	PRICE	QTY	TOTAL
N	The Guide 2000 – Great Britain & Ireland	£29.95		
O	The Guide 2000 – Europe & The Mediterranean (English, French, German Language)	£22.95		
P	The Guide 2000 – North America, Bermuda & The Caribbean	£16.95		
NEW Q	The Guide 2000 – Southern Africa, Mauritius & The Seychelles	£16.95		
R	Business Meeting Venues 2000	£20.00		
S	Privilege Card 2000 (Free with your order. Additional Cards £20 each)	£20.00		

Postage & Packing (UK) £4.50 or £2.50 for single order and CD-ROMs
Outside UK add £5 or £3 for single orders and CD-ROMs

TOTAL 2

GRAND TOTAL 1+2+P&P

Name (Mr/Mrs/Miss)

Address

Postcode

Card No.

Exp Date

Signature

I have chosen my Johansens Guides/CD-ROMs and

☐ I enclose a cheque for £ _____ payable to Johansens

☐ I enclose my order on company letterheading, please invoice (UK only)

☐ Please debit my credit/charge card account (please tick).

☐ MasterCard ☐ Diners ☐ Amex

☐ Visa ☐ Switch (Issue Number) _____

A16

GUEST SURVEY REPORT

Your own Johansens 'inspection' gives reliability to our guides
and assists in the selection of Award Nominations

Name of Hotel: _____

Location of Hotel: _____

Page No: _____

Date of visit: _____

Name of guest _____

Address of guest: _____

_____Postcode _____

Please tick one box in each category below:	Excellent	Good	Disappointing	Poor
Bedrooms				
Public Rooms				
Restaurant/Cuisine				
Service				
Welcome/Friendliness				
Value For Money				

Occasionally we may allow other reputable organisations to write with offers which may be of interest.
If you prefer not to hear from them, tick this box ☐

To: Johansens, FREEPOST (CB264), 43 Millharbour, London E14 9BR

ORDER FORM

Call our 24hr credit card hotline FREEPHONE 0800 269 397.

Simply indicate which title(s) you require by putting the quantity in the boxes provided. Choose your preferred method of payment and mail to Johansens, FREEPOST (CB 264), 43 Millharbour, London E14 9BR, England (no stamp needed). Your FREE gifts will automatically be dispatched with your order. Fax orders welcome on 0171 537 3594

CHOOSE FROM 7 SPECIAL GUIDE COLLECTIONS – SAVE UP TO £56

TITLE	Normal Price	PRICE	SAVE	QTY	TOTAL
OFFER ONE – The Basic Collection					
3 Johansens Guides A+B+C	£42.85	£36.00	£6.85		
OFFER TWO – The Extended Collection					
4 Johansens Guides A+B+C+G	£58.80	£46.00	£12.80		
OFFER THREE – The Full Selection					
5 Johansens Guides A+B+C+G+K PLUS Southern Africa Guide **FREE**	£71.75	£56.00	£15.75		
OFFER FOUR - The Executive Collection					
Business Meeting Venues Guide & CD-ROM M+R	£40.00	£30.00	£10.00		
OFFER FIVE - The Holiday Pack					
3 Johansens Guides D+E+F	£18.93	£9.99	£8.94		
OFFER SIX - The Digital Collection					
3 Johansens CD-ROMs N+O+P PLUS Southern Africa CD-ROM Q **FREE**	£69.85	£59.85	£10.00		
OFFER SEVEN - The Chairman's Collection					
Business Meeting Venues Guide & CD-ROMs M+R PLUS 5 Johansens Boxed Guides A+B+C+G+K, PLUS D+E+F, PLUS 3 CD-ROMs N+O+P PLUS Southern Africa Guide/CD ROM Q **FREE**, PLUS Mystery Gift **FREE**	£205.53	£149.00	£56.53		
Privilege Card PLUS The Millennium Guide		**FREE**			
1 Presentation box for offers 1, 2 and 3		£5.00	£20.00		

TOTAL 1

JOHANSENS PRINTED GUIDES 2000

CODE	TITLE	PRICE	QTY	TOTAL
A	Recommended Hotels – Great Britain & Ireland 2000	£19.95		
B	Recommended Country Houses & Small Hotels – Great Britain & Ireland 2000	£11.95		
C	Recommended Traditional Inns, Hotels & Restaurants – Great Britain 2000	£10.95		
NEW D	Recommended Holiday Cottages – Great Britain & Ireland 2000	£4.99		
E	Historic Houses, Castles & Gardens 2000	£4.99		
F	Museums & Galleries 2000	£8.95		
G	Recommended Hotels – Europe & The Mediterranean 2000	£15.95		
NEW H	Recommended Hotels – Europe & The Mediterranean 2000 (French Language)	£15.95		
NEW J	Recommended Hotels – Europe & The Mediterranean 2000 (German Language)	£15.95		
K	Recommended Hotels & Inns – North America, Bermuda & The Caribbean 2000	£12.95		
NEW L	Recommended Hotels & Game Lodges – Southern Africa, Mauritius & The Seychelles 2000	£9.95		
M	Recommended Business Meeting Venues 2000	£20.00		

JOHANSENS CD ROMs DIGITAL COLLECTION 2000

CODE	TITLE	PRICE	QTY	TOTAL
N	The Guide 2000 – Great Britain & Ireland	£29.95		
O	The Guide 2000 – Europe & The Mediterranean (English, French, German Language)	£22.95		
P	The Guide 2000 – North America, Bermuda & The Caribbean	£16.95		
NEW Q	The Guide 2000 – Southern Africa, Mauritius & The Seychelles	£16.95		
R	Business Meeting Venues 2000	£20.00		
S	Privilege Card 2000 (Free with your order. Additional Cards £20 each)	£20.00		

Postage & Packing (UK) £4.50 or £2.50 for single order and CD-ROMs
Outside UK add £5 or £3 for single orders and CD-ROMs

TOTAL 2

GRAND TOTAL 1+2+P&P

Name (Mr/Mrs/Miss)

Address

Postcode

Card No.

Exp Date

Signature

I have chosen my Johansens Guides/CD-ROMs and

☐ I enclose a cheque for £ _____ payable to Johansens

☐ I enclose my order on company letterheading, please invoice (UK only)

☐ Please debit my credit/charge card account (please tick).

☐ MasterCard ☐ Diners ☐ Amex

☐ Visa ☐ Switch (Issue Number) _____

A16

GUEST SURVEY REPORT

**Your own Johansens 'inspection' gives reliability to our guides
and assists in the selection of Award Nominations**

Name of Hotel: _____

Location of Hotel: _____

Page No: _____

Date of visit: _____

Name of guest _____

Address of guest: _____

_____Postcode _____

Please tick one box in each category below:	Excellent	Good	Disappointing	Poor
Bedrooms				
Public Rooms				
Restaurant/Cuisine				
Service				
Welcome/Friendliness				
Value For Money				

Occasionally we may allow other reputable organisations to write with offers which may be of interest.
If you prefer not to hear from them, tick this box ☐

To: Johansens, FREEPOST (CB264), 43 Millharbour, London E14 9BR

ORDER FORM

Call our 24hr credit card hotline FREEPHONE 0800 269 397.

Simply indicate which title(s) you require by putting the quantity in the boxes provided. Choose your preferred method of payment and mail to Johansens, FREEPOST (CB 264), 43 Millharbour, London E14 9BR, England (no stamp needed). Your FREE gifts will automatically be dispatched with your order. Fax orders welcome on 0171 537 3594

CHOOSE FROM 7 SPECIAL GUIDE COLLECTIONS – SAVE UP TO £56

TITLE	Normal Price	PRICE	SAVE	QTY	TOTAL
OFFER ONE – The Basic Collection					
3 Johansens Guides A+B+C	£42.85	£36.00	£6.85		
OFFER TWO – The Extended Collection					
4 Johansens Guides A+B+C+G	£58.80	£46.00	£12.80		
OFFER THREE – The Full Selection					
5 Johansens Guides A+B+C+G+K PLUS Southern Africa Guide **FREE**	£71.75	£56.00	£15.75		
OFFER FOUR - The Executive Collection					
Business Meeting Venues Guide & CD-ROM M+R	£40.00	£30.00	£10.00		
OFFER FIVE - The Holiday Pack					
3 Johansens Guides D+E+F	£18.93	£9.99	£8.94		
OFFER SIX - The Digital Collection					
3 Johansens CD-ROMs N+O+P PLUS Southern Africa CD-ROM Q **FREE**	£69.85	£59.85	£10.00		
OFFER SEVEN - The Chairman's Collection					
Business Meeting Venues Guide & CD-ROMs M+R **PLUS** 5 Johansens Boxed Guides A+B+C+G+K, **PLUS** D+E+F, **PLUS** 3 CD-ROMs N+O+P **PLUS** Southern Africa Guide/CD ROM Q **FREE**, **PLUS** Mystery Gift **FREE**	£205.53	£149.00	£56.53		
Privilege Card PLUS The Millennium Guide		FREE			
1 Presentation box for offers 1, 2 and 3		£5.00	£20.00		
			TOTAL 1		

JOHANSENS PRINTED GUIDES 2000

CODE	TITLE	PRICE	QTY	TOTAL
A	Recommended Hotels – Great Britain & Ireland 2000	£19.95		
B	Recommended Country Houses & Small Hotels – Great Britain & Ireland 2000	£11.95		
C	Recommended Traditional Inns, Hotels & Restaurants – Great Britain 2000	£10.95		
NEW D	Recommended Holiday Cottages – Great Britain & Ireland 2000	£4.99		
E	Historic Houses, Castles & Gardens 2000	£4.99		
F	Museums & Galleries 2000	£8.95		
G	Recommended Hotels – Europe & The Mediterranean 2000	£15.95		
NEW H	Recommended Hotels – Europe & The Mediterranean 2000 (French Language)	£15.95		
NEW J	Recommended Hotels – Europe & The Mediterranean 2000 (German Language)	£15.95		
K	Recommended Hotels & Inns – North America, Bermuda & The Caribbean 2000	£12.95		
NEW L	Recommended Hotels & Game Lodges – Southern Africa, Mauritius & The Seychelles 2000	£9.95		
M	Recommended Business Meeting Venues 2000	£20.00		

JOHANSENS CD ROMs DIGITAL COLLECTION 2000

CODE	TITLE	PRICE	QTY	TOTAL
N	The Guide 2000 – Great Britain & Ireland	£29.95		
O	The Guide 2000 – Europe & The Mediterranean (English, French, German Language)	£22.95		
P	The Guide 2000 – North America, Bermuda & The Caribbean	£16.95		
NEW Q	The Guide 2000 – Southern Africa, Mauritius & The Seychelles	£16.95		
R	Business Meeting Venues 2000	£20.00		
S	Privilege Card 2000 (Free with your order. Additional Cards £20 each)	£20.00		

Postage & Packing (UK) £4.50 or £2.50 for single order and CD-ROMs
Outside UK add £5 or £3 for single orders and CD-ROMs

TOTAL 2

GRAND TOTAL 1+2+P&P

Name (Mr/Mrs/Miss)

Address

Postcode

Card No.

Exp Date

Signature

I have chosen my Johansens Guides/CD-ROMs and

☐ I enclose a cheque for £ _____ payable to Johansens

☐ I enclose my order on company letterheading, please invoice (UK only)

☐ Please debit my credit/charge card account (please tick).

☐ MasterCard ☐ Diners ☐ Amex

☐ Visa ☐ Switch (Issue Number) _____

A16

GUEST SURVEY REPORT

**Your own Johansens 'inspection' gives reliability to our guides
and assists in the selection of Award Nominations**

Name of Hotel: _____

Location of Hotel: _____

Page No: _____

Date of visit: _____

Name of guest _____

Address of guest: _____

_____ Postcode _____

Please tick one box in each category below:	Excellent	Good	Disappointing	Poor
Bedrooms				
Public Rooms				
Restaurant/Cuisine				
Service				
Welcome/Friendliness				
Value For Money				

Occasionally we may allow other reputable organisations to write with offers which may be of interest.
If you prefer not to hear from them, tick this box ☐

To: Johansens, FREEPOST (CB264), 43 Millharbour, London E14 9BR

ORDER FORM

Call our 24hr credit card hotline FREEPHONE 0800 269 397.

Simply indicate which title(s) you require by putting the quantity in the boxes provided. Choose your preferred method of payment and mail to Johansens, FREEPOST (CB 264), 43 Millharbour, London E14 9BR, England (no stamp needed). Your FREE gifts will automatically be dispatched with your order. Fax orders welcome on 0171 537 3594

CHOOSE FROM 7 SPECIAL GUIDE COLLECTIONS – SAVE UP TO £56

TITLE	Normal Price	PRICE	SAVE	QTY	TOTAL
OFFER ONE – The Basic Collection					
3 Johansens Guides A+B+C	£42.85	£36.00	£6.85		
OFFER TWO – The Extended Collection					
4 Johansens Guides A+B+C+G	£58.80	£46.00	£12.80		
OFFER THREE – The Full Selection					
5 Johansens Guides A+B+C+G+K PLUS Southern Africa Guide **FREE**	£71.75	£56.00	£15.75		
OFFER FOUR - The Executive Collection					
Business Meeting Venues Guide & CD-ROM M+R	£40.00	£30.00	£10.00		
OFFER FIVE - The Holiday Pack					
3 Johansens Guides D+E+F	£18.93	£9.99	£8.94		
OFFER SIX - The Digital Collection					
3 Johansens CD-ROMs N+O+P PLUS Southern Africa CD-ROM Q **FREE**	£69.85	£59.85	£10.00		
OFFER SEVEN - The Chairman's Collection					
Business Meeting Venues Guide & CD-ROMs M+R **PLUS** 5 Johansens Boxed Guides A+B+C+G+K, **PLUS** D+E+F, **PLUS** 3 CD-ROMs N+O+P **PLUS** Southern Africa Guide/CD ROM Q **FREE**, **PLUS** Mystery Gift **FREE**	£205.53	£149.00	£56.53		
Privilege Card PLUS The Millennium Guide		**FREE**			
1 Presentation box for offers 1, 2 and 3		£5.00	£20.00		

TOTAL 1

JOHANSENS PRINTED GUIDES 2000

CODE	TITLE	PRICE	QTY	TOTAL
A	Recommended Hotels – Great Britain & Ireland 2000	£19.95		
B	Recommended Country Houses & Small Hotels – Great Britain & Ireland 2000	£11.95		
C	Recommended Traditional Inns, Hotels & Restaurants – Great Britain 2000	£10.95		
NEW D	Recommended Holiday Cottages – Great Britain & Ireland 2000	£4.99		
E	Historic Houses, Castles & Gardens 2000	£4.99		
F	Museums & Galleries 2000	£8.95		
G	Recommended Hotels – Europe & The Mediterranean 2000	£15.95		
NEW H	Recommended Hotels – Europe & The Mediterranean 2000 (French Language)	£15.95		
NEW J	Recommended Hotels – Europe & The Mediterranean 2000 (German Language)	£15.95		
K	Recommended Hotels & Inns – North America, Bermuda & The Caribbean 2000	£12.95		
NEW L	Recommended Hotels & Game Lodges – Southern Africa, Mauritius & The Seychelles 2000	£9.95		
M	Recommended Business Meeting Venues 2000	£20.00		

JOHANSENS CD ROMs DIGITAL COLLECTION 2000

CODE	TITLE	PRICE	QTY	TOTAL
N	The Guide 2000 – Great Britain & Ireland	£29.95		
O	The Guide 2000 – Europe & The Mediterranean (English, French, German Language)	£22.95		
P	The Guide 2000 – North America, Bermuda & The Caribbean	£16.95		
NEW Q	The Guide 2000 – Southern Africa, Mauritius & The Seychelles	£16.95		
R	Business Meeting Venues 2000	£20.00		
S	Privilege Card 2000 (Free with your order. Additional Cards £20 each)	£20.00		

Postage & Packing (UK) £4.50 or £2.50 for single order and CD-ROMs
Outside UK add £5 or £3 for single orders and CD-ROMs

TOTAL 2

GRAND TOTAL 1+2+P&P

Name (Mr/Mrs/Miss)

Address

Postcode

Card No.

Exp Date

Signature

I have chosen my Johansens Guides/CD-ROMs and

☐ I enclose a cheque for £ _____ payable to Johansens

☐ I enclose my order on company letterheading, please invoice (UK only)

☐ Please debit my credit/charge card account (please tick).

☐ MasterCard ☐ Diners ☐ Amex

☐ Visa ☐ Switch (Issue Number) _____

A16

GUEST SURVEY REPORT

**Your own Johansens 'inspection' gives reliability to our guides
and assists in the selection of Award Nominations**

Name of Hotel: _____

Location of Hotel: _____

Page No: _____

Date of visit: _____

Name of guest _____

Address of guest: _____

_____ Postcode _____

Please tick one box in each category below:	*Excellent*	*Good*	*Disappointing*	*Poor*
Bedrooms				
Public Rooms				
Restaurant/Cuisine				
Service				
Welcome/Friendliness				
Value For Money				

Occasionally we may allow other reputable organisations to write with offers which may be of interest.
If you prefer not to hear from them, tick this box ☐

To: Johansens, FREEPOST (CB264), 43 Millharbour, London E14 9BR